THE ULTRASTRUCTURE
OF HUMAN SKIN

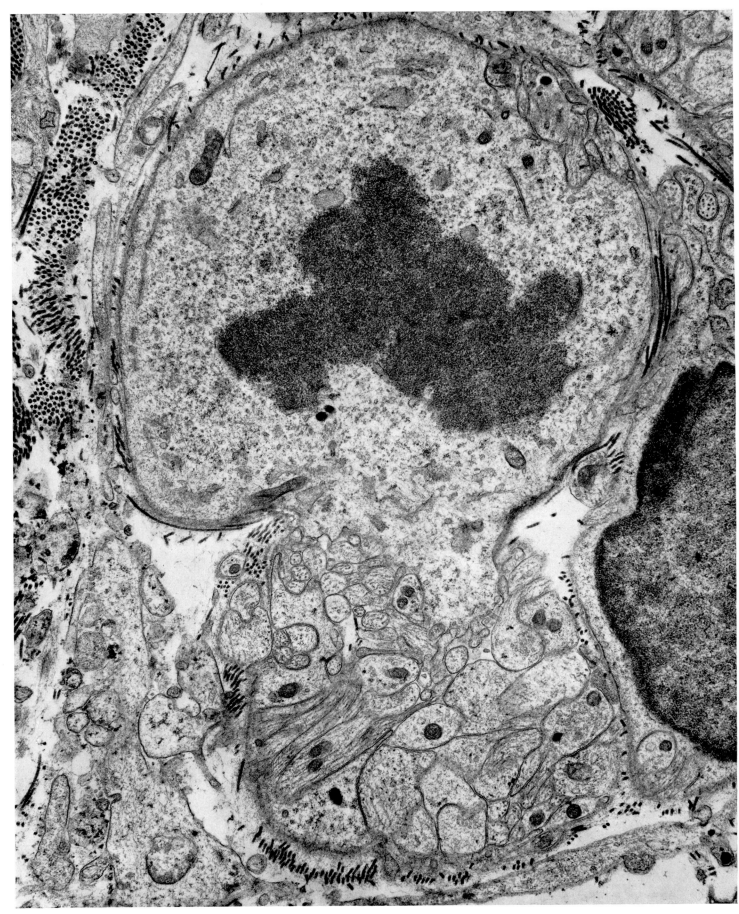

Dividing Schwann cell in dermis of arm skin of 215 mm C.R. (24 week) human fetus. Osmium fixation, uranyl acetate and lead staining. ×17,500.

AN ATLAS OF
THE ULTRASTRUCTURE
OF HUMAN SKIN

*Development, Differentiation, and Post-natal
Features*

A. S. BREATHNACH

M.Sc., M.D.

*Professor of Anatomy in the University of London
at St. Mary's Hospital Medical School*

With 305 Illustrations

J. & A. CHURCHILL

104 Gloucester Place, London

1971

First edition 1971

Standard Book Number 7000 1455 1

Printed in Great Britain by
William Clowes and Sons, Limited, London Beccles, and Colchester

Preface

This volume deals with human skin exclusively. No other mammal is featured here, not because of a lack of appreciation of the value of comparative studies, but because I felt from the outset that it was desirable to illustrate the human condition *per se*, and not a hotch-potch of the skins of a number of species. There are differences at the ultrastructural level, not yet fully appreciated, nor even documented, between elements of the skins of experimental animals and man, which make it unjustified and confusing to present micrographs of the one as representative of the other. In confining the presentation to human skin, my intention has been to provide as comprehensive a picture as possible of its fine structure for those primarily interested therein, though limitations governing the overall length and price of the book have prevented me from dealing with certain aspects as fully as I should have wished. The same considerations have necessitated exclusion of micrographs illustrating electron-histochemical and more exotic techniques, which while they are of great value in illuminating certain aspects of skin function, are not essential for illustrating the ultrastructural anatomy as such. All of the micrographs presented here have been obtained from material processed and stained by standard methods in common use.

An attempt has been made throughout this book to present the subject from a developmental point of view, since many complicated post-natal arrangements are more easily interpreted by comparison with the simpler conditions in the fetus. Approximately half the number of micrographs are of fetal skin. The inclusion of a large number of low- and medium-power survey micrographs will, I hope, justify the exclusion of light micrographs, and it is assumed that the reader will be already familiar with the general anatomy of skin at the light microscopic level. It is also assumed that he or she will have some knowledge of the general features of the cell and the common organelles as seen in electron microscopy.

The text on each left-hand page relates directly to the accompanying micrograph, and in effect represents an extended figure legend. Nevertheless, I have tried with each Section to maintain a continuous thread of description. The bibliographies at the end of each Section are not intended to be fully comprehensive, but list mainly review articles which will serve as guides to a wider literature.

This book could not have been produced without the assistance of Mrs Lucile Wyllie and Mrs Jacqueline Robins, who, as colleagues, were responsible for the collection, processing and sectioning of most of the material. It gives me great pleasure to record here my appreciation of the care and patience with which they have always, and often at short notice, dealt with exacting demands upon their skills. I should like also to express gratitude to Messrs M. Gross, B. Martin and C. Stolinski for technical assistance connected with maintenance of the microscope (provided by the Wellcome Trust) at a high level of performance, and to Miss Angela Pitman for her impeccable typing of the manuscript. The publishers, Messrs J. & A. Churchill Ltd, have done everything possible to satisfy my requirements, and I am most grateful to Mr A. Knightley for his advice and suggestions concerning layout and similar matters, and for his efforts in ensuring a high standard of reproduction of the micrographs.

The great majority of the electron micrographs have been specially prepared for this volume. Some, however, have already appeared in papers written either by myself alone, or in collaboration with colleagues, and I am grateful to the following for permission to reproduce them here. To Academic Press Inc., New York, for Figs 47, 122 and 143 (from Breathnach, in *Pigments in Pathology*, ed. Wolman, 1969), for Fig. 112 (from Breathnach and Wyllie, *J. Ultrastruct. Res.*,

v

16, 1966), and for Fig. 120 (from Breathnach, *Int. Rev. Cytol.*, **18**, 1965); to Messrs H. K. Lewis Ltd, London, for Figs 7–10, 12, 15 and 25 (from Breathnach and Robins, *Brit. J. Derm.*, **81**, 1969); to Pergamon Press Inc., New York, for Figs 126 and 127 (from Breathnach and Wyllie in *Advances in Biology of Skin*, **8**, 1967); to The Williams & Wilkins Co. Inc. for Figs 34 and 36 (from Breathnach and Wyllie, *J. invest. Derm.*, **45**, 1965) and Fig. 151 (from Breathnach *et al.*, *J. invest. Derm.*, **47**, 1966); to Cambridge University Press for Figs 45, 49, 67, 72, 189 (from Breathnach and Smith, *J. Anat.*, **102**, 1968), Figs 77 and 80 (from Gamble and Breathnach, *J. Anat.*, **99**, 1965), Fig. 124 (from Breathnach, *J. Anat.*, **98**, 1964), Figs 190, 191, 193, 194, 195, 269 (from Robins and Breathnach, *J. Anat.*, **104**, 1969) and for Figs 197, 198, 200–202 (from Robins and Breathnach, *J. Anat.*, in press, 1970). I am especially grateful to Mrs E. J. Robins for allowing me to reproduce Figs 269–272, of developing apocrine gland, which she is currently studying. Finally, I should like to thank The Medical Research Council for support over a number of years.

A. S. BREATHNACH

St. Mary's Hospital Medical School
June, 1970.

Contents

vii

I Early Development of Skin

Ectoderm and mesoderm — bilaminar epidermis: germinative layer and periderm — intercellular contacts: desmosomes — epidermal-mesodermal junction: basal lamina — pluristratification of epidermis.

FIGURE I

Human skin, like that of other vertebrates, consists of a multi-layered cellular epidermis (E) derived mainly from the surface ectoderm, and an underlying dermis of mesodermal origin. These two distinct parts of the skin meet at the epidermal-dermal junction (j), a region where important morphogenetic and other influences operate throughout fetal and post-natal life. The dermis contains a variety of elements, vessels (v), nerves (n) and individual cells (c) set in a strong meshwork of collagen fibres (f), and while it can hardly be regarded as a tissue in the same sense as the closely-knit epidermis, some of its constituents have a definite pattern of arrangement, which, however, may not be very evident at the ultrastructural level.

FIGURE 2

The outermost layers of the epidermis comprise the stratum corneum (SC) consisting of flattened squames, tough but supple as befits their protective function, and it is towards the production of these that differentiation and maturation of the underlying cells is directed during both fetal and post-natal life. This process is termed "keratinization", and evidently involves profound alterations in relationships between cells, as well as complex structural and metabolic changes within them. Many aspects of keratinization are still imperfectly understood. It has become customary to refer to cells which undergo keratinization as "keratinocytes", rather than simply as "epidermal cells" in order to emphasize the fact that the epidermis contains other cells of different lineage and function, and is in fact, a composite of ectodermal, neural-crest, and, probably, mesodermal elements.

Fig. 1. Basal layer of epidermis and dermis from forearm skin of a three-weeks' infant. Osmium fixation, lead staining. × 5,000.

Fig. 2. Upper layers of epidermis from forearm skin of a man aged 40. Osmium fixation, lead staining. × 11,600.

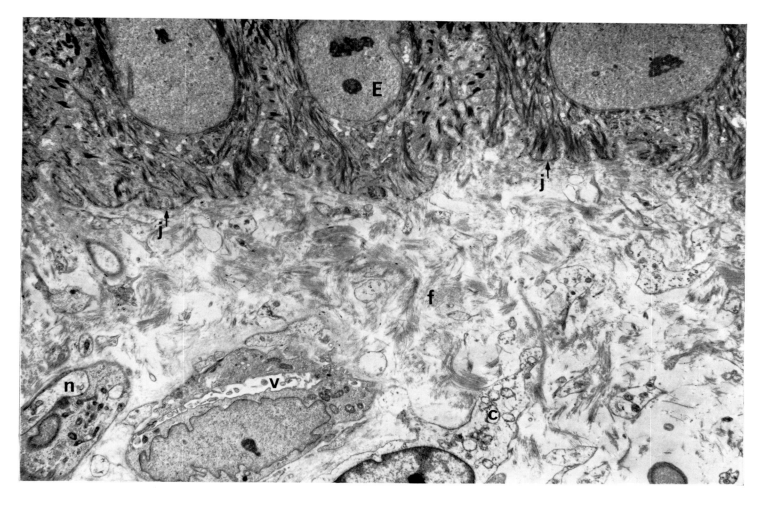

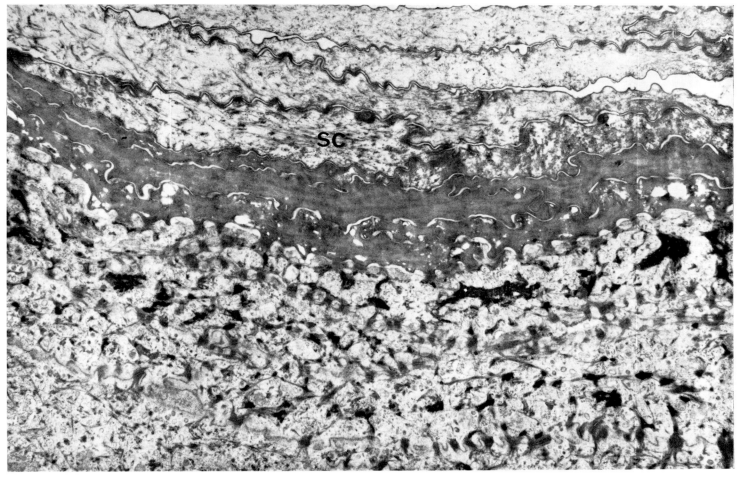

FIGURE 3

This illustrates general features of ectodermal cells from which the epidermal keratinocytes are developed. Portions of two cells and the underlying mesoderm (M) are shown. The closely apposed lateral plasma membranes of the cells (pl) exhibit no particular specializations, and appear to fuse at the surface, a segment of which just falls within the extreme upper left-hand corner of the micrograph. Within the cytoplasm are organelles commonly found in cells of all types, i.e., mitochondria (m), rough-surfaced endoplasmic reticulum (r), ribosomal particles, and membrane-limited bodies (l) resembling lysosomes. Golgi membranes are also present in ectodermal cells, though not evident in this field. Two relatively large deposits of glycogen (gl) are present in one cell—a characteristic feature, as is also what appears to be very fine fibrillar material (f) just within the basal plasma membrane, and at the angle between the surface membrane and the upper part of the lateral plasma membrane. On the mesodermal aspect of the basal plasma membrane an ill-demarcated layer of electron-dense, apparently fibrillar, material (d), stands out from the more electron-translucent general mesodermal matrix containing loosely-arranged fibrils of varying diameter.

FIGURE 4

Mesodermal cells are fairly sparsely distributed except in the area immediately deep to the ectoderm at the stage of development under consideration here. The cells are elongated, with prominent nuclei (n), and establish contact with their neighbours by means of long slender processes (pr). The cytoplasm contains the usual organelles, as well as scattered glycogen particles. Cells of this type must be responsible for producing the fibrils present in the mesodermal matrix, and bundles of these (f) are often seen closely applied to the plasma membrane. The cells, therefore, can be labelled fibroblasts, and the fibrils, pre-collagen, or micro-fibrils, since they are of finer diameter than collagen fibres of fully-developed skin.

Fig. 3. Ectoderm and mesoderm from crown of head of 14 mm C.R. (6 week) human embryo. Glutaraldehyde-osmium fixation, lead stain. × 44,200.

Fig. 4. Mesodermal cells subjacent to ectoderm of crown of head of 14 mm C.R. (6 week) human embryo. Glutaraldehyde-osmium fixation, lead stain. × 16,250.

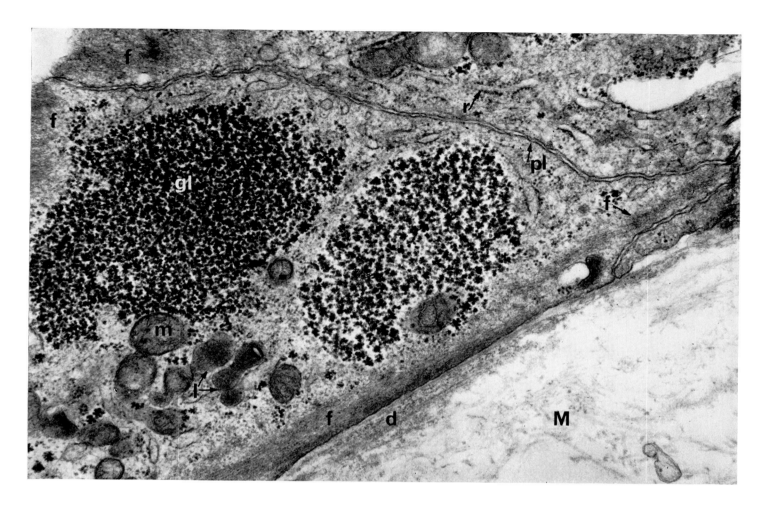

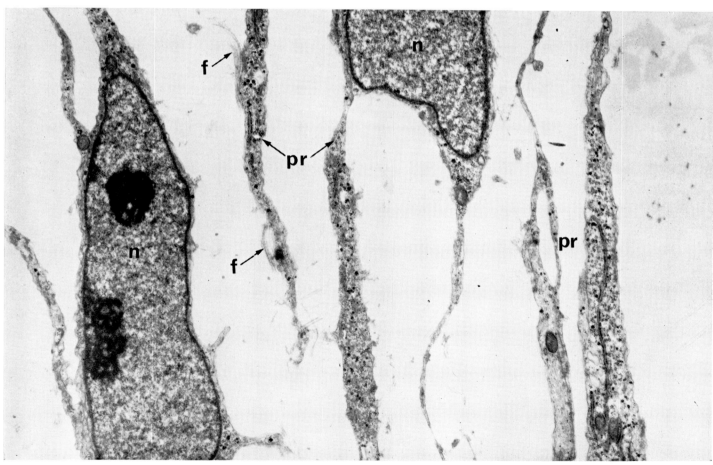

FIGURES 5 and 6

Carbohydrate is stored as glycogen in animal cells, and this polysaccharide is particularly abundant in epidermal keratinocytes at early stages of development. In sections stained with lead ions it appears very electron-dense, and is seen to be deposited in the form of particles which may occur singly (p), or aggregated into rosettes (ro) of varying size. The single particles, termed *beta* particles, are somewhat irregular in outline, and vary in diameter between 15–30 nm (150–300 Å); those present in the ectodermal cell opposite measure about 25 nm (250 Å). The rosettes are called *alpha* particles, and in turn may occur singly, or grouped together to form larger aggregates within which their individuality may not be very apparent.

Some of the cells seen in the lower micrograph are practically stuffed with glycogen (gl), so much so, that apart from the nucleus (n) they appear at this magnification to contain little else. An entirely different impression of this section would be obtained had it been stained by phosphotungstic acid (PTA), which does not render glycogen electron-dense. The cytoplasm of the glycogen-laden cells would in this case appear practically translucent or "empty", apart from the nucleus and a few sparsely distributed organelles.

Glycogen may sometimes be seen in intercellular spaces of fetal epidermis fixed primarily in osmium tetroxide, but less frequently in material fixed in glutaraldehyde. This suggests that extracellular glycogen may be an artifact of processing.

Glycogen is normally absent from keratinocytes of fully-developed interfollicular epidermis, though it may re-appear in certain diseases, or under conditions of abnormal stimulation. It is, however, normally present within cells of the sebaceous, and eccrine sweat glands, and of the outer root sheath of the hair follicle.

Fig. 5. Glycogen in ectodermal cell from crown of head of 14 mm C.R. (6 week) human embryo. Glutaraldehyde-osmium fixation, lead stain. × 80,000.

Fig. 6. Full-thickness epidermis from back of 81 mm C.R. (14 week) human fetus. Osmium fixation, lead stain. × 5,750.

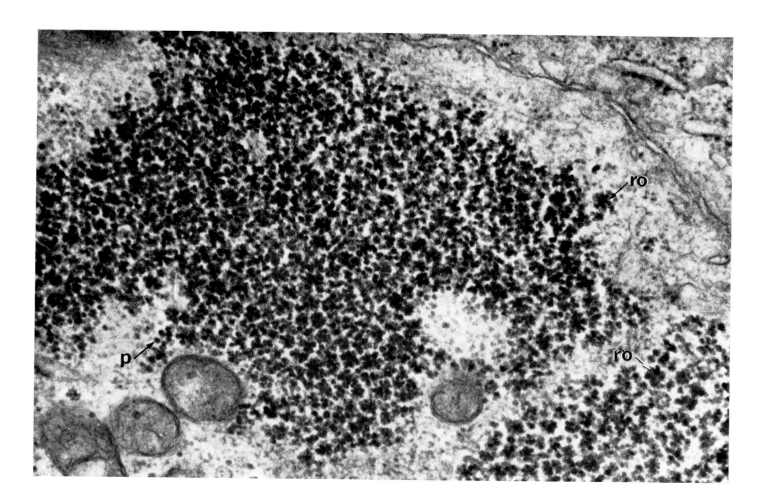

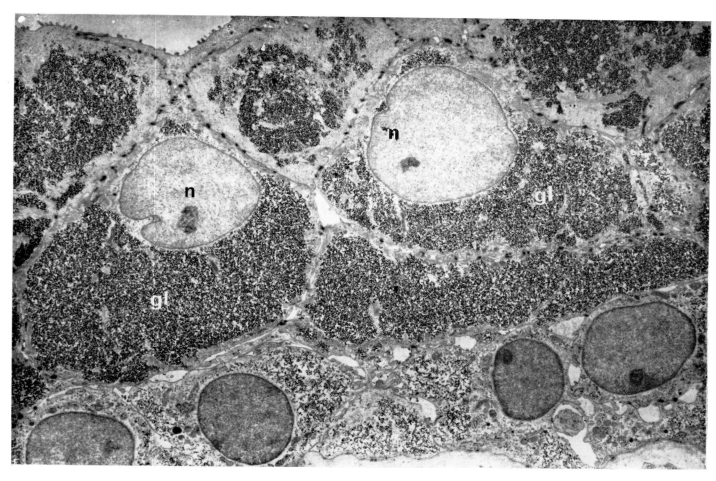

7

FIGURES 7 and 8

With the appearance of two layers of cells derived from the surface ectoderm, an epidermis proper can be said to exist. The superficial layer of cells forms the periderm (P), and this over-lies a basal or germinative layer (G). This early distinction between the two layers is a funda-mental one, since their subsequent development takes place along different and apparently independent lines. The periderm is exclusively a feature of fetal skin; over a period, its cells develop characteristics indicative of a secretory or absorptive function in relation to the amniotic fluid, but they undergo regression during the second half of intra-uterine life. The germinative layer develops into the epidermis of post-natal life, and its differentiation is directed towards a gradual attainment of the features which characterize this latter as a strati-fied, squamous, keratinizing epithelium with specialized appendages (hairs and glands). The underlying mesodermal tissues (M) have an important directive influence on epidermal differentiation and maintenance, not only in providing a substrate for the germinal cells, but also, through stimulation and control of their mitotic activity. At the same time, development of mesoderm into normal dermis requires the presence of a covering layer of epidermis, and epidermal differentiations induced by dermal influences, secondarily induce further changes in the dermis. These mutual inductive interactions remain operative to some extent throughout post-natal life, and must depend upon some form of molecular exchange at the epithelio-mesodermal, or epidermal-dermal interface, but the exact mechanisms involved remain to be determined.

While a bilaminar epidermis is in process of being developed, single ectodermal cells may be encountered bridging the gap between adjacent more advanced areas (Fig. 8). Such cells (E) are usually partially overlapped by the peripheral edges of the periderm cells (P) and are fre-quently more electron dense than neighbouring cells. A cilium (c), and small micro-villi (m), are present at the surface of the cell illustrated.

Fig. 7. Bilaminar epidermis and mesoderm from crown of head of 14 mm C.R. (6 week) human embryo. Glutaraldehyde-osmium fixation, lead stain. ×7,800.

Fig. 8. Ectodermal cell from crown of head of 14 mm C.R. (6 week) human embryo. Glutaraldehyde-osmium fixation, lead stain. ×24,100.

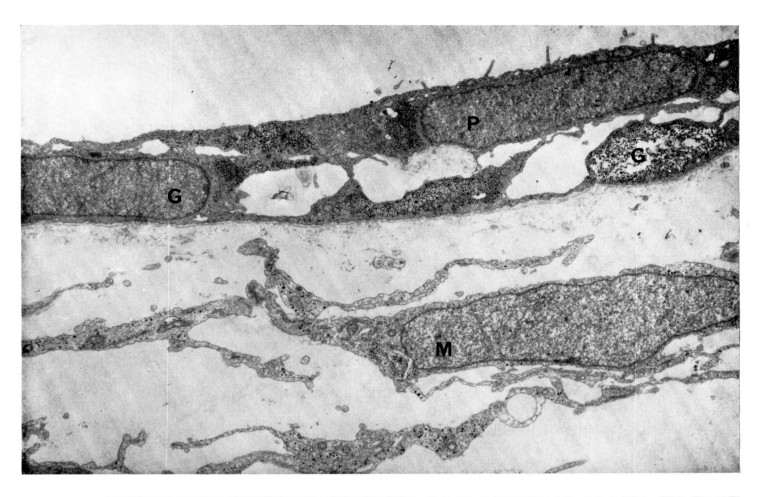

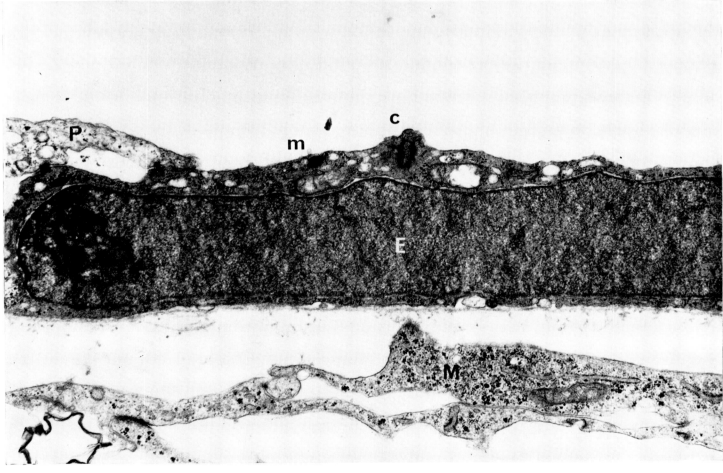

9

FIGURES 9 and 10

For some time following their original appearance, cells of both periderm (P) and germinative (G) layers are flattened parallel with the surface, and the peripheral parts of the periderm cells may be extremely attenuated as can be seen in the lower micrograph opposite. Spaces of varying size are frequently present between the two layers, and between individual overlapping cells of the germinative layer. While these spaces may be entirely due to some shrinkage of the tenous tissue during processing, they certainly indicate that intercellular adhesion is weak at this early stage of development.

In general appearance the cells of both layers are essentially similar, with large glycogen deposits (gl) in the region lateral to the nucleus; mitochondria and other organelles are also present. A single microvillus (m) projects from the amniotic surface of the periderm cell in the upper micrograph, and in both pictures, a narrow electron dense strip (b) can be distinguished just beneath the basal plasma membrane of the germinative cell. This is the basal lamina, which will receive further consideration presently.

At one point (d) along the apposed plasma membranes of periderm and germinative cells in the lower micrograph, development of a specialized zone of contact, or desmosome, is foreshadowed by an increase in density.

Fig. 9. Bilaminar epidermis from crown of head of 14 mm C.R. (6 week) human embryo. Glutaraldehyde-osmium fixation, lead stain. × 26,400.

Fig. 10. Bilaminar epidermis from crown of head of 14 mm C.R. (6 week) human embryo. Glutaraldehyde-osmium fixation, lead stain. × 22,500.

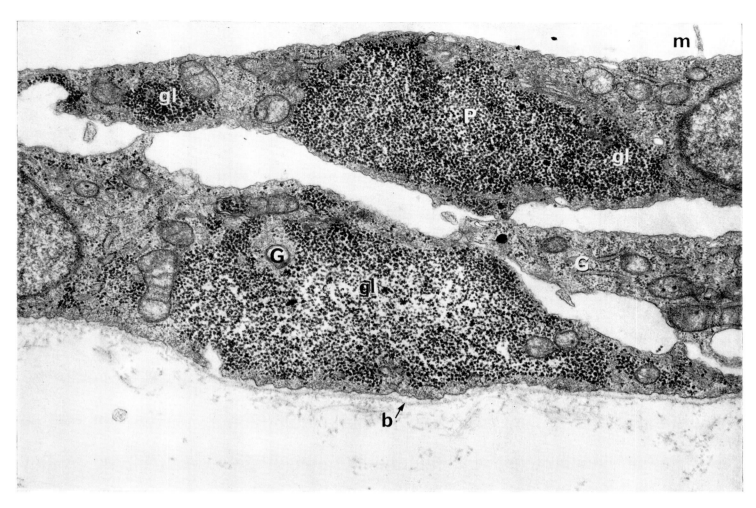

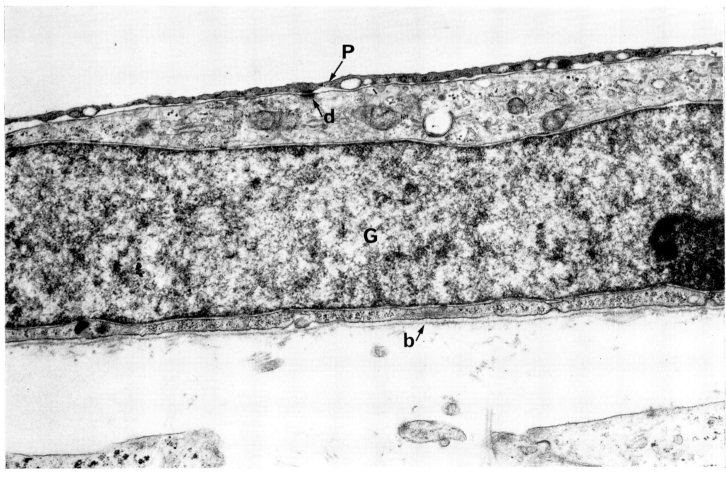

FIGURES 11 and 12

Elaboration of contacts and adhesions between cells is an important aspect of epidermal differentiation, since it is upon these features that its coherence and strength as a protective layer ultimately depends. Contact is effected, not only by apposition of stretches of parallel cell membranes, but also by means of villous processes (v) which interlock to varying degrees. Adhesion is thought to be further enhanced by secretion of an intercellular "cement" substance and by the development of special localized areas of attachment, or desmosomes. These (d) appear initially as "mirror-image" deposits of amorphous electron-dense material at intervals just within the apposed plasma membranes, and as development proceeds, they increase in size and number and acquire a structural arrangement which is highly characteristic. That they are, indeed, attachment sites of particular strength, is suggested by the fact that in pathological conditions leading to cell separation in fully developed epidermis, apposition is maintained for a longer period at desmosomes than over the rest of the plasma membrane.

At the site of peripheral surface contact of adjacent periderm cells there is a further specialization in the form of a "tight junction" (j) involving a fusion of the outer leaflets of the plasma membrane with obliteration of the intercellular space.

These micrographs were obtained from the epidermis of the upper limb-bud, which is at a more advanced stage of differentiation than that over the crown of the head of the same embryo as figured previously. The elaboration of intercellular contacts and the more numerous surface microvilli (m) are indicative of this. Golgi membranes (go) are present in the germinative cell.

Fig. 11. Features of contact surface between periderm and germinative cells of bilaminar epidermis from upper limb-bud of 14 mm C.R. (6 week) human embryo. Glutaraldehyde-osmium fixation, lead stain. × 27,000.

Fig. 12. Contacts between peripheral parts of periderm cells and germinative cell from bilaminar epidermis of upper limb-bud of 14 mm C.R. (6 week) human embryo. Glutaraldehyde-osmium fixation, lead stain. × 30,400

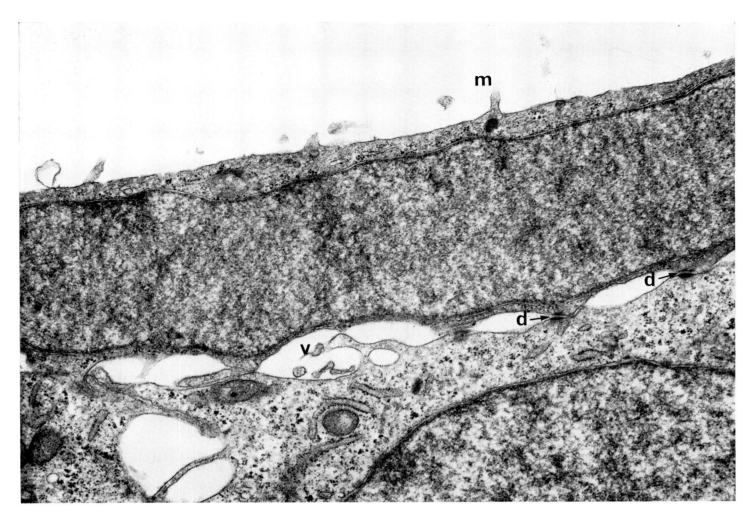

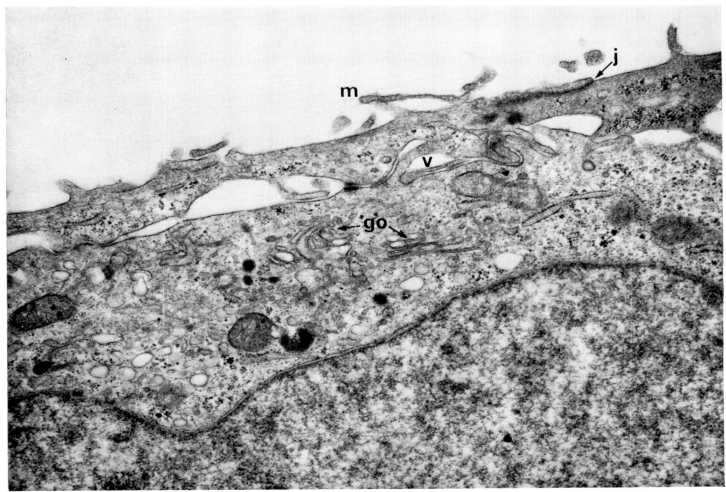

FIGURES 13–15

The micrographs opposite illustrate desmosomes in bilaminar epidermis at an early stage of development. The upper one shows that part of the ectodermal cell (E) in Fig. 8, which is overlapped by the peripheral part of a periderm cell (P) of adjacent bilaminar epidermis. Two quite well-differentiated desmosomes (d) and a tight junction (macula adherens) (t) are present along the plane of contact.

Figure 14 shows a villous process (v) of a germinative cell establishing contact at two points (arrowed) with an overlying periderm cell (P). At the lower point, the parallel apposed plasma membranes appear locally more electron dense and thickened, and the intercellular space is occupied by a barely perceptible substance of low density. This represents a very early desmosome, and one at a more advanced stage of differentiation is present at the upper point of contact. Here, and in Fig. 15, the intercellular space is seen to be bisected by an intermediate dense line, and just within each plasma membrane is a narrow band of high electron density, from the inner aspect of which an ill-defined cloud of less dense material (f) extends deeper into the cytoplasm. In desmosomes of later embryonic and fully developed epidermis, filaments are characteristically present in this latter situation, and though none such can be resolved at the present stage, their appearance is already clearly fore-shadowed. Desmosomes sectioned in the same plane as the plasma membrane are seen to be rounded or oval in shape.

The "mirror-image" character of the two halves of a desmosome suggests that mutual interactions are concerned in their formation, but whether these processes commence simultaneously in each cell, or are initiated by one or other is not known. It is not clear either what factors are concerned in determining the precise location of individual desmosomes along a length of apposed plasma membranes. Indeed, the general phenomenon of intercellular adhesion is at present poorly understood, though physico-chemical factors such as ionic conditions and electrical potentials at the cell surface are undoubtedly concerned in its maintenance.

Fig. 13. Contacts between ectodermal cell and overlapping peripheral part of periderm cell from crown of head of 14 mm C.R. (6 week) human embryo. Glutaraldehyde-osmium fixation, lead stain. × 99,600.

Fig. 14. Contacts between periderm cell and process of germinative cell from crown of head of 14 mm (6 week) human embryo. Glutaraldehyde-osmium fixation, lead stain. × 100,800.

Fig. 15. Desmosome from bilaminar epidermis of crown of head of 14 mm (6 week) human embryo. Glutaraldehyde-osmium fixation, lead stain. × 136,840.

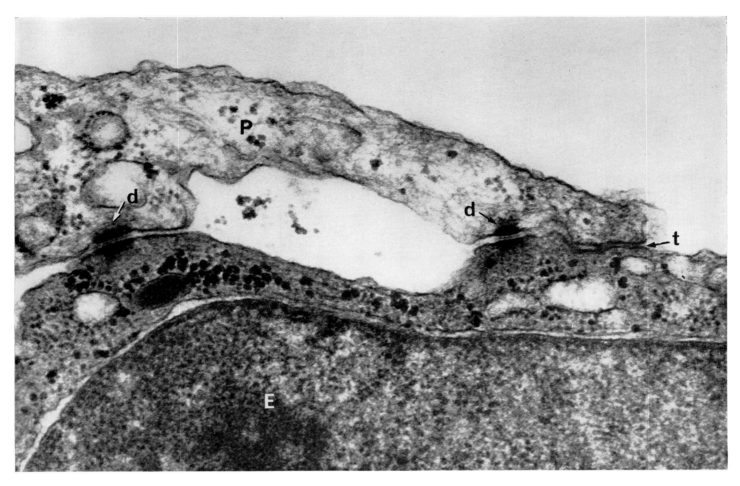

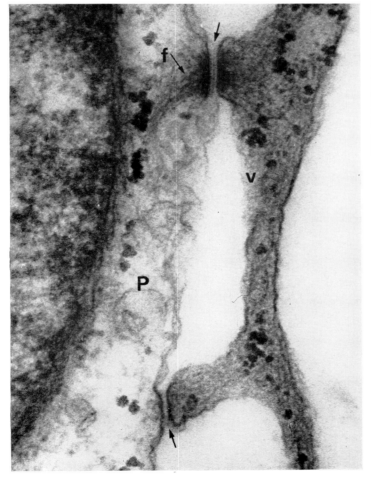
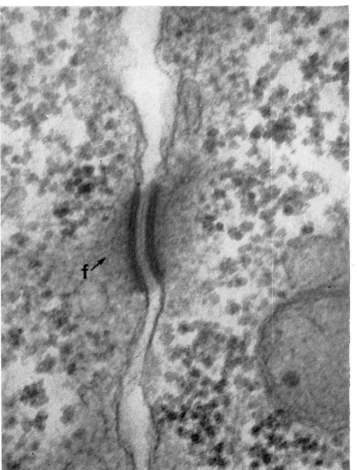

FIGURES 16 and 17

These two micrographs illustrate the filaments (f) which become associated with desmosomes at later stages of development. They have a diameter of 7–9 nm (70–90 Å) and are termed tono-filaments, and bundles of them (tonofibrils) appear to terminate upon the dense band, or attachment plaque (p), just within the plasma membrane at the site of the desmosome (d). Some authorities maintain that individual tonofilaments do not actually terminate at the desmosome, but merely make contact with it and loop back into the cytoplasm. Tonofilaments on cross-section are seen at f_1 in the upper micrograph.

Tonofilaments and tonofibrils are perhaps the most characteristic feature of the epidermal keratinocyte, and it may be emphasized here that they are not confined to the neighbourhood of desmosomes, but are present throughout the cytoplasm of fully developed cells. Observations on fetal skin suggest, however, that they appear initially in the former situation. Further details of tonofilaments and tonofibrils will be given as they are repeatedly referred to at later stages.

Fig. 16. Desmosomes and tonofilaments of cells from upper intermediate level of epidermis of a 215 mm C.R. (24 week) human fetus. Osmium fixation, lead stain. × 83,600.

Fig. 17. Desmosomes and tonofilaments of cells from stratum spinosum of forearm epidermis of an 18 year old girl. Osmium fixation, lead stain. × 116,500.

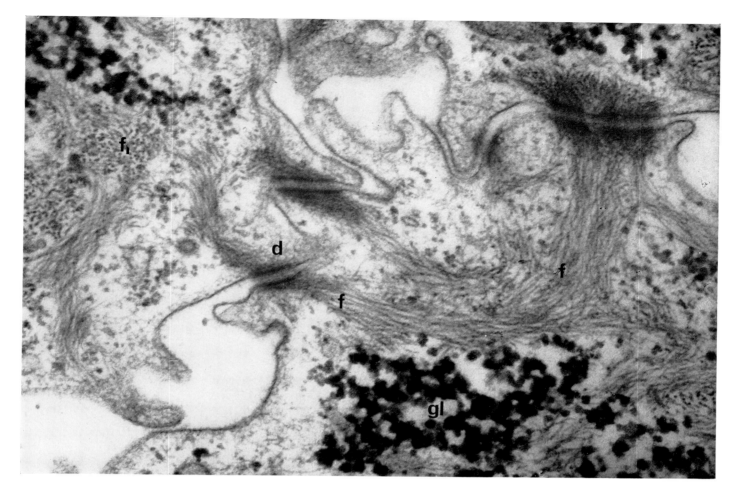

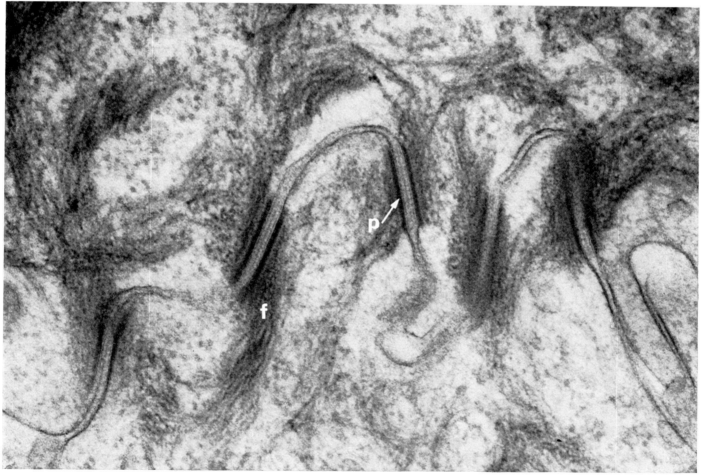

17

FIGURE 18

These remarks on intercellular contacts, stemming from a consideration of early bilaminar epidermis, may be rounded off by presenting a micrograph showing the complexity of arrangement which may be encountered at the fully developed post-natal stage. There is a marked
interdigitation of cellular processes, and the intercellular space between the apposed plasma
membranes is narrow, measuring 15–20 nm (150–200 Å). Segments of plasma membrane lying
in the plane of section (p), present an amorphous appearance. Desmosomes, and tonofilamentous bundles (t) sectioned in different planes are seen.

Fig. 18. Intercellular contacts in basal layer of forearm epidermis of an 18 year old girl. Osmium
fixation, lead stain. × 79,800.

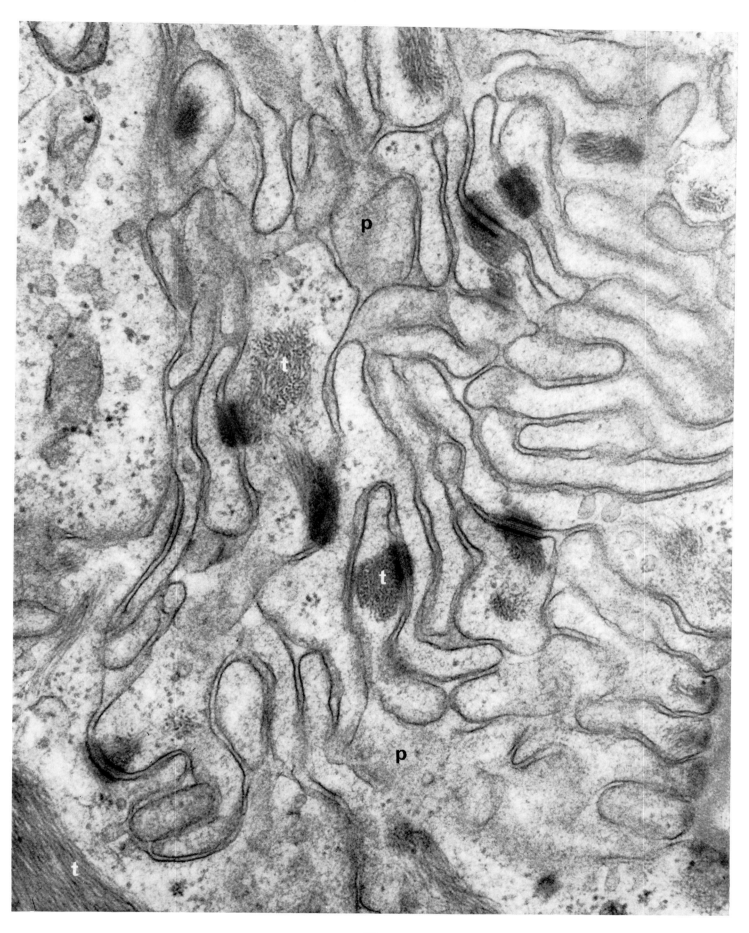

19

FIGURE 19

A zone of relatively greater density (d) compared with the general mesodermal matrix is present from an early stage just beneath the basal plasma membrane (pl) of the ectodermal cell (E). This zone varies in depth between 0·1 and 0·2 μm, and appears to consist of scattered 10–12 nm (100–120 Å) fibrils set in an amorphous matrix. In places, a narrow (approximately 15 nm (150 Å)) more electron-translucent interval can be distinguished between the dense zone and the basal plasma membrane, but it is not continuous over any great extent. On the cytoplasmic aspect of the plasma membrane another zone of localized density (f), approximately 0·19 μm in depth but with ill-defined upper limit, can be observed. One gets the impression that this zone also is fibrillar in nature, though if so, the fibrils must be exceedingly fine as none can with certainty be resolved within it.

FIGURE 20

This shows the character of the junctional region at a stage when a bilaminar epidermis is present. A continuous, narrow layer of moderately electron-dense material (b) now parallels the basal plasma membrane of the germinative cell (G) being separated from it by a relatively electron-translucent interval (s) of approximately 35 nm (350 Å). This is the basal lamina, or "adepidermal membrane", and though its limits are ill-defined, its depth is about 20 nm (200 Å). It presents a rather fuzzy homogenous appearance, and is thought to consist of very fine tropocollagenous fibrils running mainly in the plane of the lamina and embedded in an amorphous matrix containing acid mucopolysaccharides and probably some protein. The interval (s) between the basal lamina and the plasma membrane of the germinative cell is occupied by similar material, less densely arranged, but which in places seems to consist of fine filamentous strands connecting the two. The source and mode of production of the basal lamina remains obscure. Most workers would agree that it receives a material contribution from the mesoderm, but evidence of epidermal participation in its formation, apart from an inductive influence, is equivocal.

The dense zone (f) on the cytoplasmic aspect of the basal plasma membrane is more compacted than in the ectodermal cell above. It is not possible to say anything about the origin, nature, or significance of whatever substance may be responsible for this localized density. A similar zone present in epidermal basal cells cultured on millipore filter in the presence of high levels of embryo extract has been thought to have an internal supportive or "scaffolding" function. However this may be, this is a transient feature of the germinative cells, and by the time tonofilaments are beginning to appear in the cytoplasm, it is no longer apparent.

Fig. 19. Ectodermal-mesodermal interface from crown of head of 14 mm C.R. (6 week) human embryo. Glutaraldehyde-osmium fixation, lead stain. × 80,500.

Fig. 20. Interface between mesoderm and germinative cell from bilaminar epidermis of upper limb-bud of 14 mm C.R. (6 week) human embryo. Glutaraldehyde-osmium fixation, lead stain. × 79,500.

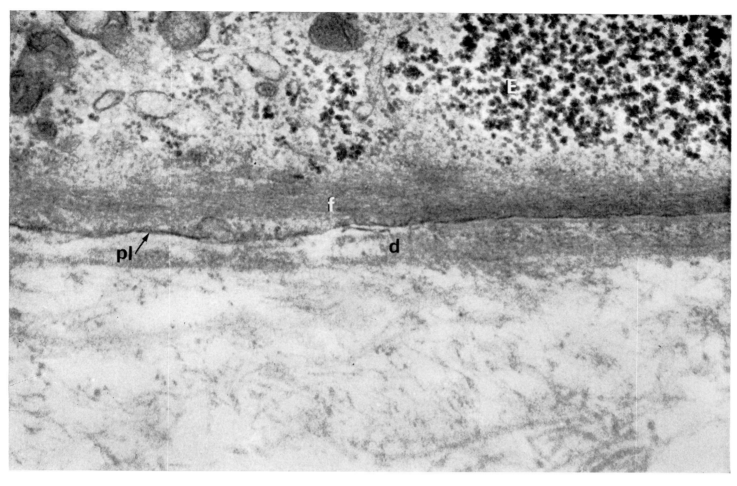

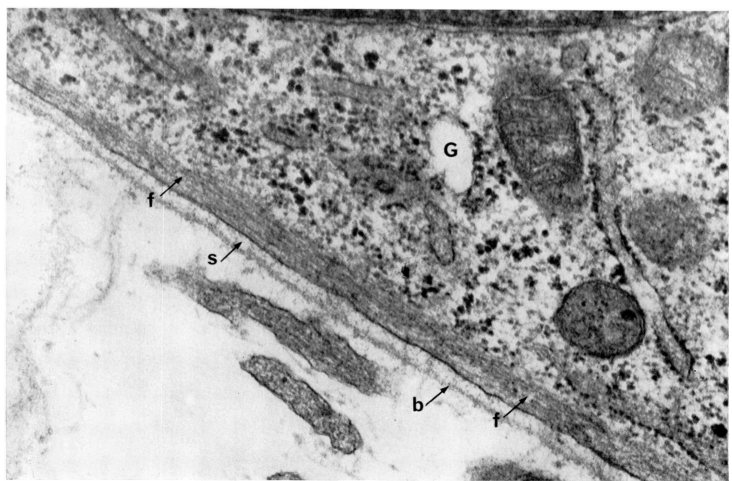

21

FIGURE 21

These germinative cells of bilaminar upper limb-bud epidermis are less overlapped, and be-coming more regularly arranged compared with similar cells from the less advanced crown of head region figured in earlier illustrations. Tissue culture experiments have established that development of such an ordered epithelial habit as well as maintenance of the basal orientation and mitotic activity of the germinal cells requires a suitable substrate. The basal lamina (b) is thought to function as such *in vivo*, and therefore to be of considerable morphogenetic signifi-cance. Some authorities believe it forms a barrier to free ionic exchange between epidermis and mesoderm, and if this be so, it is evidently in a position selectively to regulate the passage across it in either direction of factors influencing cytodifferentiation.

In certain epidermal tumours, and in regenerating epidermis, the basal lamina may not be completely continuous, and in these circumstances dilated bladder-like processes of basal cell cytoplasm are found protruding into the dermis through the gaps. This suggests that an intact, normal basal lamina is essential in limiting basal cell growth in a dermal direction, and in determining the exact boundary between the two.

FIGURE 22

This illustrates features of the epidermal-mesodermal (or dermal) junctional region present at later stages of development, though exactly when they first appear cannot definitely be stated. Localized areas of increased density (d) are present at intervals along the basal plasma mem-brane, and opposite these, mirroring them so to speak, the basal lamina is correspondingly more locally dense (d_1). The arrangement is reminiscent of early desmosomes, and indeed in some situations an intermediate dense line (l) is present in the interval (30–40 nm) between plasma membrane and basal lamina (25–30 nm) though closer to the former. At a slightly later stage of development, tonofilaments, already fairly abundant in the cytoplasm (t), are associated with these structures which are known as hemi-desmosomes. This implies they are regions of particularly strong attachment of the basal plasma membrane to the basal lamina. It may be observed that the compact dense zone present at an earlier stage just within the basal plasma membrane is no longer evident.

Two types of fibrils are present in the region deep to the basal lamina. Directly beneath, and in fact running into, or attached to it, are finer, 10–20 nm (100–200 Å) fibrils (f) arranged as an irregular meshwork; interspersed with these are fibres (c) of larger diameter (25–40 nm). The smaller fibrils are reticular fibrils, and the larger ones are young collagen, or precollagen fibres.

Fig. 21. Germinative cells and basal lamina from bilaminar epidermis of upper limb-bud of 14 mm C.R. (6 week) human embryo. Glutaraldehyde-osmium fixation, lead stain. × 22,800.

Fig. 22. Epidermal-mesodermal junction from scalp skin of 113 mm C.R. (16 week) human embryo. Osmium fixation, lead and uranyl acetate staining. × 63,800.

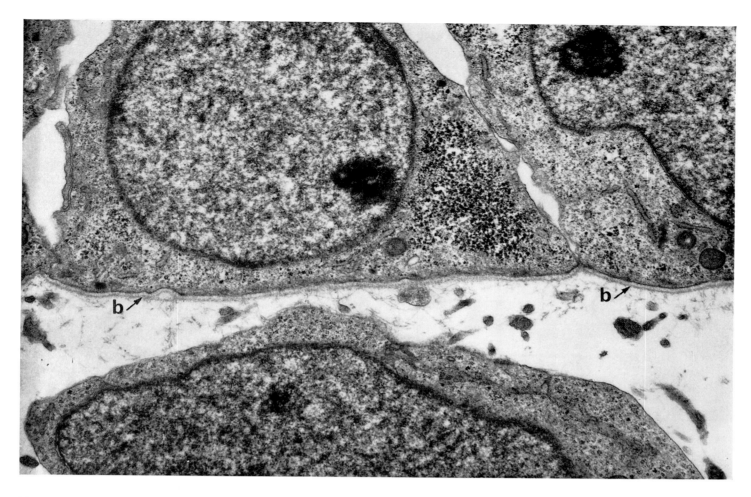

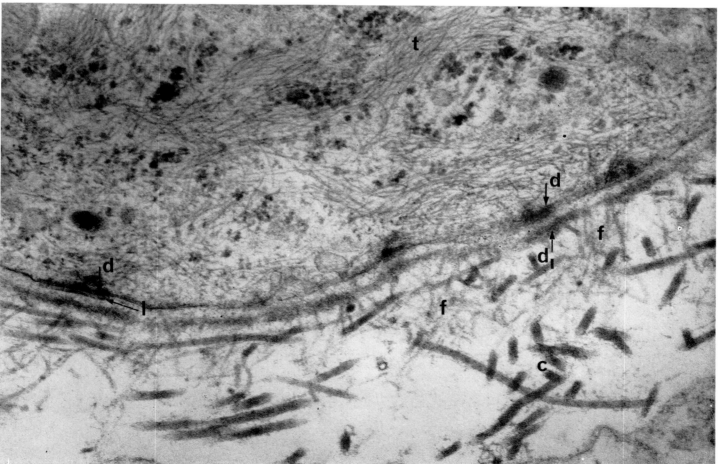

FIGURES 23 and 24

As development proceeds, the interface between the basal epidermal cell and the underlying tissue, which can now be referred to as the dermis, appears more undulant on section, and this feature is very marked in post-natal skin as seen in the lower micrograph. Hemi-desmosomes (h) present along the basal plasma membrane are numerous, and some present a highly characteristic appearance. Instead of being of uniform thickness throughout its extent, the dense plaque just within the basal plasma membrane is seen to be composed of a number of triangular bobbins (b), and in places, what are presumably single bobbins are evident. These differences in appearance of hemi-desmosomes are very likely due to differences in orientation to the plane of section, or, assuming that they are oval or rounded structures, dependent upon how close or otherwise to the central diameter an individual hemi-desmosome happens to have been sectioned.

The basal lamina (l) of late fetal and post-natal epidermis is not significantly different to that of earlier developmental stages, and while the fibres underlying it gradually increase in numerical density, two types of different diameter remain distinguishable. These are larger diameter, pre-collagen or collagen fibres as the case may be, and fibres of smaller diameter (f) many of which are directly attached to the basal lamina. The majority of these latter are classed as "reticular fibrils" in fully developed skin, but some, which often present a branched appearance and an irregular banding have been termed "anchoring fibrils".

Fig. 23. Epidermal-dermal junction from back skin of 230 mm C.R. (26 week) human fetus. Osmium fixation, lead stain. × 52,500.

Fig. 24. Epidermal-dermal junction from forearm skin of an 18 year old girl. Osmium fixation, lead and uranyl-acetate staining. × 35,000.

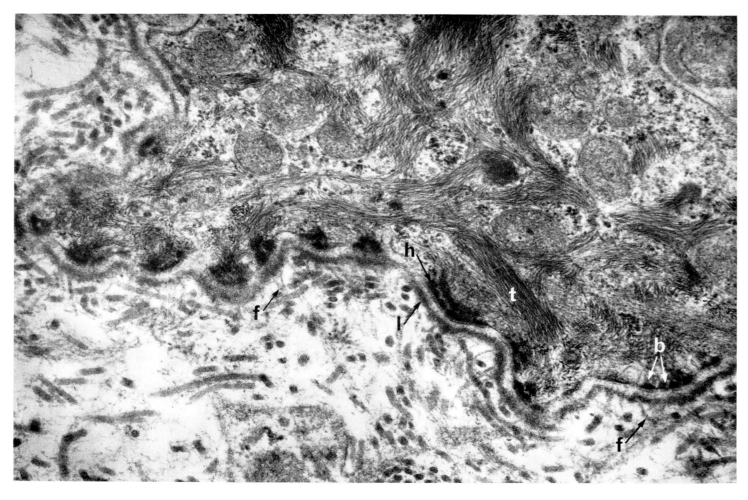

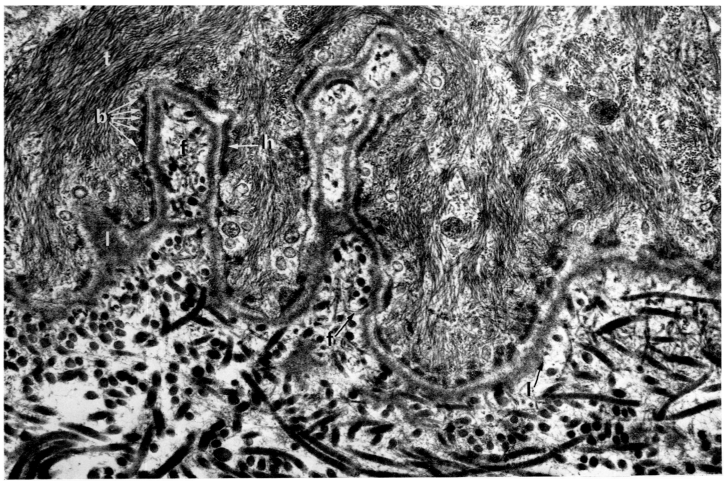

FIGURES 25 and 26

Individual cells (M) of the type illustrated in these micrographs are occasionally seen between periderm (P) and germinative (G) cells. Desmosomes are absent from the plasma membrane, and there is little or no glycogen present in the cytoplasm. Round globules (g) of high electron density, and closely resembling lipid in appearance are numerous, and vesicles (v) either empty or containing less dense material, are also present. From their position, it is possible that these cells could be first generation intermediate layer cells derived from the germinative layer, though their appearance is totally different to that presented by such cells at a slightly later stage of development. The other possibility is, that they may be immigrant cells of mesodermal origin. If so, the presence of a non-ectodermal component in epidermis at this early stage of development is a matter of some interest.

Fig. 25. Cell of possible mesodermal origin in bilaminar epidermis from upper limb-bud of 14 mm C.R. (6 week) human embryo. Glutaraldehyde-osmium fixation, lead stain. × 20,100.

Fig. 26. Similar cell of possible mesodermal origin in bilaminar epidermis from upper limb-bud of 14 mm C.R. (6 week) human embryo. Glutaraldehyde-osmium fixation, lead staining. × 26,000.

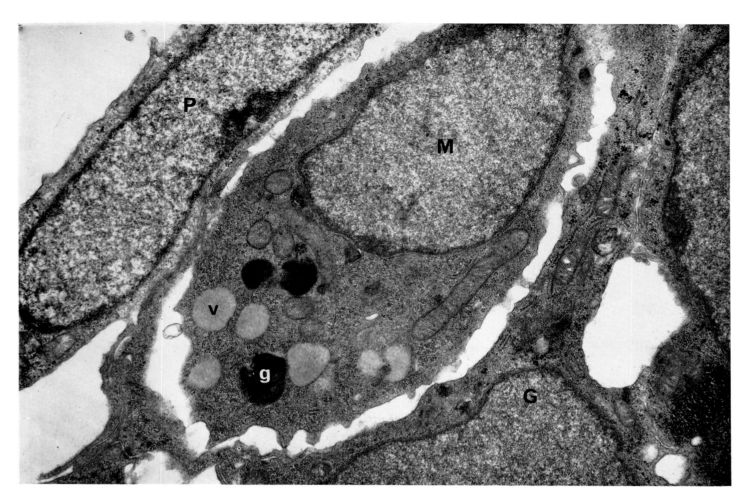

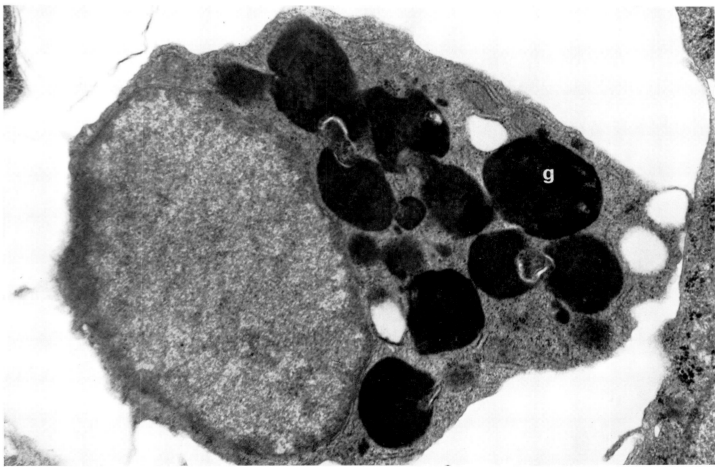

27

FIGURE 27

The appearance of one or more intermediate layers of cells (I) between the periderm (P) and the germinative layer (G) leads to pluristratification of the epidermis, but the time and rate at which this occurs is not uniform throughout the embryo. In general, development tends to be further advanced cephalad than caudad, and on the body, it progresses from the region of the mid-axillary line ventrally. By about the 9th week, an intermediate layer is present on the face (eyebrows, lips, nose), and appears progressively later on the back, abdomen and limbs. Since differentiation therefore is not synchronous throughout all regions, it should not be thought of purely in terms of the age of the fetus.

The intermediate cells (I) are initially flattened parallel with the surface, a feature which is exaggerated somewhat in the micrograph opposite, as nuclei are not included in the section. Cohesion between cells of all layers soon becomes well established in comparison with the previous two cell-layered stage, as evidenced by closer apposition of plasma membranes and interlocking processes, and more numerous desmosomes. Glycogen is a very prominent feature of the epidermis at this stage, large deposits being present within cells at all levels.

FIGURE 28

By the time one or more layers of intermediate cells are present, small rounded cells (M) with high nuclear-cytoplasmic ratio and containing relatively little glycogen are encountered with increasing frequency among the germinative cells (G) and at higher levels. They are usually separated at first from adjacent cells by spaces of varying size, and desmosomes are absent from the plasma membrane. These cells are representatives of an important epidermal element —the non-keratinocytes—which comprises melanocytes and Langerhans cells. Melanocytes stem from the neural crest and begin to enter the epidermis from the underlying dermis from about the 11th week onwards—depending upon the region. The origin of the Langerhans cells is less certain, but they are also immigrant cells, though it is not known when they first enter the epidermis. It is very remotely possible that the cells in the previous two micrographs (Figs. 25 and 26) are stem cells destined to differentiate into Langerhans cells. Melanocytes and Langerhans cells ultimately develop highly characteristic cytoplasmic organelles by which they may be individually identified, but previous to this it is not easy at times to distinguish them with certainty, and the cell illustrated here might belong to either category.

The fetal epidermis can thus be said to contain four components: (1) Germinal and intermediate cells which, since they give rise ultimately to the keratinized elements of late fetal and post-natal life, are termed keratinocytes; (2) Melanocytes, or pigment forming cells; (3) Langerhans cells of rather uncertain function; and (4) the periderm, which unlike the other three is a purely fetal structure.

Fig. 27. Multi-stratified epidermis from back skin of 57 mm C.R. (12 week) human fetus. Glutaraldehyde-osmium fixation, lead staining. × 13,000.

Fig. 28. Non-keratinocyte in germinative layer of epidermis from back skin of 57 mm C.R. (12 week) human fetus. Glutaraldehyde-osmium fixation, lead staining. × 29,600.

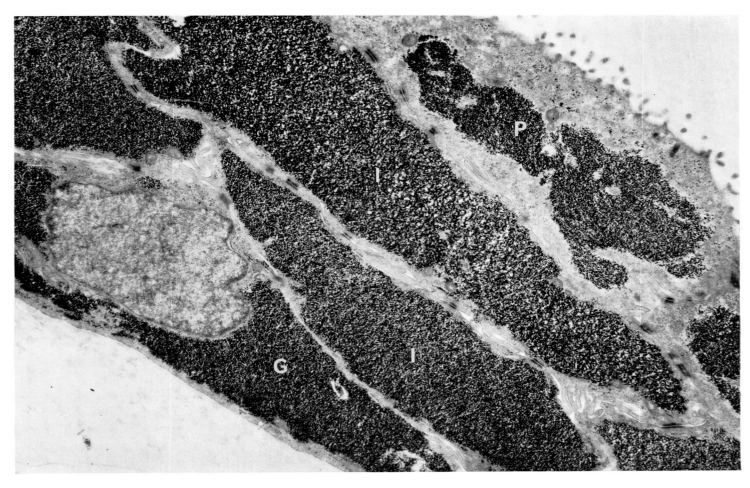

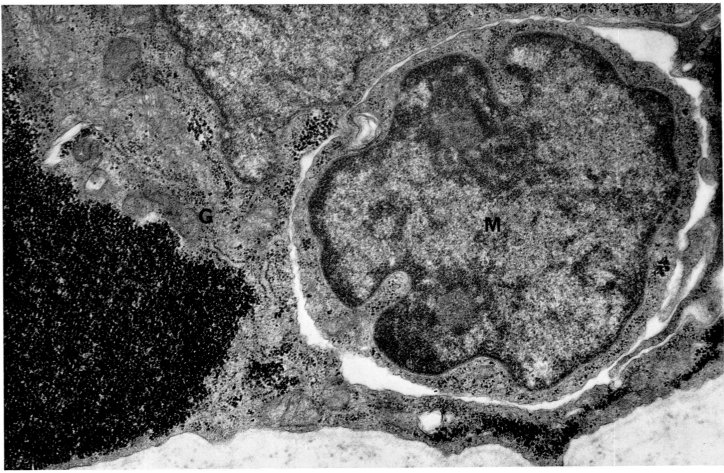

REFERENCES

GENERAL CELL STRUCTURE

Brachet, J. and Mirsky, A. E. (eds.). "The Cell", Vols. I–VI. New York, Academic Press, 1959–64.
Fawcett, D. W. "The Cell. Its organelles and inclusions". Philadelphia, W. B. Saunders Co., 1966.

TISSUE INTERACTIONS AND CYTODIFFERENTIATION

Billingham, R. E. and Silvers, W. K. The origin and conservation of epidermal specificities. *New Eng. J. Med.*, **268**:477, 1963.
Fleischmajer, R. and Billingham, R. E. (eds.). "Epithelial-Mesenchymal Interactions". Baltimore, Williams and Wilkins Co., 1968.
Mercer, E. H. "Keratin and keratinization". Oxford, Pergamon, 1961.
Wessels, N. K. Differentiation of epidermis and epidermal derivatives. *New Eng. J. Med.*, **277**:21, 1967.

GLYCOGEN

Drochmans, P. Morphologie du glycogène. *J. Ultrastruct. Res.*, **6**:141, 1962.
Revel, J. P. Electron microscopy of glycogen. *J. Histochem. Cytochem.*, **12**:104, 1964.

INTERCELLULAR CONTACTS, DESMOSOMES

Abercrombie, M. Cell contacts in morphogenesis. *Arch. Biol. (Liège)*, **75**:351, 1964.
Curtis, A. S. G. "The cell surface: its molecular role in morphogenesis". New York, Academic Press, 1967.
Farquhar, M. G. and Palade, G. E. Cell junctions in amphibian skin. *J. Cell Biol.*, **26**:263, 1965.

EPIDERMAL MESODERMAL JUNCTION, BASAL LAMINA

These receive consideration in some of the references listed above. See also:
Dodson, J. W. Differentiation of epidermis. 1. Inter-relationship of epidermis and dermis in embryonic chicken skin. *J. Embryol. & Exper. Morphol.*, **17**:83, 1967.
Goel, S. C. and Jurand, A. Electron microscopic observations on the basal lamina of chick limb buds after trypsin and EDTA treatment. *J. Cell. Sci.*, **3**:373, 1968.

2 Development of Epidermis—the Periderm

Globular elevations: differentiation of vesicles: microvilli and filaments — regression: fibrillar transformation.

FIGURES 29 and 30

From an early stage, mitotic figures can be observed in the periderm, and it is now generally thought that this layer is maintained by the mitotic activity of its own cells rather than by recruitment of underlying intermediate cells (I) stemming from the germinative layers.

From being originally flattened, the periderm cells (P) gradually increase in depth, due to an elevation of the central part of the cell. This renders the amniotic surface of the epidermis regularly undulant. At the same time, the surface microvilli (m) become larger and more numerous. The cell organelles at this stage are mainly located in the supra-nuclear cytoplasm which is relatively free of glycogen, in contrast to the infra-nuclear cytoplasm, where large deposits (gl) extending lateral to the nucleus are located. Golgi membranes and vesicles (go) though present are not particularly prominent at this stage, and mitochondria (mi) are not very numerous. Scattered clusters of ribosomes (r) are present, and loosely arranged bundles of fine filaments (f) are barely perceptible in sections stained with lead, though more clearly evident in those stained with phosphotungstic acid.

Fig. 29. Periderm and intermediate cells from epidermis of back of 50 mm C.R. (11 week) human fetus. Osmium fixation, lead staining. × 7,000.

Fig. 30. Supra-nuclear region of periderm cell from epidermis of back of 50 mm C.R. (11 week) human fetus. Osmium fixation, lead staining. × 15,600.

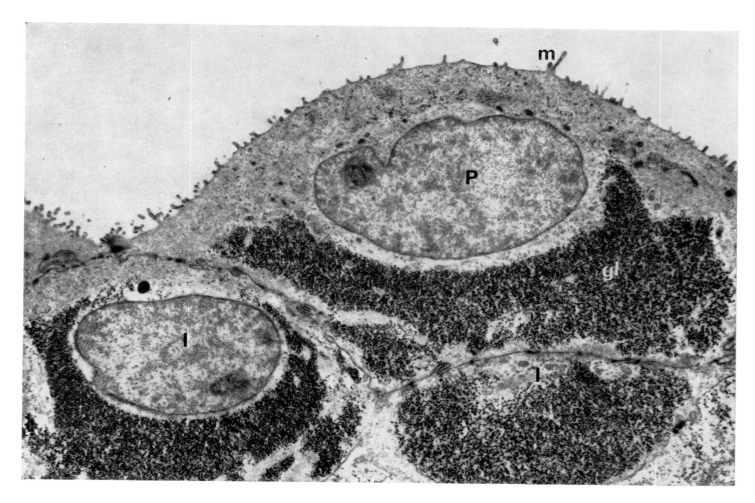

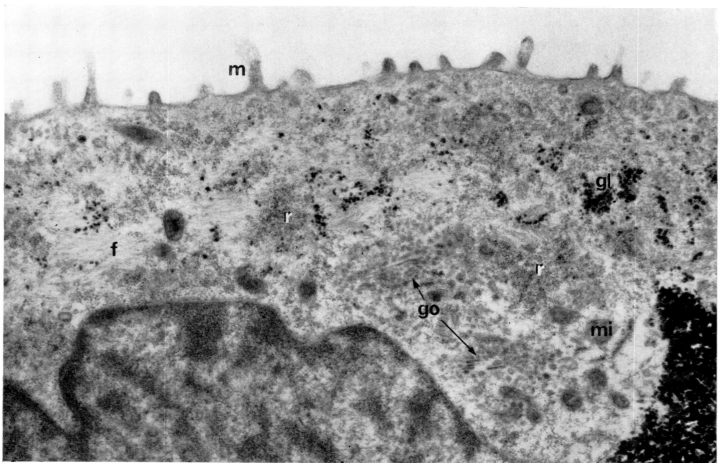

FIGURE 31

As development proceeds, the surface elevation of the periderm becomes more irregular, and indentations of the plasma membrane (in) which partly undermine the elevations lead to the formation of globular protrusions which are connected to the remainder of the cell by one or more pedicles of cytoplasm. The nucleus (n) may, or may not be included in these globular elevations, which correspond to the "bladder-cells" of light microscopy. Owing to the tortuosity of the indentations of the plasma membrane, these may appear to be intracellular canaliculi lined by microvilli, but it is doubtful if they should be regarded as such in any functional sense.

The bulk of the glycogen (gl) still occupies the infra-nuclear region of the cytoplasm, but within the globular elevations, increased amounts are observed in a supra-nuclear position with advancing age. Whether this is due to redistribution of glycogen already present, or to new deposition in this latter situation it is not possible to say. Junction between periderm cells occurs at (j).

FIGURE 32

This shows a globular elevation at a more advanced stage. Its attachment to the rest of the cell is undermined to an even greater extent than earlier by indentations of the plasma membrane (in) so much so, that were this to proceed much further, one might expect the elevated portion to become completely detached as a free element in the amniotic fluid. This indeed is the fate of many of the globular elevations as will be seen. Glycogen (gl) is now abundantly present superficial to the nucleus (n), the marked indentation of which is indicative of the advancing age of the cell.

Fig. 31. Periderm cell from epidermis of back of 81 mm C.R. (14 week) human fetus. Osmium fixation, lead staining. × 5,000.

Fig. 32. Globular elevation of periderm cell from scalp epidermis of 120 mm C.R. (17 week) human fetus. Glutaraldehyde-osmium fixation, lead staining. × 7,400.

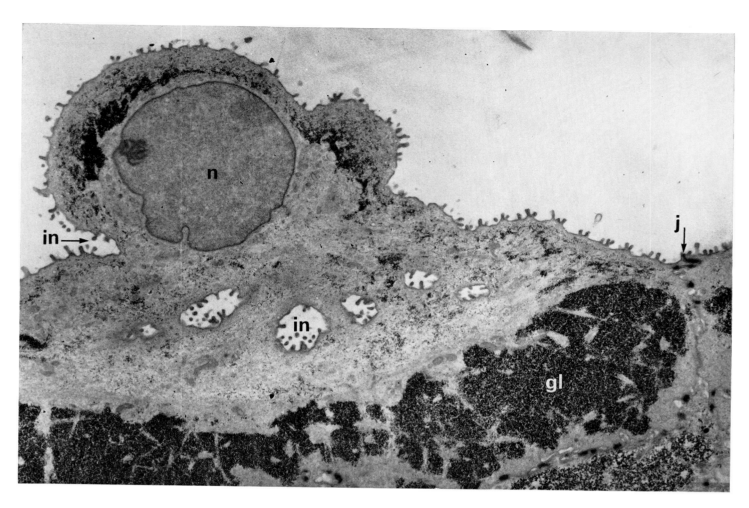

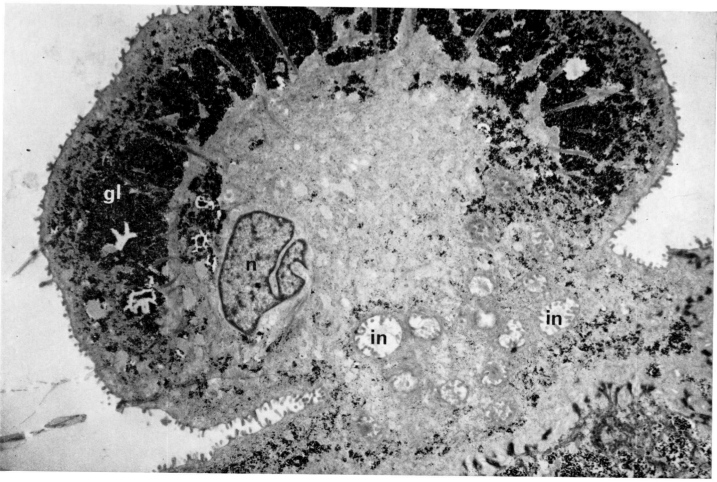

FIGURE 33

While globular elevations are developing at the surface of the periderm (10–12th week on-wards, depending upon site) smooth membrane-bound vesicles (v) appear in the supra-nuclear cytoplasm, in the neighbourhood of the Golgi apparatus (go). Many of the vesicles contain reticular material of low density, and the variation in size is well seen in this micrograph. Over the next few weeks these vesicles become widely distributed throughout all areas of the cyto-plasm showing a tendency to become concentrated in the zone just deep to the surface mem-brane. They represent one of the most characteristic features of the periderm cell over the period 10–16 weeks.

FIGURE 34

This micrograph of the peripheral cytoplasm of a more advanced periderm cell shows numer-ous cytoplasmic vesicles (v) and an exuberant development of microvilli (m). A line of desmo-somes (d) marks the junction between periderm and an underlying intermediate layer cell (I). The cytoplasm of this latter appears characteristically "empty", because the section is stained with PTA, and the glycogen (gl) which practically fills the cell, in fact, is not rendered electron dense by this stain.

Fully developed microvilli are constricted basally and often exhibit a bulbous terminal ex-pansion. The majority arise singly from the plasma membrane, but occasionally several may be seen arising from a common stem.

Fig. 33. Supra-nuclear cytoplasm of periderm cell from epidermis of back of 57 mm C.R. (12 week) human fetus. Glutaraldehyde-osmium fixation, lead staining. × 47,200.

Fig. 34. Peripheral region of periderm cell from forearm epidermis of 130 mm C.R. (17 week) human fetus. Osmium fixation, phosphotungstic acid staining. × 14,700.

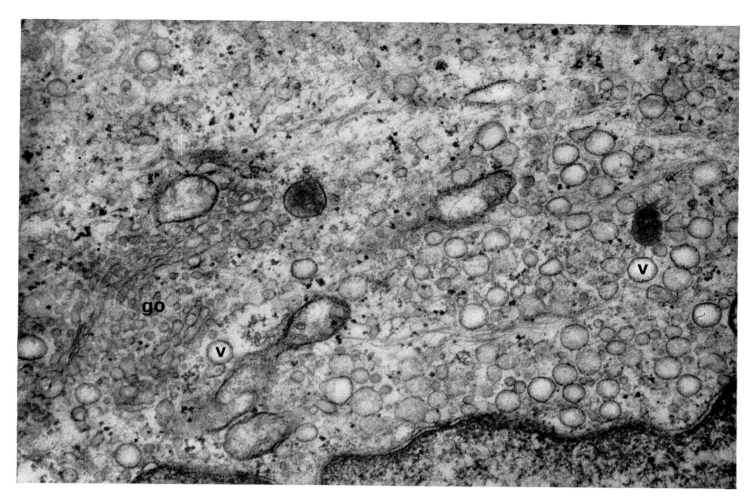

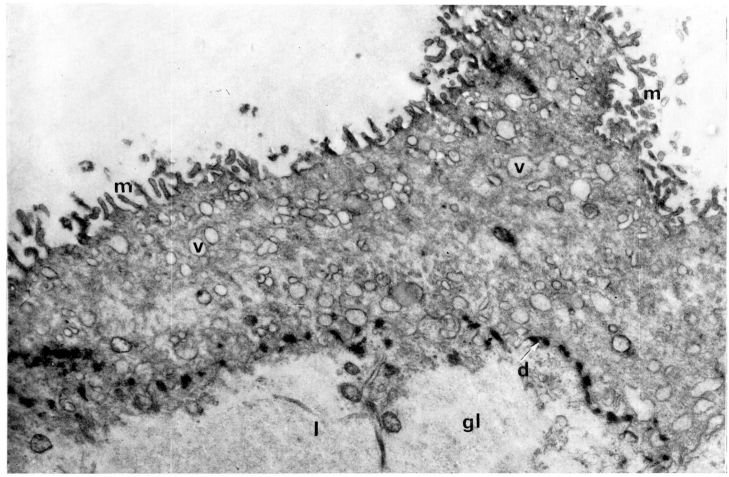

37

FIGURES 35 and 36

Phosphotungstic acid (PTA) is preferable to lead as a stain for revealing the cytoplasmic filaments (f) of the periderm cell, since they stand out more clearly in the absence of any significant staining of glycogen (gl). Filaments are concentrated around the nucleus, in the region just deep to the surface membrane and its indentations (in), and in the peripheral areas of the cell as seen in the upper micrograph, they form a meshwork within which the vesicles (v) lie. Apparently empty vesicles, and others containing reticular material are seen in both micrographs, and there seems to be no relation between the size of a vesicle and its location within the cell.

There is no information available as to the origin of the vesicles nor as to the nature of their contents. They may be produced within the cell, possibly from the Golgi apparatus, in which case they could be regarded as secretory or excretory in nature, perhaps delivering some product to the amniotic fluid. Or, they may develop as infoldings of the surface membrane which are nipped off—a process akin to micropinocytosis. This would suggest they may be concerned with absorption of fluid or other substances from the liquor amnii. In either instance, vesicles in open communication with the surface might be encountered. This, however, is rarely, if ever the case.

Fig. 35. Surface cytoplasm of periderm cell from forearm epidermis of 130 mm C.R. (17 week) human fetus. Osmium fixation, phosphotungstic acid staining. × 55,400.

Fig. 36. Perinuclear cytoplasm of periderm cell from forearm epidermis of 130 mm C.R. (17 week) human fetus. Osmium fixation, phosphotungstic acid staining. × 22,500.

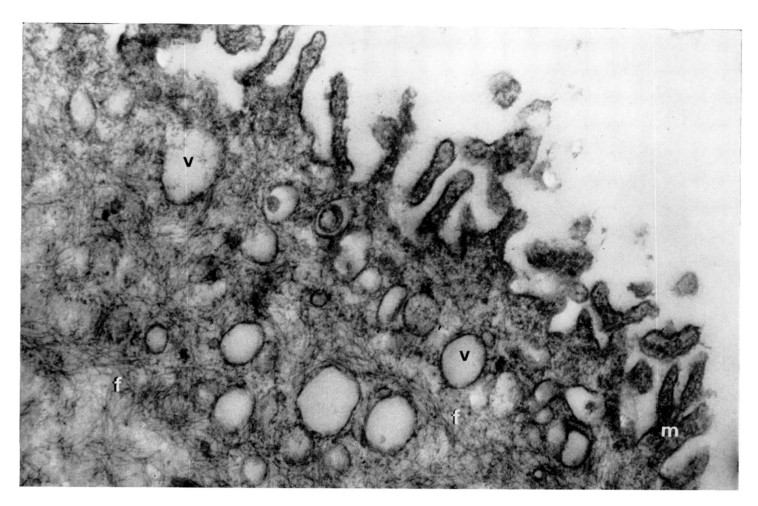

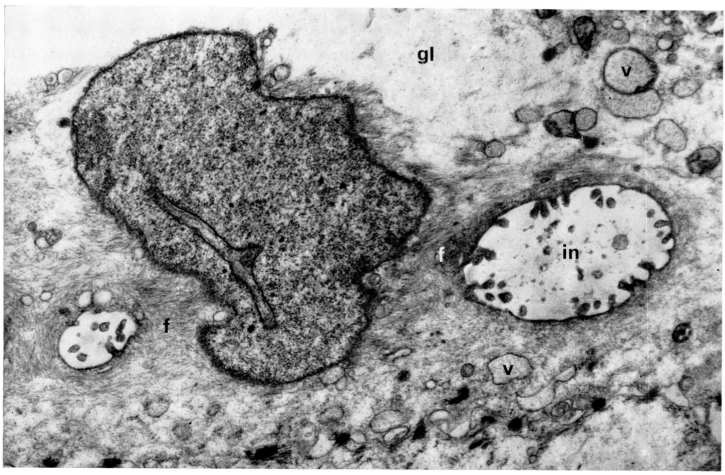

FIGURE 37

This micrograph is from a section stained with lead, therefore glycogen particles are revealed, but filaments are much less evident than in the previous figures. Staining with lead provides no additional information concerning the cytoplasmic vesicles, some of which are very close to the surface plasma membrane, particularly in relation to the indentation (in) in the centre of the field. As in the previous micrographs, however, no vesicles can be seen actually opening onto the surface.

Fine filamentous material (f) is frequently found on the surface of the microvilli. There is electron-histochemical evidence that this contains acid mucopolysaccharide, and it has been suggested that the surface of the periderm is covered by a thin mucous coat as in fully developed amphibian epidermis. If this be so, the most likely source of the mucous material is the periderm itself, though attempts so far to demonstrate it within the cells have not been successful. That the periderm should be capable of secreting mucus is not however beyond the bounds of possibility. Embryonic chick and human epidermis undergo a (reversible) mucous metaplasia when cultured in medium containing excess Vitamin A, and the periderm vesicles figured here closely resemble what have been identified as mucin containing globules in electron micrographs of metaplastic cells.

The progressive development of globular elevations, surface indentations, and more numerous and larger microvilli leads to a great increase in the surface area of peridermal plasma membrane exposed to the amniotic fluid. This certainly suggests that the periderm may be concerned with fluid, or other exchange in one or both directions between liquor and fetus, and the cytoplasmic vesicles may have some connection with this. At any rate, the features described require that the periderm be regarded as an actively functioning epithelium, rather than a purely passive protective layer of cells. It appears to reach its peak of differentiation in this connection over the period 12–16 weeks, after which it begins to regress, and it is finally transformed into a layer of flattened squames with purely filamentous internal structure.

Fig. 37. Surface cytoplasm of periderm cell from forearm epidermis of 130 mm C.R. (17 week) human fetus. Osmium fixation, lead staining. × 46,000.

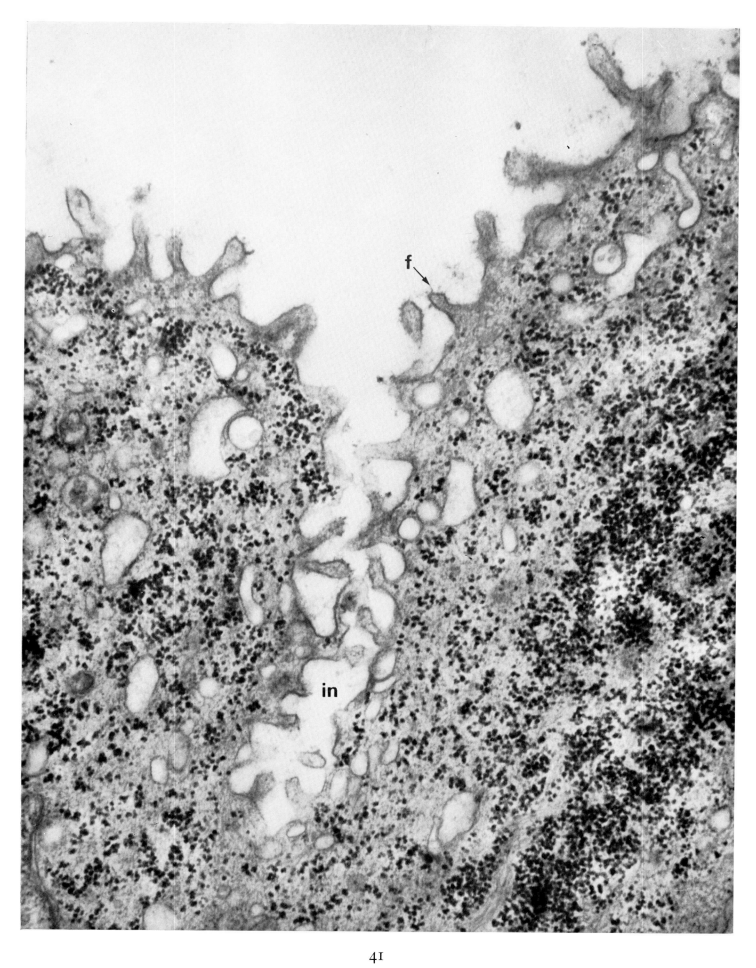

41

FIGURE 38

Undermining of globular protrusions (G) by indentation of the surface membrane proceeds to the extent that many entirely lose their connection with the basal part of the cell from which they stem (P) and are shed into the amniotic fluid. From the 16th to the 20th week and later, these elements make a significant contribution to the cellular content of the liquor, and some of the glucose present in the latter may be derived from breakdown of their contained glycogen.

FIGURE 39

Loss of protrusions as development proceeds leads to a diminution in the depth of the periderm (P) and a general smoothing out of its surface, though protrusions of variable size and irregular shape remain for some time. Associated with these alterations are dispersal and diminution of glycogen deposits, disappearance of cytoplasmic vesicles and reduction of other organelles, and a tendency for the microvilli to become shorter and more uniform in size. These features, taken together are indicative of the progressive retrogression of the periderm, prior to its transformation into a layer of cells containing little other than a meshwork of fine filaments.

Fig. 38. Periderm from scalp epidermis of 120 mm C.R. (16½ week) human fetus. Glutaraldehyde-osmium fixation, lead staining. × 5,200.

Fig. 39. Periderm and intermediate cells from forearm epidermis of 169 mm C.R. (21 week) human fetus. Osmium fixation, lead staining. × 13,000.

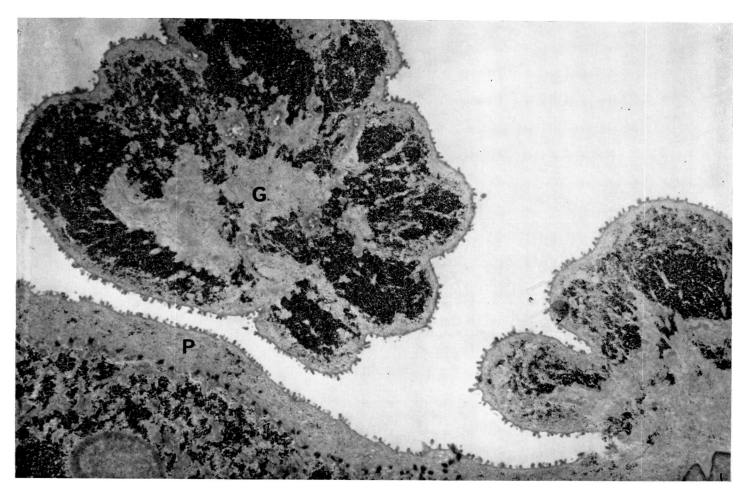

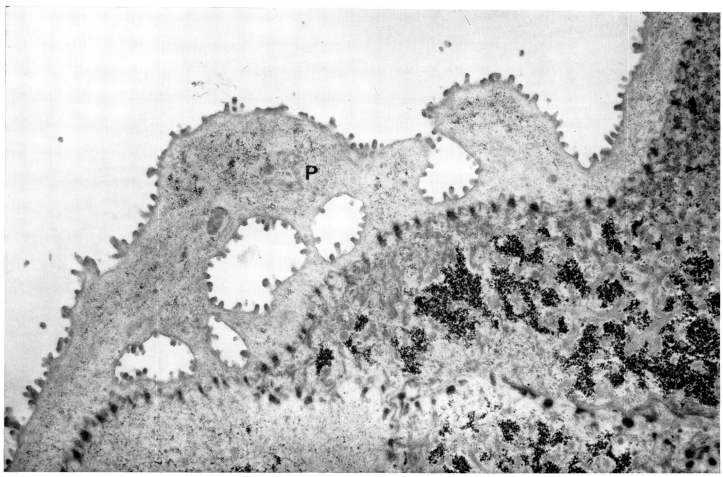

43

FIGURE 40

In this micrograph portions of two periderm cells of totally different appearance are seen. The cell on the left (P) is similar to that in the previous figure, and apart from an absence of organelles in the segment shown, the cytoplasm is not significantly different to that of the underlying uppermost intermediate layer cell (I). The cell on the right (P_1) is different in three respects: (1) the cytoplasm is more electron translucent, presenting an apparently granular matrix which at higher magnification can be resolved into a meshwork of fine filaments; (2) glycogen is absent, and (3) the plasma membrane appears thickened. Short microvilli are still present at the surface of both cells.

FIGURE 41

This illustrates an irregular protrusion from a periderm cell of similar appearance. In addition to the features mentioned above, remnants of cytoplasmic organelles (o) are present within the filamentous matrix (f), and nuclei in various stages of degradation are also occasionally seen in cells of this type. With the disappearance of nuclear and other remnants, the periderm cell can be said to have undergone its final transformation, into an essentially flattened, or in places, irregular surface filamentous flake. As such it remains attached to the underlying cells for some time, but is eventually shed, either independently, or with one or more layers of these latter as they in turn become transformed into squamous elements.

The thickened appearance of the plasma membrane of the transformed periderm cell seems to be due to development of a narrow zone of increased density on its cytoplasmic aspect. A similar feature is characteristic of keratinized stratum corneum cells of fully developed epidermis.

Fig. 40. Periderm and intermediate cells from forearm epidermis of 169 mm C.R. (21 week) human fetus. Osmium fixation, lead staining. × 17,100.

Fig. 41. Transformed periderm from forearm epidermis of 169 mm C.R. (21 week) human fetus. Osmium fixation, lead staining. × 13,200.

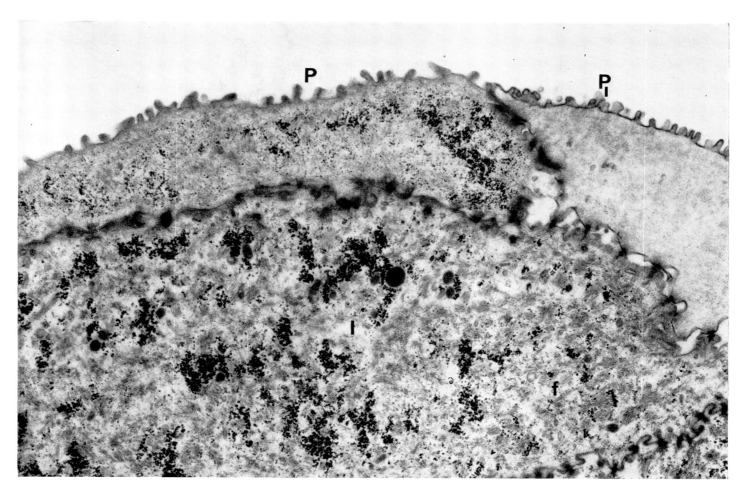

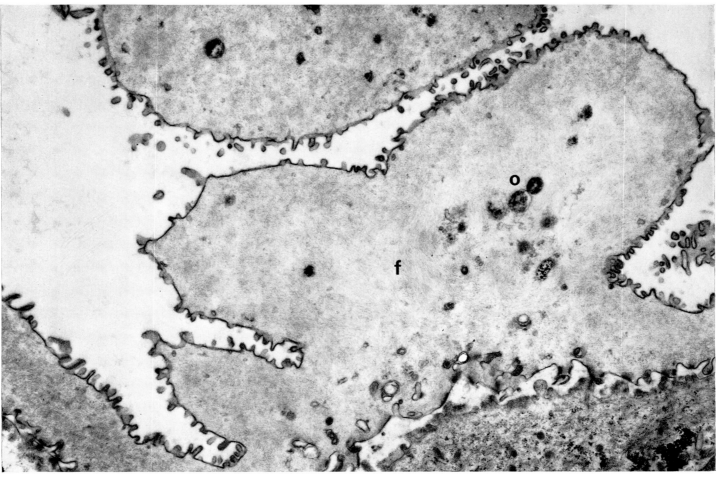

FIGURES 42 and 43

These two micrographs illustrate the internal filamentous structure of the transformed peri-derm cell (P). The filaments are uniformly distributed, and show little or no tendency to aggregate into bundles as do the tonofilaments (f) present in the underlying uppermost inter-mediate layer cell (I). One gets the impression that individual periderm filaments are shorter than tonofilaments, and of somewhat smaller diameter on transverse section.

In its final condition, the transformed periderm cell, though superficially resembling the keratinized stratum corneum cell of late fetal and post-natal epidermis, is yet essentially dif-ferent, as will become apparent when the latter are considered. In fact, it resembles more the stratum corneum cell of amphibian epidermis, which, like it, is exposed to a fluid medium.

Throughout this account, the periderm has been regarded as formed of a single layer of cells. However, in certain situations, e.g. the face, two layers of cells exhibiting features characteristic of periderm may be encountered. This could suggest, contrary to what was stated at the outset, that the periderm is populated in part by reception of cells from the underlying uppermost intermediate layer.

Granules of characteristic appearance are present in cells of chick periderm. They have a mesh-like internal structure of interlocking strands, very different to that of keratohyalin. Such periderm granules are not seen in the human fetus.

Fig. 42. Transformed periderm from forearm epidermis of 169 mm C.R. (21 week) human fetus. Osmium fixation, lead staining. × 32,000.

Fig. 43. Intermediate cell and periderm from forearm epidermis of 169 mm C.R. (21 week) human fetus. Osmium fixation, lead staining. × 53,200.

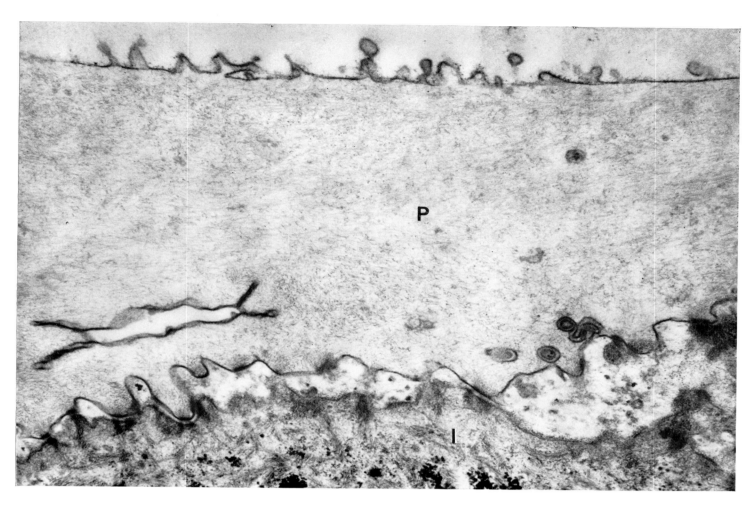

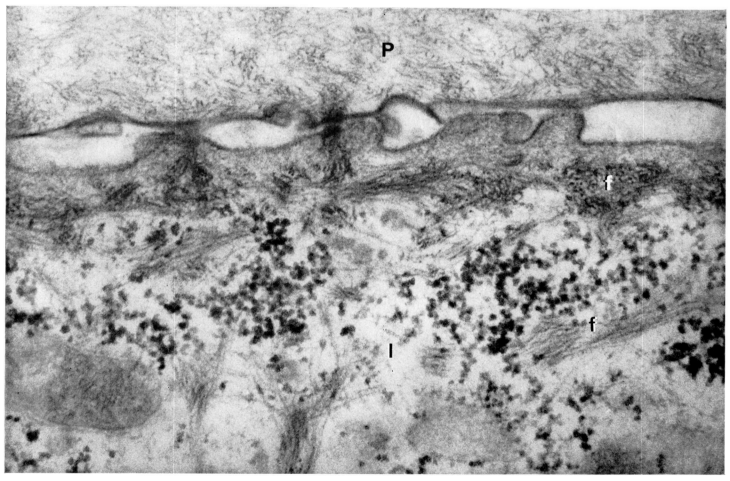

REFERENCES

PERIDERM

Breathnach, A. S. and Wyllie, L. M. Fine structure of cells forming the surface layer of the epidermis in human fetuses at fourteen and twelve weeks. *J. Invest. Derm.*, **45**:179, 1965.

Hoyes, A. D. The ultrastructure of the periderm, etc. Ph. D. thesis, University of London, 1968.

Hoyes, A. D. Electron microscopy of the surface layer (periderm) of human fetal skin. *J. Anat.*, **103**:321, 1968.

Parakkal, P. F. and Matoltsy, A. G. An electron microscopic study of developing chick skin. *J. Ultrastruc. Res.*, **23**:403, 1968.

Wolf, J. Structure and function of periderm. *Folia Morph. (Praha)*, **15**:296, 1967.

MUCOUS SECRETION

Fell, H. B. and Jackson, S. F. Epidermal fine structure in embryonic chicken skin during atypical differentiation induced by Vitamin A in culture. *Develop. Biol.*, **7**:394, 1963.

Hoyes, A. D. Acid mucopolysaccharide in human fetal epidermis. *J. Invest. Derm.*, **48**:598, 1967.

Lasnitski, I. The effect of carcinogens, hormones, and vitamins on organ cultures. *Int. Rev. Cytol.* **7**:79, 1958.

CELLS OF AMNIOTIC FLUID

Hoyes, A. D. Ultrastructure of the cells of the amniotic fluid. *J. Obstet. Gynaec. Brit. Cwlth.*, **75**:164, 1968.

3 Development of Sub-Peridermal Interfollicular Epidermis

Basal layer: melanocyte: cilia: lipid — intermediate layers: keratohyalin: granular layer and stratum corneum: keratinization — Langerhans cell — Merkel cell.

FIGURE 44

As the fetus grows older and larger, continuing mitotic activity of the cells of the basal layer provides for the necessary increase in the overall surface area of the epidermis and for the build up of intermediate layers of cells (I). By the time globular elevations are evident on the periderm (P), differentiation of the underlying layers has reached the stage illustrated opposite. There is significantly less glycogen now in the basal layer cells than in those lying more superficially, and irregular intercellular spaces are present between them. It is always a difficult matter to assess the significance of such spaces between cells of developing epithelial tissues. As already mentioned they may be in part artefactual, or, as some would have it, they may provide channels for the passage of fluid etc. from the mesoderm to various levels of the epidermis, or vice versa. At any rate, such spaces are consistently present between the basal cells in fetuses at this stage, and may be present to varying degrees for some time later. Desmosomes (d) help to outline individual cells of the various layers.

Melanocytes (M) are seen with increasing frequency in the basal layer, as development proceeds, and also occasionally at supra-basal levels. They are never encountered above the basal layer in fully-developed epidermis.

The epidermal-mesodermal interface or epidermal-dermal junction (j) as it may be termed from here on, is slightly undulant, and becomes progressively more so as the fetus matures. At intervals along it, crowding of cells in the basal layer foreshadows the appearance of hair-germs which later project into the dermis (see Fig. 189).

Fig. 44. Full-thickness epidermis from back of 81 mm C.R. (14 week) human fetus. Osmium fixation, lead staining. × 5,000.

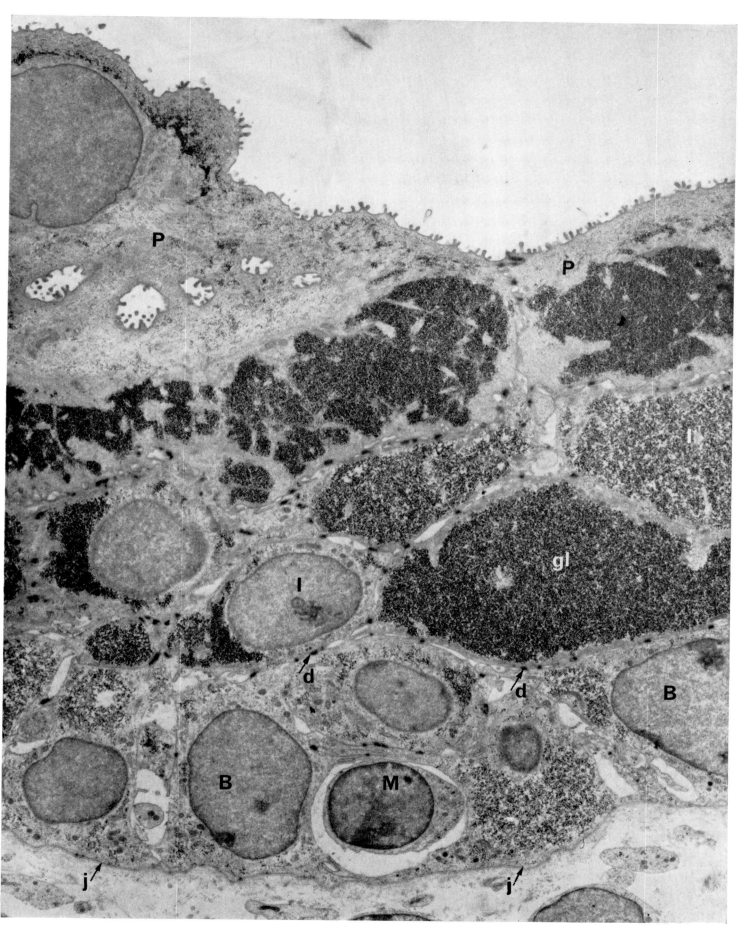

FIGURE 45

This micrograph illustrates most of the features of basal cell cytoplasm at the stage of development seen in the previous micrograph. Glycogen particles (gl), mitochondria (m), membranes
of the rough endoplasmic reticulum (r) and occasional round granules (gr) are present, as well
as fine filaments which show a tendency to aggregate into loose bundles (f). Golgi membranes,
though not included in the segments of the two cells shown, are also present. An intercellular
space (s) of moderate dimensions is present, and a narrower one surrounds the melanocyte
(M) at the top right corner of the field. In many preparations, glycogen is present in these
intercellular spaces, and it is difficult to say whether or not it occupies such a position *in vivo*.
It is seen more frequently in material fixed with osmium tetroxide than with glutaraldehyde,
and when present in large amounts in an intercellular position, there is frequently collateral
evidence of imperfect fixation, or damage to the tissue during some other stage of processing.

The basal lamina (b) closely parallels the basal plasma membrane of the cell, and a single
hemi-desmosome (h) is evident. As already mentioned (p. 22), it is not possible to say at what
stage basal hemi-desmosomes first appear, but they are certainly of later development than
desmosomes. Fine collagenous (c) and reticular fibres are associated with the mesodermal
aspect of the basal lamina, and portion of a fibroblast (F) can also be seen.

Fig. 45. Cytoplasm of basal layer cells of epidermis from arm of 81 mm C.R. (14 week) human fetus.
Osmium fixation, lead staining. × 28,500.

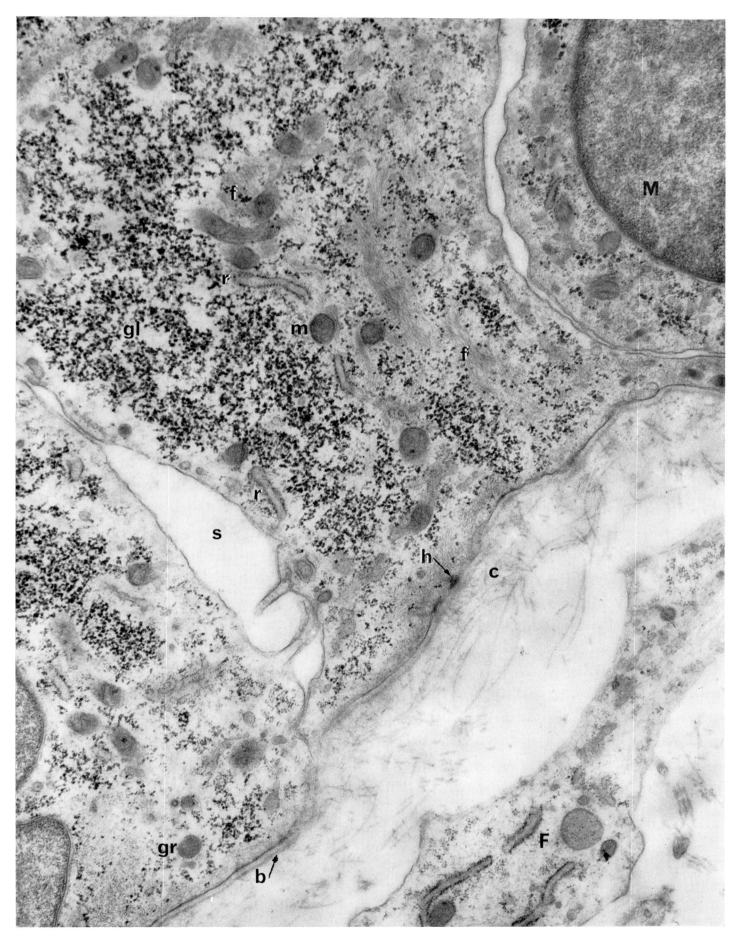

53

FIGURE 46

In place of a clearly defined nucleus, individual chromosomes (ch) are seen in the centre of this dividing basal cell, and only isolated fragments of a nuclear membrane (m) are present. The cytoplasmic organelles and glycogen granules occupy the peripheral area of the cytoplasm, and desmosomes (d) and hemi-desmosomes (h) are present along the plasma membrane.

It has already been stressed that the mesenchyme appears to regulate the rate and type of differentiation of embryonic and adult epidermis, and it is believed that control of epidermal cell mitosis is an essential part of this regulation. Apparently, differentiation does not occur without prior division. Exactly what are the factors concerned with mitotic control, and how they operate *in vivo*, remains to be determined. An active fraction obtainable from homogenates of whole embryos, or dermis, can support basal cell mitosis, and a protein "epidermal-growth factor" which stimulates mitosis has been isolated from mouse sub-maxillary gland. These, however, are ineffective unless the epidermis is attached to a suitable substrate which, under normal conditions is provided by the mesenchyme or dermis. An inhibitory regulator of mitotic activity, produced by the epidermal cells themselves is thought to be of importance by some workers. This factor, possibly a glycoprotein, is known as the epidermal "chalone", and is thought to act by forming an active complex with adrenaline. It may be that the actual mitotic rate at a given time is determined by the relative concentrations of stimulators and inhibitors.

Mesodermal factors are also of importance in regulating differentiation of the expanding post-mitotic population of epidermal cells, and such features as local variations in thickness and type of keratinization are dependent upon the nature of the underlying mesoderm. Other extrinsic factors, such as Vitamin A, can affect differentiation by influencing the type, or possibly sequence, of specific synthetic processes within the cell. Cell-surface phenomena concerned with permeability, adhesiveness etc., are at present receiving considerable attention as regulators of cytodifferentiation, particularly in closely-knit epithelia like the epidermis, where the influence of individual cells on their neighbours seems to be of significance.

Fig. 46. Dividing basal epidermal cell from back of 81 mm C.R. (14 week) human fetus. Osmium fixation, lead staining. × 19,200.

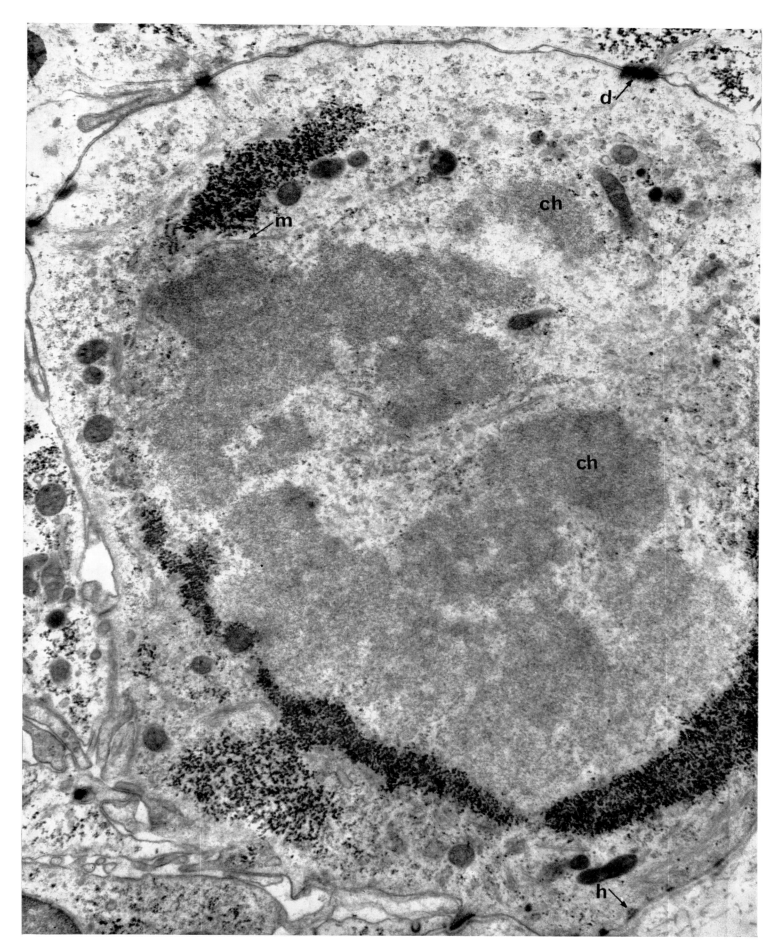

FIGURE 47

This cell has already commenced production of the characteristic cytoplasmic organelles by which it is identified. These, depending upon plane of section, appear as round or elongated granules of variable electron density. The less dense granules are termed premelanosomes (p) and they represent an earlier stage in development of the more dense melanosomes (m). The greater density of the latter is due to deposition of melanin upon the protein matrix of the pre-melanosome, and some granules at an intermediate stage of melanization are present. These exhibit characteristic 7–9 nm (70–90 Å) periodicity (*inset*). Premelanosomes are thought to develop from vesicles arising in the Golgi region (go), and their detailed structure will be considered later (p. 140). Mitochondria and rough membranes (r) are present in the cytoplasm, which contains a fine scattering of glycogen and R.N.P. particles, but no filaments, though these latter are present in melanocytes of post-natal epidermis (see Fig. 109).

Desmosomes (d) are associated with the apposed plasma membranes of the surrounding basal keratinocytes (K) but are absent from the plasma membrane of the melanocyte, which does not interdigitate to any extent with the membranes of neighbouring cells. These two features must mean that there is less strong cohesion between melanocyte and keratinocyte, than between adjacent keratinocytes, and in this sense one might regard melanocytes as recurring weak links in the chain of cells which constitute the basal layer, particularly in connection with any process tending to produce lateral separation.

Fully developed melanocytes are dendritic cells with processes distributed horizontally along the epidermal-dermal interface, and vertically to ramify among the basal and supra-basal keratinocytes. At the early stage of development at present being considered, the cells are rounded, with few dendrites, but one such (de) is seen on section. D, indicates dermis.

Fig. 47. Basal melanocyte in epidermis from arm of 81 mm C.R. (14 week) human fetus. Osmium fixation, lead staining. × 24,500. *Inset:* Melanosome. × 100,000.

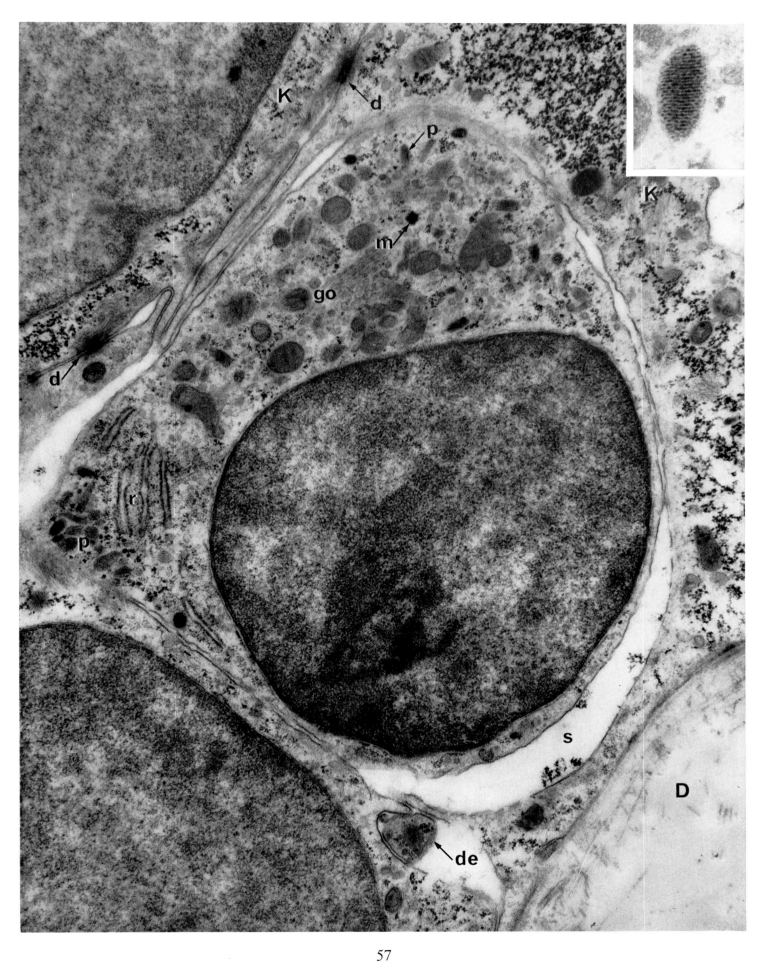

57

FIGURE 48

This micrograph shows features of basal keratinocytes (K) and a melanocyte (M) at a more advanced stage of development. Very little glycogen (gl) is present in the basal cells though it is still abundant in overlying intermediate cells (I). Filaments (f) are aggregated into bundles which form a mesh-work throughout the cytoplasm, and hemi-desmosomes (h) are frequent along the basal plasma membrane. The melanocyte shows evidence of active melanogenesis with numerous premelanosomes and melanosomes (m) in the cytoplasm. Some melanosomes have already been transferred to the keratinocytes. They are rarely at this stage dispersed singly in the cytoplasm of the latter, but are aggregated in clusters of two or more within membrane limited organelles as "compound melanosomes" (co *and inset*). Round or oval electron-dense granules (a) are very likely precursors of the organelles containing melanosomes. In fully developed epidermis, compound melanosomes are frequently seen, and are thought to represent lysosomes which engulf and degrade the melanosomes.

Apart from further reduction in glycogen, and an increase in the number and coarseness of tonofilamentous bundles, little further differentiation of basal keratinocytes takes place beyond the stage figured here. The melanocyte has also reached a stage of differentiation comparable to that seen in post-natal epidermis (Fig. 108).

Fig. 48. Basal keratinocytes and melanocyte of epidermis from arm of 169 mm C.R. (21 week) human fetus. Osmium fixation, lead staining. ×22,800. *Inset:* Compound melanosome. ×98,000.

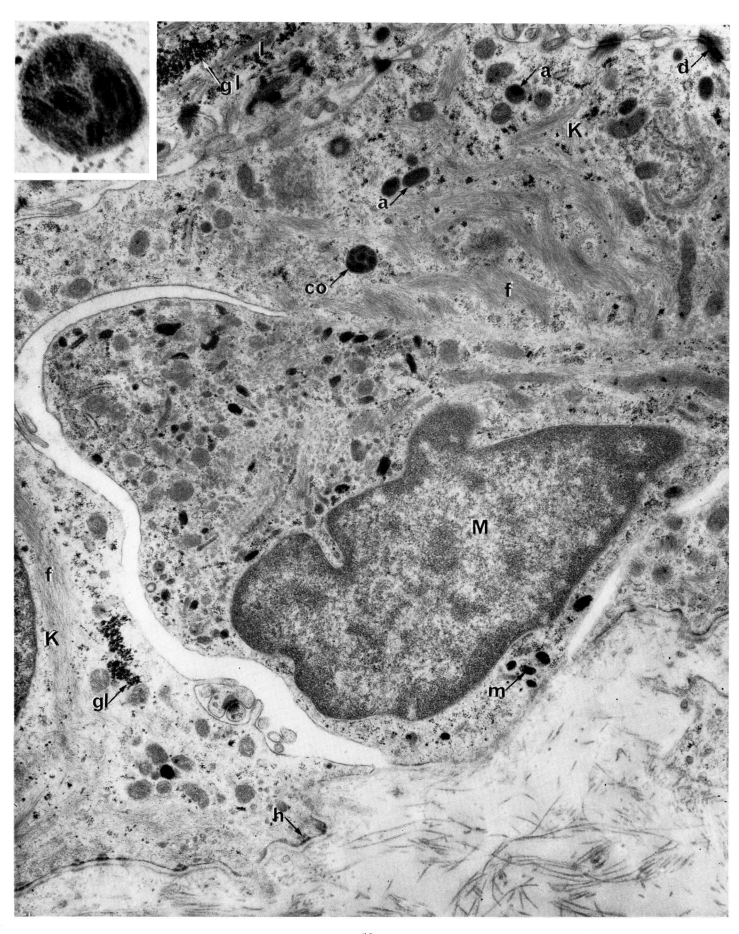

59

FIGURE 49

Cilia are not uncommonly associated with the plasma membrane of the basal cell at early and intermediate stages of intra-uterine life. Here a cilium (c) is seen projecting from the surface of a basal germinative cell (G) and invaginating the plasma membrane of the overlying intermediate cell (I). A basal body (b) is associated with the base of the cilium, and glycogen (gl), filaments (f) and R.N.P. particles (r) are also seen in the cytoplasm of the basal cell.

Cilia may also be present at the surface of central cells of the hair germ, and of melanocytes at this stage of development.

FIGURE 50

Lipid droplets (li) may be seen in developing basal cells, and, as here, are not intensely osmiophilic, suggesting a relatively high degree of saturation. In the living cell, lipid droplets are circular in outline, but they frequently appear irregular in electron micrographs due to distortion during fixation and dehydration. A narrow zone of more intense osmiophilia (o) at the periphery of the droplet could be interpreted as a limiting membrane, but this is not its nature, since lipid accumulates free in the cytoplasm and not within membrane-limited organelles or spaces. Similar lipid droplets are occasionally seen in keratinocytes of fully developed epidermis (see Fig. 93).

Fig. 49. Cilium of basal epidermal cell from leg of 81 mm C.R. (14 week) human fetus. Osmium fixation, lead staining. × 96,000.

Fig. 50. Lipid droplets in basal epidermal cell from back of 215 mm C.R. (24 week) human fetus. Osmium fixation, lead staining. × 57,200.

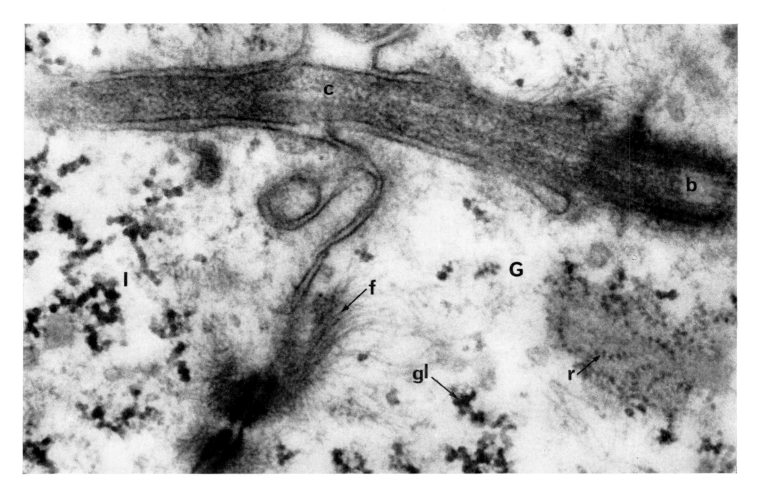

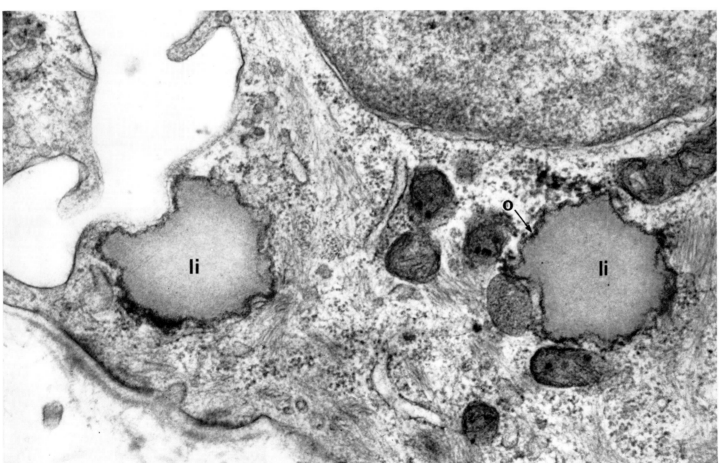

FIGURE 51

A high content of glycogen, and a relative poverty of cytoplasmic organelles characterizes the intermediate cells (I) for a considerable period following their appearance between the basal germinative cells (B) and the overlying periderm. As development proceeds and more layers are built up there is a gradual reduction in glycogen concentration within the cells, an increase in organelles and filaments, and the more superficial cells acquire specialized features in contrast to those more deeply placed which differentiate along lines very similar to basal layer cells.

FIGURE 52

This micrograph figures basal (B) and overlying lower intermediate cells (I) which are practically fully differentiated. Their appearance is to all intents and purposes identical, and one may note desmosomes present along the apposed plasma membranes, as well as a variety of organelles—mitochondria, centriolar structures, membrane bound vesicles, and a few profiles of rough-surfaced endoplasmic reticulum. A small aggregation of glycogen particles is still present in the basal cell, but only scattered individual particles can be seen in the intermediate cells. A cilium (c) springs from one of these latter. It is difficult to see what function cilia can have in relation to these deeply situated cells at this stage of development. Cilia are usually associated with the surface of cells facing an open environment, and their presence on ectodermal cells has already been noted. Since the cells in question here are derived (at many removes) from the latter, it is not entirely surprising that they should have transmitted to them some of the potentialities of their forebears, but that this particular one should become manifest in an entirely different environment seems strange.

Fig. 51. Intermediate layer cells of epidermis from back of 81 mm C.R. (14 week) human fetus. Osmium fixation, lead staining. × 5,600.

Fig. 52. Basal, and lower intermediate layer cells of epidermis from arm of 215 mm C.R. (24 week) human fetus. Osmium fixation, lead staining. × 28,000.

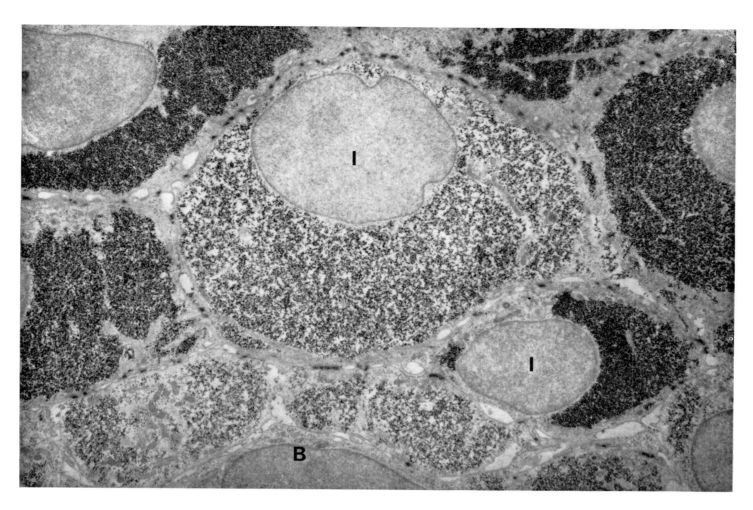

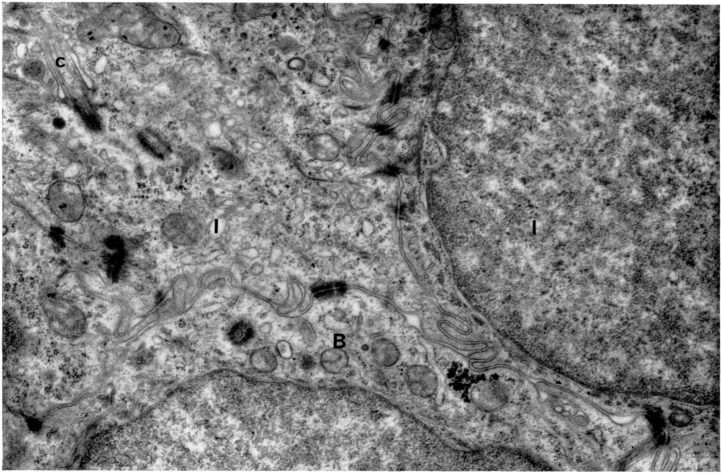

FIGURE 53

At the stage when the periderm is undergoing its final transformation, the cytoplasm of the uppermost intermediate cells contains a high concentration of filaments (f) aggregated into short bundles, moderate amounts of glycogen (gl) and scattered organelles. This is their condition immediately before, or coincident with the appearance of their most characteristic product—keratohyalin.

FIGURE 54

Small areas of increased density (d) due to accumulation of amorphous substance can be observed within some filamentous bundles (f) of cells at a stage similar to or slightly more advanced than that illustrated above. These enlarge, apparently by extension along the filaments which they incorporate, becoming highly electron dense, to form keratohyalin granules (k). The origin, chemical nature, and function of keratohyalin are matters which continue to exercise the attention of those investigating the process of keratinization in fully developed epidermis. Ribosomes are thought by some to be of importance in synthesis of the granules, and it has been suggested that the amorphous material is a product of nuclear degradation. Some workers have doubted that the granules are discrete entities at all, and consider them to be merely intensely staining regions of tono-fibrillar bundles. It might be expected that examination of graded fetal material would throw light on these matters. The picture opposite presents as early a stage in the development of keratohyalin as one could reasonably hope to obtain. All it does is to confirm the initial site of appearance of amorphous electron dense material within filamentous bundles, but it provides no information on its primary source or chemical constitution. It might be added that ribosomes are not particularly concentrated in association with it.

Fig. 53. Cytoplasm of uppermost intermediate layer cell of epidermis from arm of 169 mm C.R. (21 week) human fetus. Osmium fixation, lead staining. × 28,800.

Fig. 54. Keratohyalin forming in upper intermediate layer cell of epidermis from arm of 215 mm C.R. (24 week) human fetus. Osmium fixation, lead staining. × 88,400.

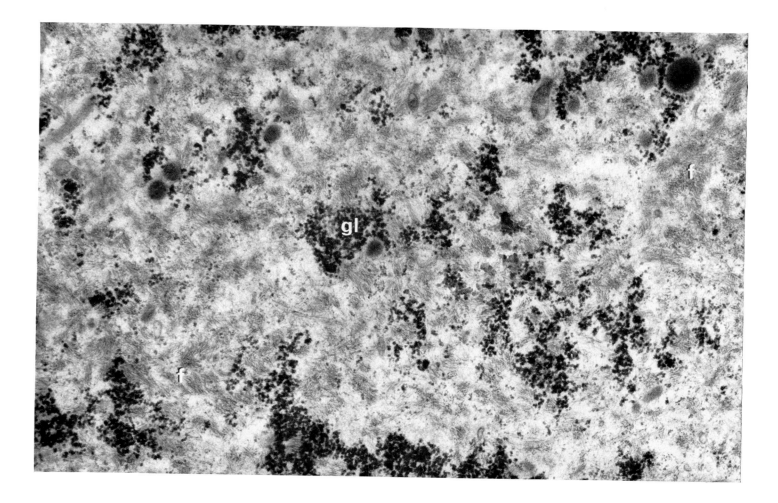

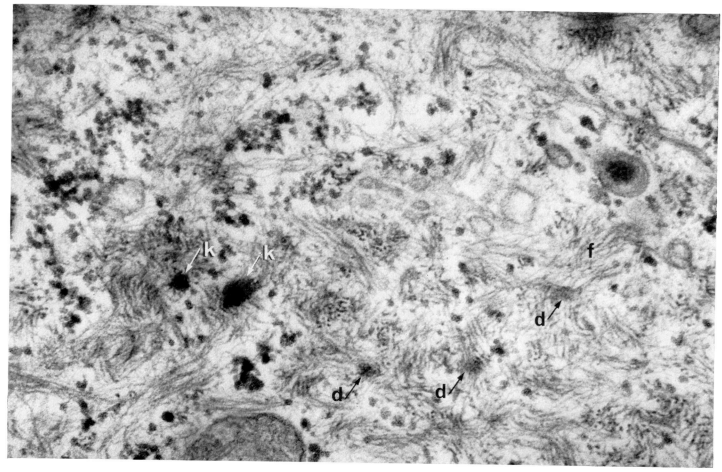

FIGURE 55

With the appearance of keratohyalin granules (k) the cells containing them can be referred to as "granulosa cells", and they ultimately form a "stratum granulosum" of one or more layers. In this micrograph of a later stage than the previous, two layers are represented. The cell of the lower layer—outlined by desmosomes (d)—is flattened, and contains early keratohyalin granules (k) in characteristic relation to tonofilamentous bundles. The granulosa cell superficial to this, of which only a small segment is shown, has larger keratohyalin granules, and a less electron dense cytoplasm (c). This type of granulosa cell is further illustrated in the lower micrograph.

FIGURE 56

The superficial granulosa cells (G) contain large, irregularly-shaped keratohyalin granules (k). As these accumulate, the general cytoplasm of the cell becomes more translucent, organelles of all types become reduced in number, and the nucleoplasm becomes less granular. Directly superficial to cells of this type are keratinized cells of a stratum corneum (SC), and a major problem of both fetal and fully developed epidermis is elucidating the sequence of events at the ultra-structural and molecular level involved in transformation of granulosa cells into flattened squames lacking nuclei or cytoplasmic organelles.

Fig. 55. Granulosa cells of epidermis from back of 230 mm C.R. (26 week) human fetus. Osmium fixation, lead staining. × 42,000.

Fig. 56. Granulosa cell and stratum corneum of epidermis from arm of 215 mm C.R. (24 week) human fetus. Osmium fixation, lead staining. × 10,000.

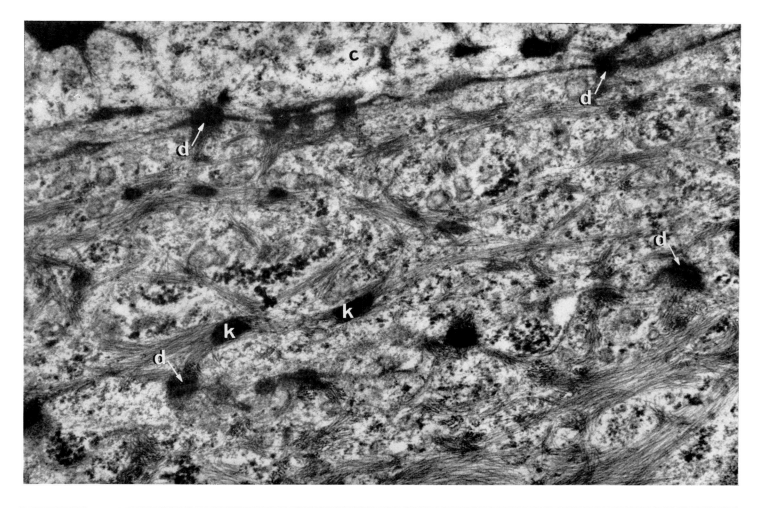

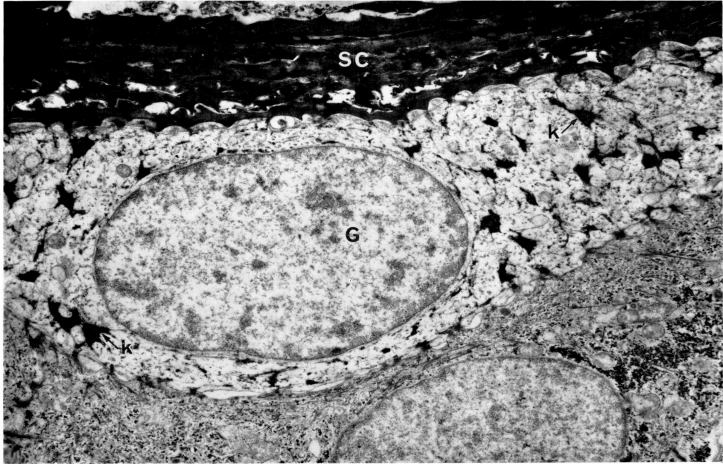

FIGURE 57

This micrograph shows the upper layers of the epidermis at a slightly earlier stage of differentiation than that shown in the previous one (Fig. 56). The granulosa cell (G) contains irregular keratohyalin granules (k) and scattered organelles in relatively electron translucent general cytoplasm. Superficial to it in ascending order are: (a) one or two irregularly flattened cells (SC) similar in appearance to stratum corneum cells of fully developed epidermis; (b) a layer of somewhat similar cells (K_2) apparently extremely friable and undergoing disintegration; (c) two layers of flattened cells (K_1) with filamentous matrix and some organelles, and (d) the transformed periderm (P). It is evident from their position that of these various layers, SC is of more recent development than K_2, and the latter than K_1. The micrograph therefore presents a static picture of a sequence of developments which have taken place in uppermost intermediate layer cells beyond the stage illustrated in Fig. 53. One might conclude that for a brief period, the superficial cells differentiate to a final K_1 condition, for another limited period, at a time when some keratohyalin has been formed, to the condition represented at K_2, and finally from the later granulosa cell (G) condition to the fully keratinized state as seen at SC. The implication is, that K_1 and K_2 represent transient stages of partial keratinization, not necessarily to be regarded as intermediate stages in the transformation of a granulosa type cell (G) into a fully keratinized SC type, which takes place at a later stage. This is confirmed by the fact that, to date, K_1 and K_2 type cells have not been seen intervening between the two former types.

FIGURE 58

This illustrates features of K_1 type cells at higher magnification. The filaments which form the bulk of the matrix are evidently denser than those in the periderm (P). Organelles (o) and a nuclear remnant (n) can be seen. Further characteristic of this type of cell are electron translucent areas (t). It might be thought that these represent tears or processing defects in the tissue, but examination of a large number of sections indicates this is probably not the case. In so far as K_1 cells may represent a further stage of differentiation of cells such as that in Fig. 53, these translucent areas could result from loss of glycogen present in the latter. The cell in Fig. 53 contains no keratohyalin, and it may be that until this is produced, final differentiation in the direction of keratinization cannot progress beyond a K_1 stage. K_2 type cells may be derived from cells containing some keratohyalin, but insufficient to allow them to become fully keratinized. This interpretation is very tentative and may well prove incorrect as further observations accumulate. It suggests that keratohyalin is essential for development of full keratinization.

Fig. 57. Upper layers of epidermis from back of 230 mm C.R. (26 week) human fetus. Osmium fixation, lead staining. × 10,500.

Fig. 58. Periderm and subjacent layers of epidermis from back of 230 mm C.R. (26 week) human fetus. Osmium fixation, lead staining. × 36,000.

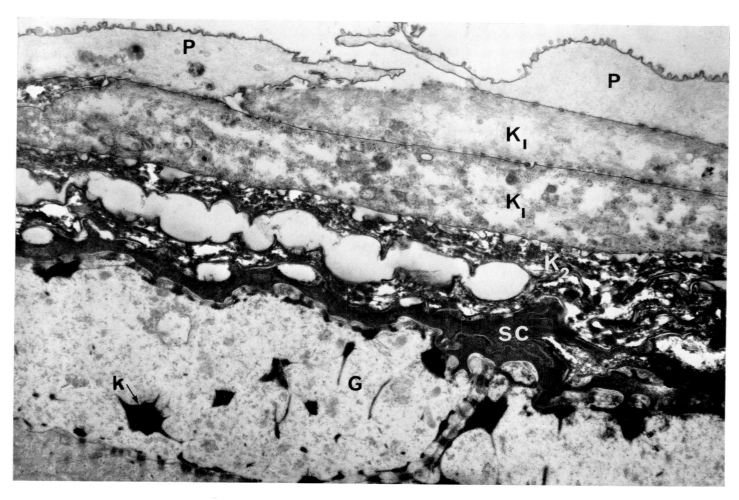

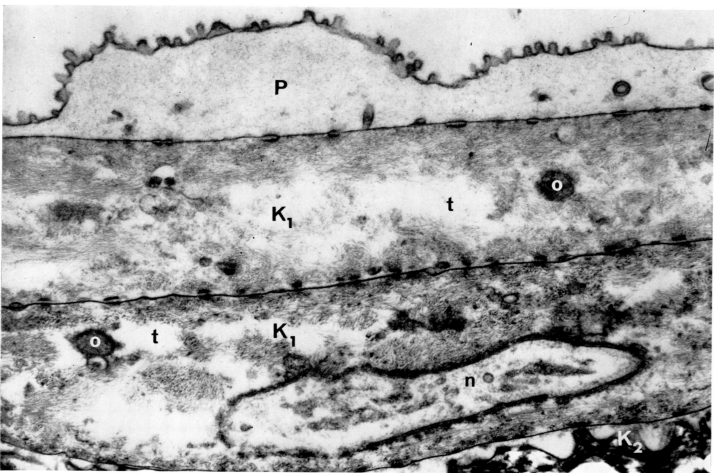

FIGURE 59

This micrograph of full thickness interfollicular epidermis gives an overall picture of the various layers at a stage when a definite stratum corneum has differentiated. The basal layer (B), separated from the dermis (D) at the epidermal-dermal junction (j), consists of keratino-cytes with characteristic tono-filaments (t). A non-keratinocyte (M) is also present in the basal layer, and this might be thought to be a melanocyte, because it contains numerous dense cytoplasmic granules. However, at higher magnification, these granules are seen not to be melanosomes, but granules typical of another type of cell infrequently present—the Merkel cell (see Fig. 61). Above the basal layer are two or three layers of intermediate or spinous cells (S) still containing moderate amounts of glycogen (gl) and a single layer of granulosa cells (G) intervenes between the uppermost of these and the stratum corneum (SC).

In its general arrangement, the epidermis at this stage is essentially similar to the post-natal condition. The individual layers of keratinocytes have established their final relationships, and even at a detailed level, undergo little further differentiation, apart from the spinous layer cells, which gradually lose their remaining glycogen.

Fig. 59. Full thickness of epidermis from back of 230 mm C.R. (26 week) human fetus. Osmium fixation, lead staining. × 5,000.

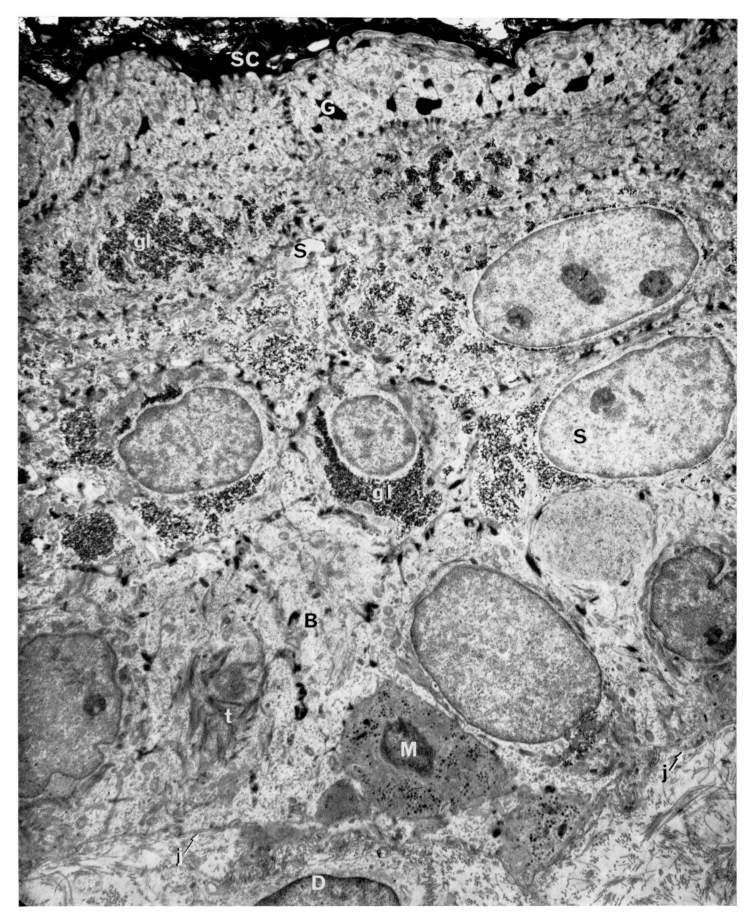

71

FIGURE 60

From the 12th week onwards, non-keratinocytes with characteristic features can be identified in the basal and supra-basal layers of interfollicular epidermis, and among cells of the outer root sheath of the hair follicle. These are Langerhans cells (L) which are dendritic (de) in shape, and which can be distinguished from surrounding keratinocytes by an absence of desmosomes and tonofilaments, and from melanocytes because melanosomes are not present in the cytoplasm. The most typical feature of this cell, however, is a rod-shaped cytoplasmic organelle (r) which is the sectional profile of what is commonly termed a "Langerhans granule". The detailed structure of these is considered in Section 6 (pp. 156–8). In addition to the specific granules, Langerhans cells contain vesicles (v), numerous mitochondria, a Golgi apparatus (go) and a variety of membrane limited organelles (l) resembling lysosomes.

Since originally described in post-natal epidermis by Langerhans in 1868, the nature and significance of this cell has remained controversial. For a long time it was thought to be an "effete" or defunct melanocyte, but its ultrastructural appearance and the fact that it is present in fully differentiated form at a comparatively early stage of development, renders this view no longer tenable. It is now thought to be an immigrant of mesodermal origin, though exactly when it enters the epidermis is difficult to say, because until the characteristic Langerhans granules are developed, it is impossible to distinguish from a melanocyte which has not yet commenced production of melanosomes. Melanocytes begin to enter the epidermis at about the 11th week, so one might assume that non-keratinocytes with general features common to both types of cell encountered earlier than this, are probably Langerhans cells. However, this is a matter which requires further study.

Fig. 60. Langerhans cell in outer root sheath of hair follicle from arm of 215 mm C.R. (24 week) human fetus. Osmium fixation, lead staining. × 15,300.

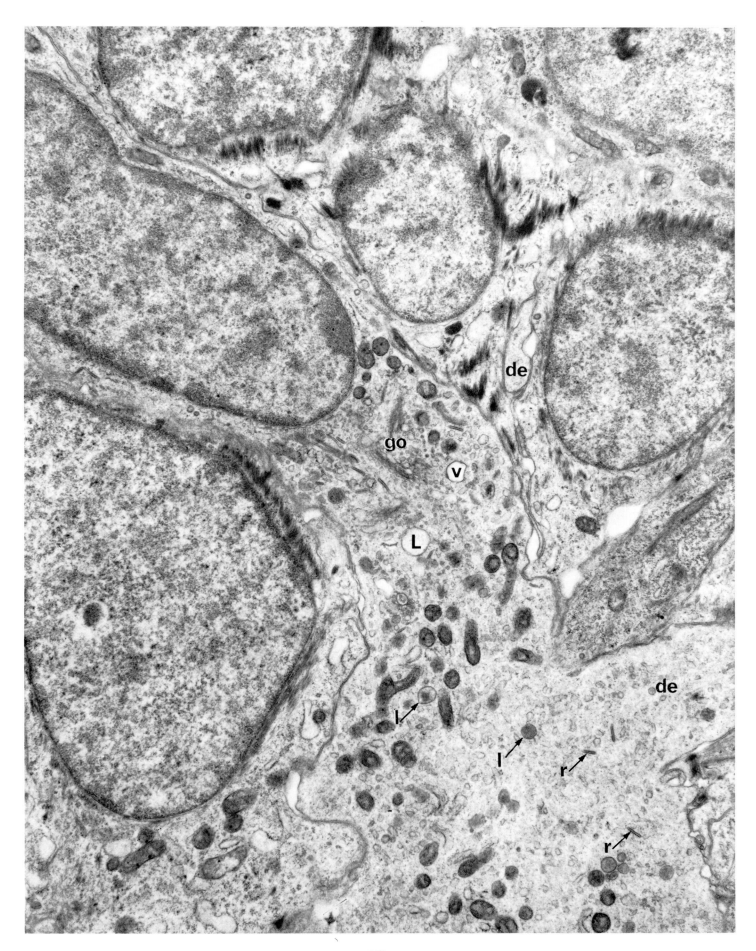

73

FIGURE 61

The Merkel cell is a specialized type of cell closely associated with neurites, first described in the snout skin of the mole. It is also frequently present in distal (digital) non-hairy human skin, but very rarely in interfollicular epidermis of hairy skin. The earliest it can be reported as being observed in the human fetus is at C.R. length 115 mm (16 weeks) where it may be present in the interfollicular epidermis, and, very frequently among the cells of the "bulge" of developing hair follicles. These early Merkel cells are not invariably associated with neurites as are those of fully developed post-natal epidermis.

Since the Merkel cell lacks tonofilaments, and apparently does not undergo keratinization, it can be classed as a non-keratinocyte, but is unlike other non-keratinocytes (melanocytes and Langerhans cells) in that desmosomes (de) connect it to adjacent keratinocytes (K). Round, electron-dense cytoplasmic granules (gr), smaller than, and structurally distinct from melanosomes are specific to this type of cell, and make it readily distinguishable. It has a well-developed Golgi region (go), vesicles (v) of varying size and content, as well as lysosome-like membrane limited granules (l).

FIGURE 62

This shows some further features of Merkel cell cytoplasm such as glycogen (gl), large electron-dense granules (dg), collections of small vesicles, probably Golgi (v), and irregular apparently membrane limited spaces containing fine reticular material (r). These resemble sacs of rough endoplasmic reticulum, and the fact that one appears to be continuous with the outer nuclear membrane could favour this identification.

The process (pr) insinuated between the Merkel cell and the keratinocyte (K) is, as far as could be determined, the tip of a dendrite of a melanocyte.

Fig. 61. Merkel cell in basal layer of interfollicular epidermis from arm of 215 mm C.R. (24 week) human fetus. Osmium fixation, lead staining. × 14,000.

Fig. 62. Cytoplasm of Merkel cell in basal layer of interfollicular epidermis from arm of 215 mm C.R. (24 week) human fetus. Osmium fixation, lead staining. × 21,700.

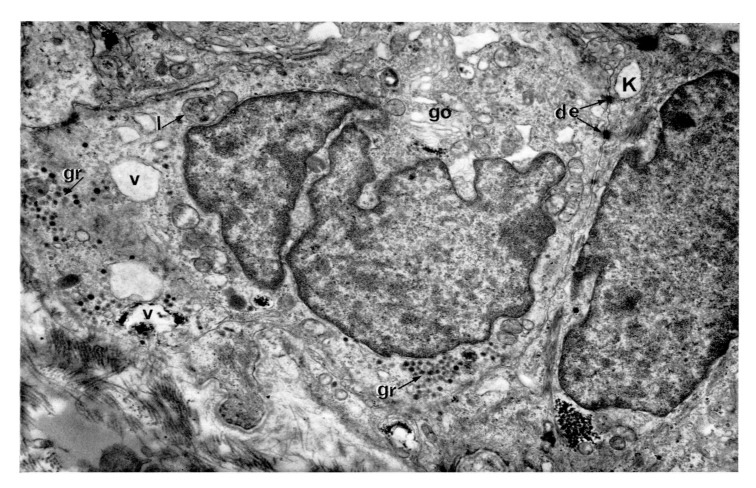

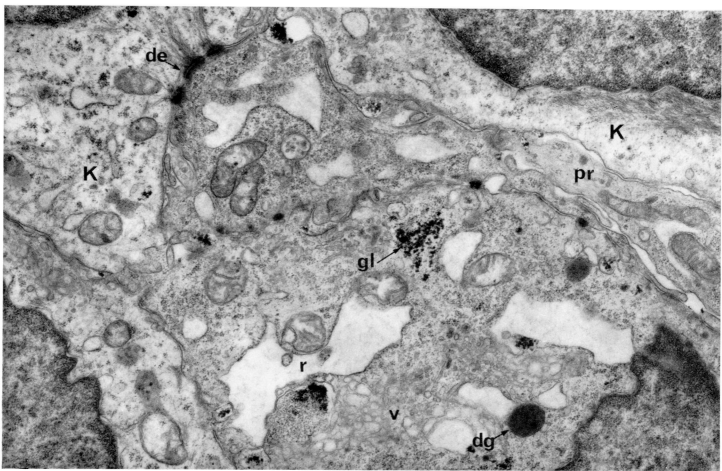

FIGURE 63

Little is known of the developmental origin of the Merkel cell. It is unlikely to be a modified keratinocyte, even though it be connected to its neighbours in the basal layer by desmosomes. Pictures such as that opposite strongly suggest that it is actually an immigrant cell which enters the epidermis from the mesoderm. The bulk of the Merkel cell (M) shown lies at a deeper level than the keratinocytes of the outer root sheath, and is separated over a considerable extent from their basal plasma membranes (b) by a narrow space containing fine axonal terminals (a). The micrograph could be interpreted as illustrating a Merkel cell in process of migrating from the mesoderm into the outer root sheath. S, is a segment of a Schwann cell.

A number of axonal terminals (a) are associated with the Merkel cell, and one (aa) has penetrated for some distance between cells of the outer root sheath. Intra-epidermal nerve fibres such as this are very rarely encountered in the human fetus (or adult for that matter), and, to date, have only been seen in the immediate neighbourhood of a Merkel cell.

FIGURE 64

This illustrates axonal terminals (a) related to the Merkel cell seen above. The largest one is characteristically located close to the granular region (g) of the cell, and a branch of it, or perhaps another terminal (a_1) is penetrating between the two keratinocytes (K); b is the basal lamina. The axoplasmic matrix of these terminals appears very tenuous, apart from isolated clusters of small vesicles (v).

The close association of axonal terminals with Merkel cells recalls the similarly close relation between them and Schwann cells. This could lead to the suggestion that the Merkel cell may be a modified Schwann cell, or at any rate of similar lineage.

Fig. 63. Merkel cell associated with outer root sheath of hair follicle from arm of 215 mm C.R. (24 week) human fetus. Osmium fixation, lead staining. × 8,000.

Fig. 64. Neurites associated with Merkel cell and outer root sheath of hair follicle from arm of 215 mm C.R. (24 week) human fetus. Osmium fixation, lead staining. × 35,100.

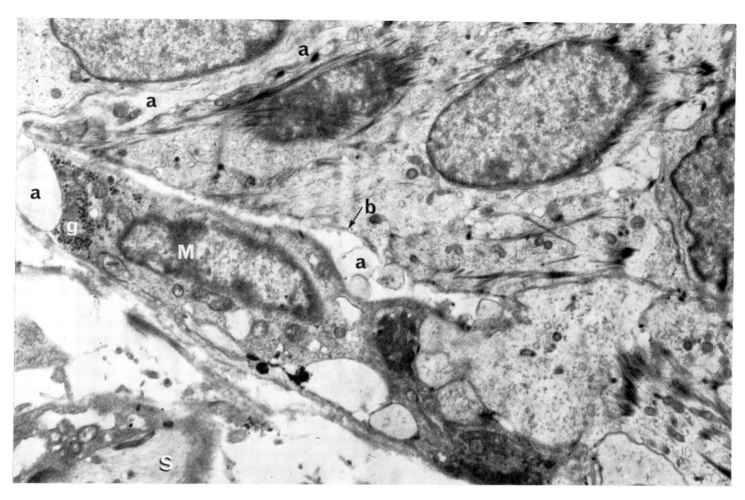

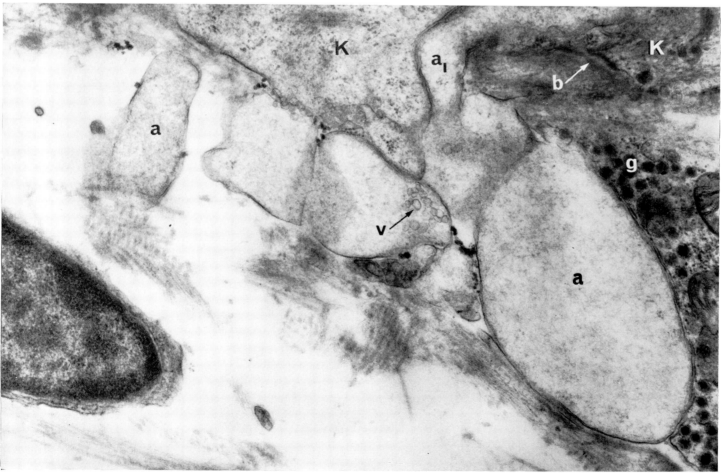

77

REFERENCES

GENERAL DEVELOPMENT AND DIFFERENTIATION OF EPIDERMIS

Bullough, W. S. and Laurence, E. G. The control of epidermal mitotic activity in the mouse. *Proc. Roy. Soc. B.*, **151**:517, 1960.

Bullough, W. S., Laurence, E. B., Iversen, O. H. and Elgjo, K. The vertebrate epidermal chalone. *Nature*, **214**:578, 1967.

Hashimoto, K., Gross, B. G., Di Bella, R. J. and Lever, W. F. The ultrastructure of the skin of human embryos. IV. The epidermis. *J. Invest. Derm.*, **47**:317, 1966.

Mercer, E. H. "Keratin and keratinization". Oxford, Pergamon, 1961.

Mercer, E. H. Protein synthesis and epidermal differentiation. In: "The Epidermis", W. Montagna and W. C. Lobitz, eds., New York, Academic Press, 1964.

Wessels, N. K. Differentiation of epidermis and epidermal derivatives. *New Eng. J. Med.*, **277**:21, 1967.

MELANOCYTE

Breathnach, A. S. and Wyllie, L. M. Electron microscopy of melanocytes and Langerhans cells in human fetal epidermis at fourteen weeks. *J. Invest. Derm.*, **44**:51, 1965.

Mishima, Y. and Widlan, S. Embryonic development of melanocytes in human hair and epidermis. *J. Invest. Derm.*, **46**:263, 1966.

Zimmerman, A. A. and Becker, S. W. Jr. Melanoblasts and melanocytes in fetal Negro skin. Illinois monographs in medical sciences, **6**. Urbana, University of Illinois Press, 1959.

LANGERHANS CELL

Breathnach, A. S. and Wyllie, L. M. The problem of the Langerhans cells. In: "Advances in Biology of Skin", **8**, W. Montagna and Funan Hu, eds. Oxford, Pergamon, 1967.

Breathnach, A. S., Silvers, W. K., Smith, J. and Heyner, S. Langerhans cells in mouse skin experimentally deprived of its neural crest component. *J. Invest. Derm.*, **50**:147, 1968.

Wolff, K. Die Langerhans-Zelle. Ergebnisse neuerer experimenteller Untersuchungen. *Arch. klin. exp. Derm.*, **229**:54, 1967.

MERKEL CELL

Munger, B. L. The intraepidermal innervation of the snout skin of the opossum. *J. Cell Biol.*, **26**:79, 1965.

4 Development of Dermal Elements

Mesenchymal cells—fibroblasts and collagen—cells of doubtful lineage—mast cell: nerve—
Schwann cells and axons — perineurium — micro-vasculature: endothelial cells.

FIGURE 65

The main structural component of the dermis, collagen, is synthesized by fibroblasts, which are differentiated from the mesodermal cells present from an early stage just beneath the epidermis. In low-power micrographs these latter appear as elongated cells with large nuclei and fine elongated processes which may or may not establish contact with similar processes of neighbouring cells. The overall impression is of a very loose arrangement of cells with a minimal degree of contact adhesion. However, at higher powers of magnification, it becomes evident that the plasma membranes of adjacent cells, and processes, may be closely apposed over quite considerable distances (c, c,).

The cytoplasm of undifferentiated mesodermal cells contains the common organelles and some glycogen (gl). The rough endoplasmic reticulum (r) is not particularly prominent.

FIGURE 66

This micrograph illustrates specialized sites of contact between sub-epidermal mesodermal cells. The cell M, makes contact with two of its neighbours, M_1 and M_2, and in each case at the point p along the plane of contact, the intercellular space is indistinct, and a narrow zone of increased density is present just within the plasma membrane. The appearance is identical with that of the "macula adherens" of epithelial cells. The presence of such specialized zones of attachment between mesodermal cells indicates a degree of adhesion beyond what might at first sight be expected. However, considering their low distribution density per unit area, and the as yet poorly developed intercellular fibrous framework, adhesion between them could be associated with the necessity to provide some support to the overlying epidermis.

Re-examination of Fig. 65 will reveal a specialized contact (p) at one point along the contact surface between the two cells, on the left hand side of the picture.

Fig. 65. Sub-ectodermal mesodermal cells from crown of head of 14 mm C.R. (6 week) human embryo. Glutaraldehyde-osmium fixation, lead staining. × 18,200.

Fig. 66. Contacts between mesodermal cells from crown of head of 14 mm C.R. (6 week) human embryo. Glutaraldehyde-osmium fixation, lead staining. × 44,500.

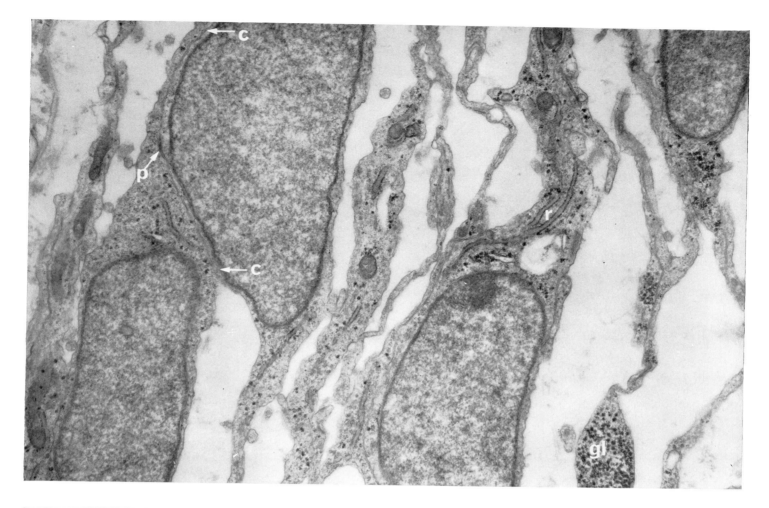

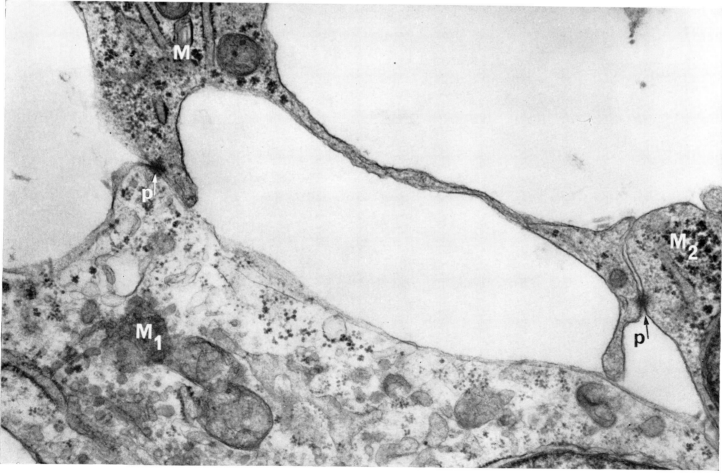

FIGURES 67 and 68

These two micrographs illustrate general features of fibroblasts which differentiate from meso-dermal cells of the type seen in the previous two figures. The cells are elongated or spindle-shaped, and in less intimate contact, being separated by the increasing number of collagen fibres (c) which have been produced, and the fine elongated processes characteristic of their forebears (cf. Fig. 65) are hardly evident. The most prominent feature of the cytoplasm is the well developed rough endoplasmic reticulum (r) and indeed it is this more than anything else which allows one to identify the cells as fibroblasts. An extensive rough endoplasmic reticulum is characteristic of cells that are actively synthesizing protein for export, and in the present instance, the exuberance of its development can be correlated with the production of large amounts of collagen precursors.

Fine cytofilaments (f) randomly dispersed throughout the cytoplasm or aggregated into loose bundles are commonly seen in fibroblasts. It has been suggested that these represent pre-cursor collagen fibrils which are released from the cell through discontinuities in the plasma membrane. This view is based entirely upon ultrastructural morphology, and micrographs apparently showing mature fibrils within the vertebrate fibroblast, or fibrils in process of being shed into the surrounding milieu, should be treated with extreme caution. Apparent deficien-cies in the plasma membrane can result from it being sectioned tangentially, and stains such as PTA which are most suitable for revealing the banding of collagen fibrils, quite frequently give a poor image of the cell membrane, which if it be close to intra- or extra-cellular fibrils may be almost indistinguishable, or appear to merge into them. Besides, collateral evidence of poor fixation or sectioning defects (not always avoidable unfortunately) which can lead to apparent local membrane deficiency, is often present in such micrographs. It is more likely that the cytofilaments in question are similar to those present in a variety of other cells, e.g. endothelial cells and melanocytes, not concerned with collagen synthesis. The function of these filaments is obscure, but they may be concerned with cell contractility and motility, or they may have an internal supportive ("skeletal") role.

Fig. 67. Fibroblasts from dermis of back of 81 mm C.R. (14 week) human fetus. Osmium fixation, lead staining. × 10,800.

Fig. 68. Fibroblasts from dermis of face of 142 mm C.R. (19 week) human fetus. Osmium fixation, phosphotungstic acid staining. × 30,800.

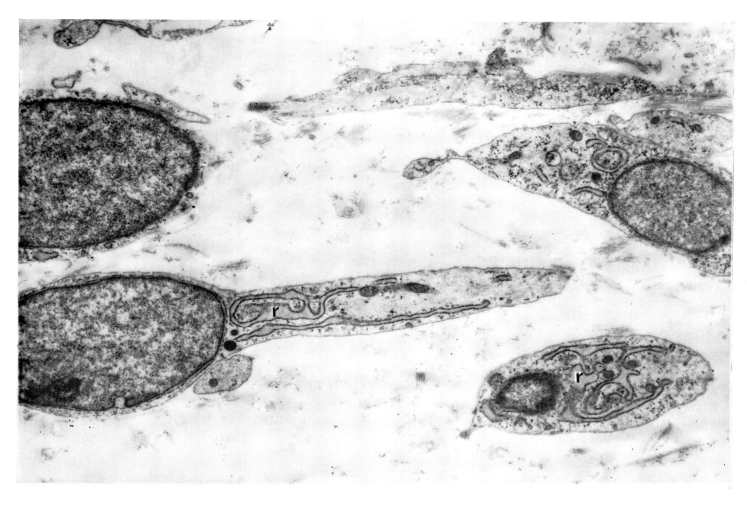

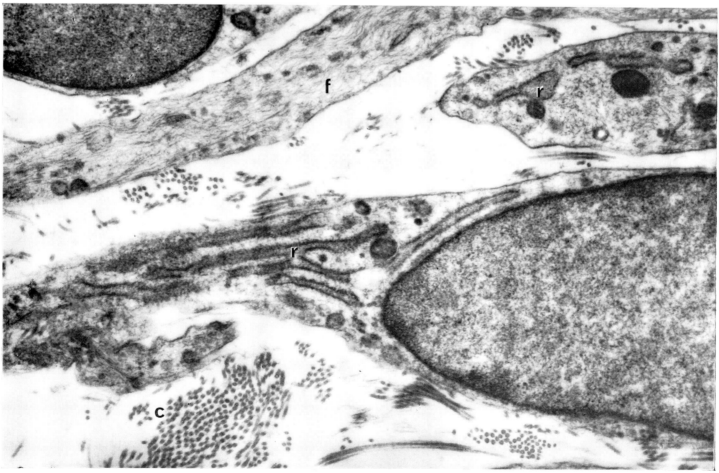

FIGURE 69

This shows the extensive endoplasmic reticulum (r) characteristic of the active fibroblast. The cisternae have a tendency to be arranged in parallel array, and contain flocculent or reticular material of slightly greater density than the cytoplasmic matrix. Where sectioned normally, the cisternal membranes are seen to have a single row of ribosomes attached to the cytoplasmic aspect, but where sectioned tangentially (as at t) a ribosomal pattern of curves, spirals, or parallel rows is evident. The cell has cytofilaments (f), a Golgi apparatus (go), with which numerous vesicles are associated, and similar vesicles (v) are present in the peripheral cytoplasm just within the plasma membrane.

FIGURE 70

Collagen is a protein of unusual composition in that it contains in addition to common amino-acids such as glycine, proline, glutamic and alanine, two of very limited distribution, i.e. hydroxyproline and hydroxylysin. Production of the final 54–70 nm (540–700 Å) banded collagen fibril of the dermis and other connective tissues is a complicated process on which volumes have been, and are being, written, and it cannot really be analysed here. It involves activation of amino-acids, their assembly to form polypeptide chains, the aggregation of these latter to form a helically-coiled macromolecule—tropocollagen—and the further aggregation and polymerization of tropocollagen macromolecules to form fibrils. The aggregations of ribosomes attached to the rough endoplasmic reticulum are concerned with stages leading to the production of tropocollagen, which is thought to be sequestered in the cisternae and intermittently released, either by fusion of cisternal and plasma membranes (as perhaps at x), or by means of peripheral vesicles (? of Golgi origin) which attach to the latter and liberate their contents. Further aggregation of tropocollagen into fibrils which gradually increase in diameter and exhibit banding takes place extra-cellularly. This final process is still probably influenced by the fibroblast and by the muco- and protein-polysaccharides which it also secretes to form the interfibrillar ground-substance.

Macromolecules of tropocollagen are estimated to have a diameter of 1·4 nm (14 Å), and are unlikely therefore to be individually identifiable in routine electron micrographs; the flocculent material within the cisternae of the endoplasmic reticulum (r) may however, represent this substance. The cytofilaments (f) which, by comparison with the 15 nm (150 Å) ribosomes (ri) are seen to have a diameter of 5–8 nm (50–80 Å), should not be referred to as "tropocollagenous fibrils". Neither should they be regarded as precursors of the 10–15 nm (100–150 Å) microfibrils (m) seen just external to the plasma membrane. Such microfibrils are commonly associated with active collagen formation, but whether they represent an early stage in the development of larger, more mature fibrils (c) is impossible to say on the basis of purely static morphological appearances.

Features of mature collagen are considered in Section 7 (pp. 170–3).

Fig. 69. Cytoplasm of fibroblast from dermis of back of 215 mm C.R. (24 week) human fetus. Osmium fixation, lead staining. × 39,600.

Fig. 70. Fibroblasts and collagen from dermis of back of 215 mm C.R. (24 week) human fetus. Osmium fixation, lead staining. × 61,200.

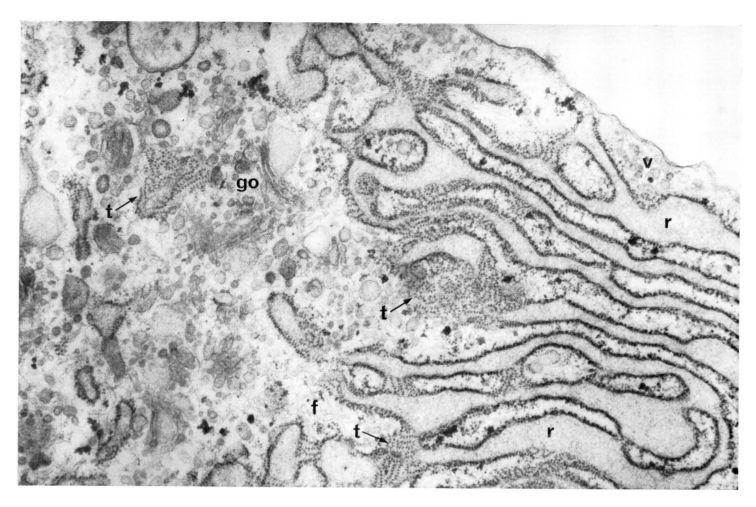

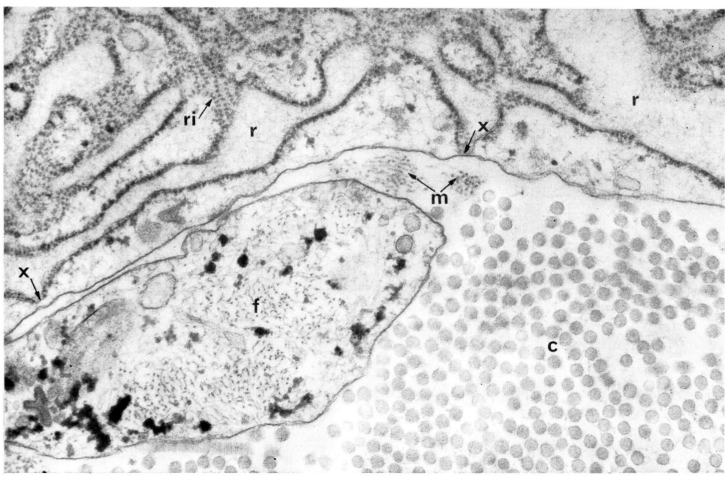

FIGURES 71 and 72

In addition to fibroblasts and other cells which can be identified by specific features, a variety of elements of indeterminate type and lineage are encountered at random levels beneath the epidermis at mid-fetal stages. Two examples from a varied collection are presented here. The upper one (Fig. 71) is characterized by large membrane-limited cytoplasmic vesicles (v) and a moderately well developed rough endoplasmic reticulum. The lower one (Fig. 72) has very prominent, darkly staining mitochondria (m), a Golgi apparatus (go) and vesicles (v) of varying size and content. A rough endoplasmic reticulum is not evident. These cells might be referred to as "histiocytes" or "wandering cells", but this seems unjustified in the absence of any evidence as to their function.

It is worth stating that not once in any section of skin from over 150 human fetuses ranging in age from 6 to 26 weeks examined during the past five years, has a cell been seen in the dermis which by any criterion could be labelled a melanoblast. Such cells must be present in fair numbers here preparatory to their invasion of the epidermis. However, in the absence of cytoplasmic premelanosomes they cannot be identified with certainty in routine preparations. Application of Mishima's dopa-silver technique to fetal skin might solve this problem.

Fig. 71. Cell of indeterminate type from dermis of back of 57 mm C.R. (12 week) human fetus. Glutaraldehyde-osmium fixation, lead staining. × 9,000.

Fig. 72. Cell of indeterminate type from dermis of leg of 81 mm C.R. (14 week) human fetus. Osmium fixation, lead staining. × 27,900.

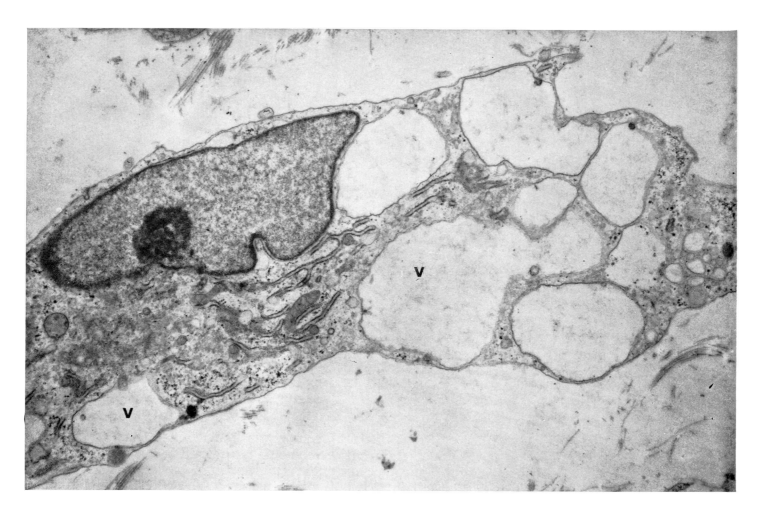

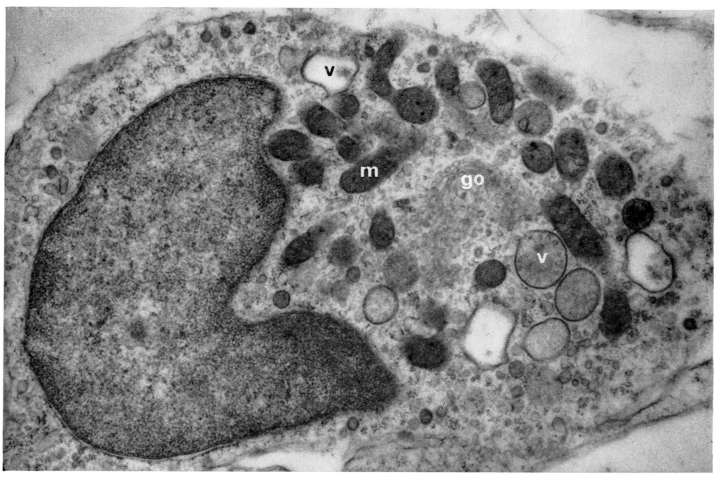

FIGURES 73 and 74

These show a cell with highly characteristic features which is encountered with reasonable frequency in the dermis over the period 16 to 20 weeks. It has prominent Golgi membranes (go), moderate numbers of mitochondria (m), and unusual cytoplasmic organelles (o). These appear to be very friable but when preserved intact, as in the lower figure, are seen to be membrane-limited (me) collections of tubules, and whorled membranes arranged in irregular concentric fashion. These organelles bear some resemblance to lysosomal bodies present in macrophages of fully developed dermis, and if such be their nature, one might be justified in labelling the cell which contains them a fetal macrophage. On the other hand, some of the organelles, e.g. the one marked gr, are not unlike mast-cell granules, and it may be that the cells are developing mast cells. These are of mesodermal origin, and the less differentiated representatives might well contain granules differing in some respects from those present in mature cells. In this connection it is of interest to compare these micrographs with those overleaf which present an undoubted fetal mast cell.

Fig. 73. Cell of doubtful lineage from dermis of arm of 140 mm (18 week) human fetus. Osmium fixation, lead staining. × 15,300.

Fig. 74. Cytoplasmic organelles present in cell of type illustrated in Fig. 73. Osmium fixation, lead staining. × 43,400.

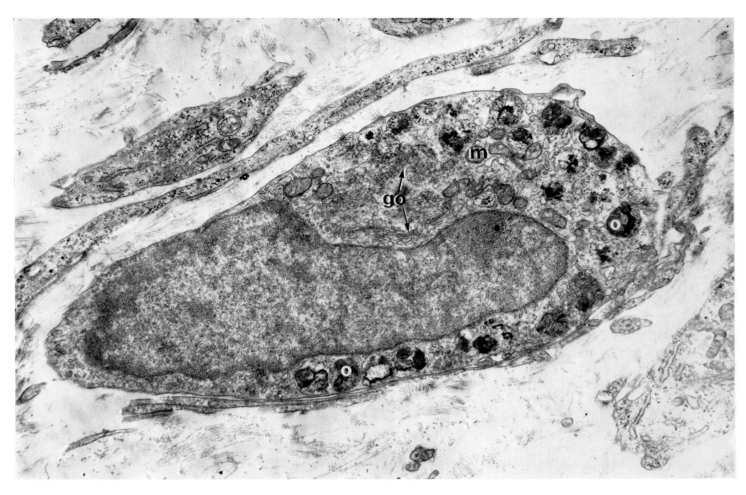

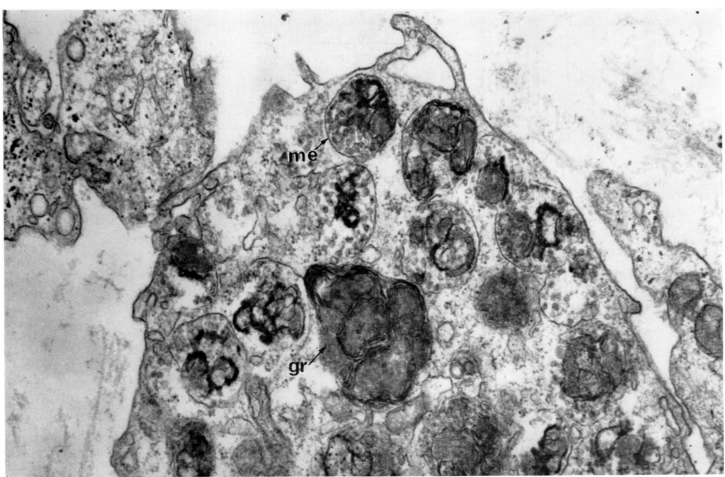

FIGURES 75 and 76

The most obvious features of this cell are the round electron-dense cytoplasmic granules (g) and the villous processes (p), which protrude from the plasma membrane. These two features alone would be sufficient, were the cell present in post-natal skin, to justify identifying it as a mast cell, though many more granules would be present. At higher magnification as in the lower micrograph, the granules are seen to have a limiting membrane (m) and an electron dense core, which in some cases is coarsely particulate. They are sufficiently similar in appearance to granules which are present in mature mast cells to make it reasonable to conclude that the cell containing them is, in fact, a mast cell.

The suggestion in the older literature that mast cells and melanocytes are closely related, has recently been revived by authors who claim there is strong circumstantial evidence that the two are of similar lineage, and that melanocytes may pass through a stage of mast granulation before entering the epidermis. Alleged similarities in the structure of mast granules and melanosomes, which are not very convincing, have been presented in support of this view. If it were to be accepted, the presumed mast cell in question here might equally well be regarded as a melanoblast, as also might the cells figured in the previous two micrographs. However, there is an impressive volume of experimental embryological evidence that mast cells and melanocytes are of entirely different lineage, and this must surely outweigh evidence to the contrary, which amounts to little more than superficial morphological resemblances, and some histochemical reactions common to both.

Mast cells of post-natal skin are considered in Section 7 (pp. 184–7).

Fig. 75. Mast cell from dermis of scalp of 120 mm C.R. (17 week) human fetus. Glutaraldehyde-osmium fixation, lead staining. ×16,200.

Fig. 76. Granules in cytoplasm of presumptive mast cell from dermis of 120 mm C.R. (17 week) human fetus. Glutaraldehyde-osmium fixation, lead staining. ×74,100.

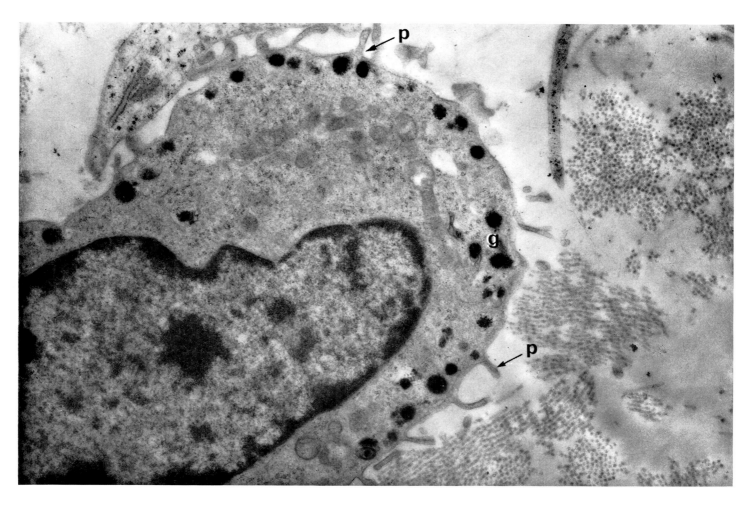

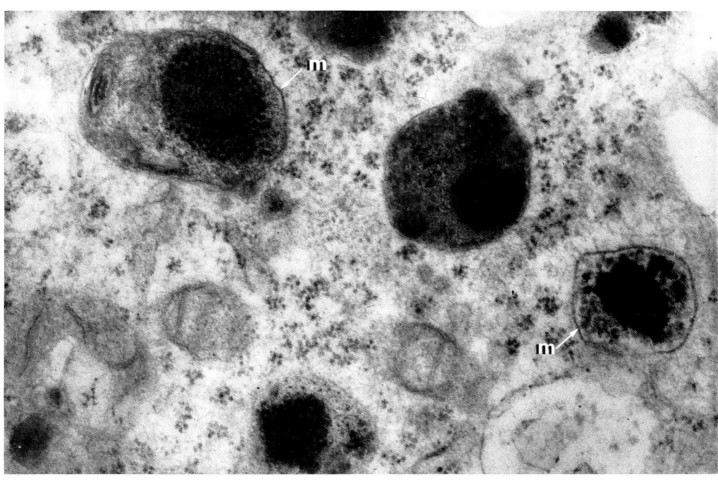

FIGURE 77

The superficial nerves of fully developed skin (see Section 8) comprise axons and Schwann cells—intimately related in different fashion so as to permit a distinction between myelinated and unmyelinated fibres—embedded in endoneurial collagen, and surrounded by a continuous cellular perineurial sheath which peters out at a pre-terminal level. These elements are of varied developmental origin. The axons grow out from the spinal cord and posterior root ganglia, Schwann cells stem from the neural crest, and the endoneurial collagen is probably the product of local fibroblasts, though Schwann cells are also thought to be capable of synthesizing collagen. It is not quite clear where the perineurial cells stem from; some believe they are of neural crest origin, others that they are derived from local mesodermal cells.

The micrograph shows the relationship established between these various components of a cutaneous nerve from a fetus aged 18 weeks. Individual axons (A), or bundles of up to 30 (A_1) are loosely enveloped and isolated from the surrounding endoneurial milieu (E), by cytoplasmic processes (c) stemming from the juxta-nuclear region of the Schwann cell (S). The tips of these processes approaching from different directions can be seen to establish contact at various points (t) along the surface outline of the complex. Golgi membranes, mitochondria and cisternae of rough endoplasmic reticulum are present in the Schwann cytoplasm. The majority of the axons are in direct contact with their neighbours and not individually segregated as in fully developed nerves. The mature Schwann cell is enveloped by a basal lamina but only tenuous traces of this can be seen associated with the plasma membrane of this cell. Schwann-cell axon complexes formed of two Schwann cells which from opposite sides enwrap as many as 150 axons are commonly seen at this stage of development. At earlier stages the relation between Schwann cell and axons is essentially the same, but simpler, in that only one or two axonal bundles may be associated with a single cell; as development proceeds the bundles are broken up by invasion of cytoplasmic processes.

There is little for comment about the endoneurial collagen (E) at this stage, and the perineurium is considered overleaf.

FIGURE 78

This is a longitudinal section along a Schwann cell/axon complex similar to the one above. A Schwann cell (S) and its cytoplasmic extensions (c) can be seen, as well as axons (A), and, in the upper part of the field, a perineurial cell (P).

Fig. 77. Schwann cell/axonal complex from dermis of arm of 140 mm C.R. (18 week) human fetus. Osmium fixation, lead staining. × 17,100

Fig. 78. Longitudinal section of Schwann cell/axonal complex from dermis of arm of 140 mm C.R. (18 week) human fetus. Osmium fixation, lead staining. × 19,100

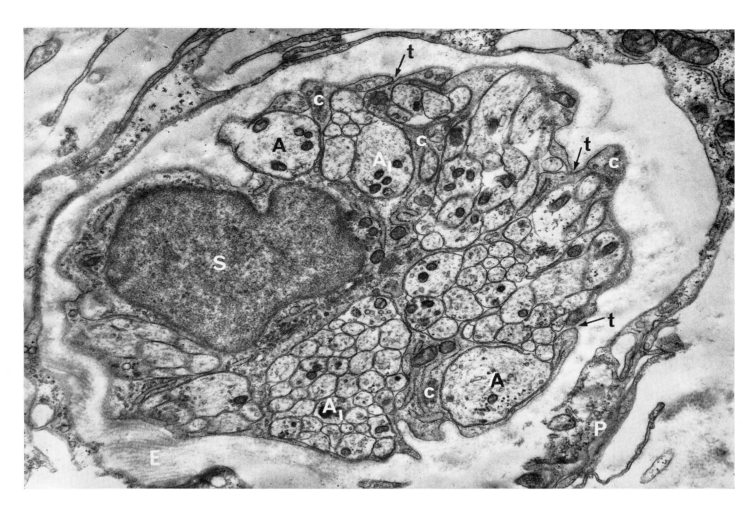

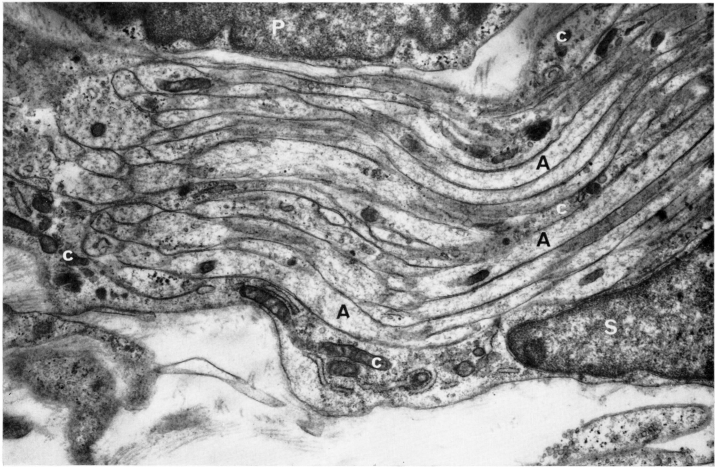

FIGURE 79

Here, a perineurial cell (P) is seen investing a Schwann cell/axonal complex which does not include the nucleus, and consists of two bundles of axons (A) enveloped by Schwann cytoplasm (S). An ill-defined basal lamina is just discernable at places along the Schwann cell plasma membrane, and an appreciable amount of endoneurial collagen (E) is present.

The perineurial cell is flattened in appearance, and the part furthest from the nucleus narrows considerably to become an elongated fine process which establishes overlapping contact with similar processes (pr) of other cells lying outside the field. The perineurial investment of the Schwann cell/axonal complex in Fig. 77 is made up in the main of such processes. There is nothing very characteristic about the cytoplasm of fetal perineurial cells—the usual organelles are present, but the rough endoplasmic reticulum is more prominent than post-natally. Indeed, they closely resemble fibroblasts, and it is only their association with Schwann cell/axonal complexes which permits separate identification. Fully developed perineurial cells, like Schwann cells, are invested by a basal lamina, but there is no trace of this at the stage of development figured here, and it is not possible to say when it first appears.

FIGURE 80

Close to the epidermis, and at deeper levels, Schwann cell/axonal complexes (S, A) devoid of perineurial investment may be seen, and readily recognized by the characteristic relation between the two components. They frequently accompany small vessels (V). Whether these will subsequently be invested, with the vessels becoming endoneurial in position it is not possible to say in individual cases. As previously mentioned, axonal terminals have not been seen entering the epidermis, except in association with Merkel cells (Fig. 64).

Fig. 79. Perineurial cell associated with Schwann cell/axonal complex from dermis of arm of 140 mm C.R. (18 week) human fetus. Osmium fixation, lead staining. × 19,000.

Fig. 80. Schwann cell/axonal complex and vessel from dermis of arm of 140 mm C.R. (18 week) human fetus. Osmium fixation, lead staining. × 18,200.

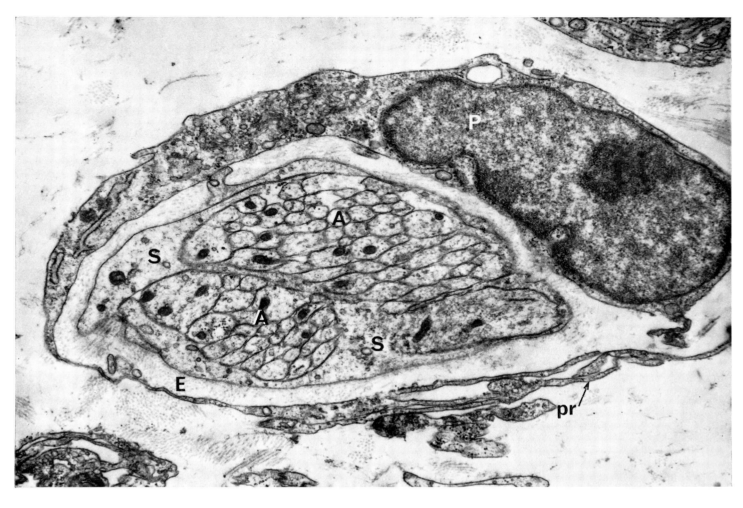

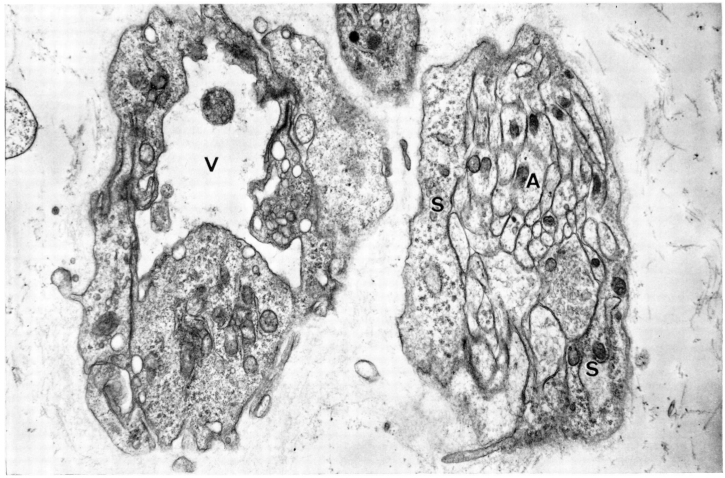

FIGURE 81

As development proceeds (cf. Fig. 77) there is a progressive reduction in the number of axons associated with a single Schwann cell (S). This reduction could be achieved by multiplication of Schwann cells, which seems very likely, possibly accompanied by extrusion and loss of a proportion of axons. Pictures such as that opposite suggest that the latter process may indeed be involved. Quite a number of axons (a) are only partially enveloped by Schwann cytoplasm, and are in direct contact with the surrounding milieu, or separated from it only by basal lamina (b). A few (a_1) are entirely lacking any Schwann cell investment and may well be axons which have been extruded, ultimately to degenerate and disappear. Of the remaining axons (a_2) some have already established a relationship with the Schwann cell which is seen in unmyelinated nerves of post-natal skin (Section 7, pp. 192–3) with typical mesaxon (m) formation in individual instances. Myelination occurs at a later stage.

FIGURE 82

This shows axonal terminals (A) in contact with the basal plasma membrane of a cell (OR) of the outer root sheath of a hair follicle from a 24 week fetus. There is a high concentration of mitochondria and other organelles within the terminals, and each retains a covering of Schwann cytoplasm (S) to the very end. Completely "naked" axons are rarely, if ever, encountered, either in fetal or post-natal skin.

Fig. 81. Schwann cells from dermis of arm of 215 mm C.R. (24 week) human fetus. Osmium fixation, lead staining. × 19,200.

Fig. 82. Nerve terminals associated with outer root sheath cell of hair follicle from arm of 215 mm C.R. (24 week) human fetus. Osmium fixation, lead staining. × 16,500.

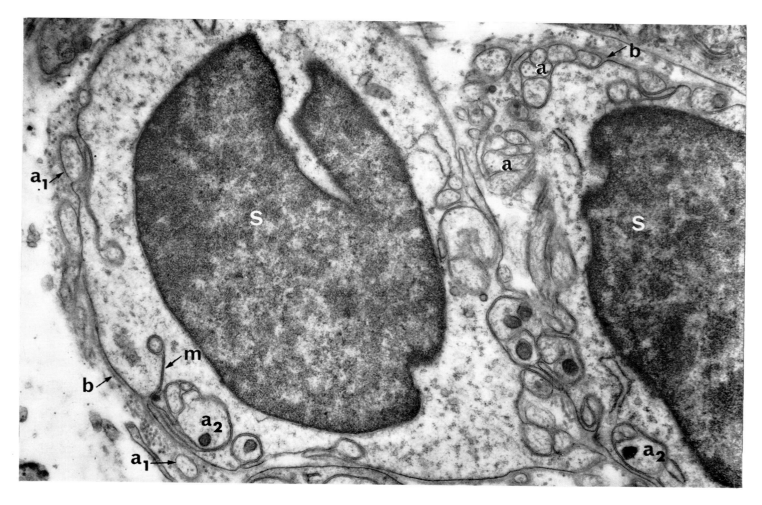

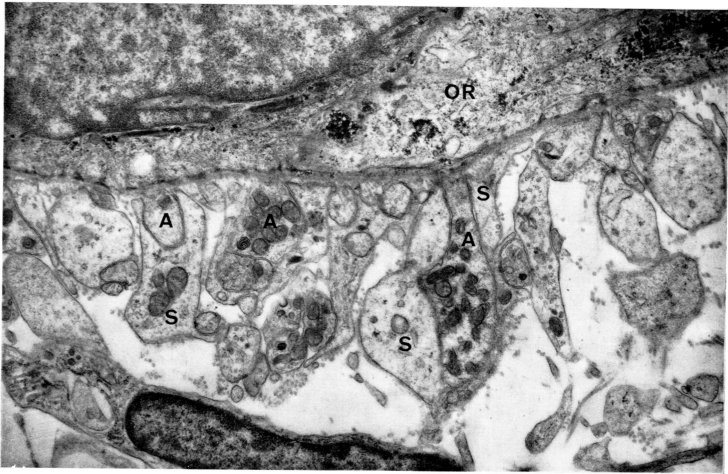

FIGURE 83

Small blood-vessels are present from the earliest stage within the sub-ectodermal mesoderm. Flattened endothelial cells (E) enclose a lumen (L) within which nucleated red cells (R) and other formed elements may be seen, and when the cells meet or overlap (j), there is close apposition of the plasma membranes. A characteristic feature of these early endothelial cells is the presence of processes (pr) which extend for quite considerable distances into the surrounding matrix, where they may establish loose contact with similar processes of undifferentiated mesodermal cells. The cytoplasm contains the common organelles, and does not differ in any significant respect from that of surrounding mesodermal cells. At a later stage of development, and post-natally, a basal lamina is associated with the outer plasma membrane of the endothelial cell. No trace of this can be detected in connection with the cells of this vessel, and it is not possible to say where it first appears.

FIGURE 84

This shows portion of an endothelial cell lining a vessel from a fetus approximately 6 weeks older than that from which the vessel in the upper micrograph was taken. The most striking feature of this cell is the high concentration of free ribosomes (ri) in the cytoplasm, which also contains mitochondria (m) and cisternae of rough endoplasmic reticulum (r). These latter are not nearly as dilated or prominent as in fibroblasts at the same stage of development. Projections (p) of varying shape and dimension extend from the luminal (L) surface of the cell, and the root of a process (pr) extending from the opposite surface also appears in the section. At one point along the external plasma membrane barely perceptible evidence of a basal lamina (l) is present.

Fig. 83. Sub-ectodermal vessel from crown of head of 14 mm C.R. (6 week) human embryo. Glutaraldehyde-osmium fixation, lead staining. × 10,000.

Fig. 84. Cytoplasm of endothelial cell lining vessel in dermis of back of 57 mm C.R. (12 week) human fetus. Glutaraldehyde-osmium fixation, lead staining. × 39,600.

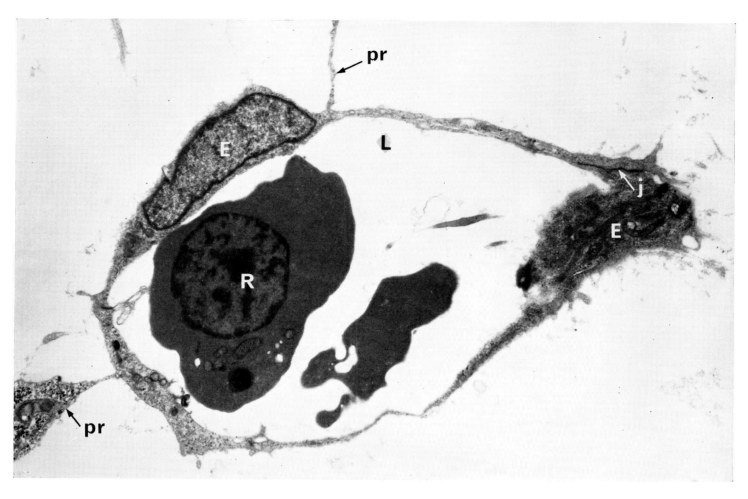

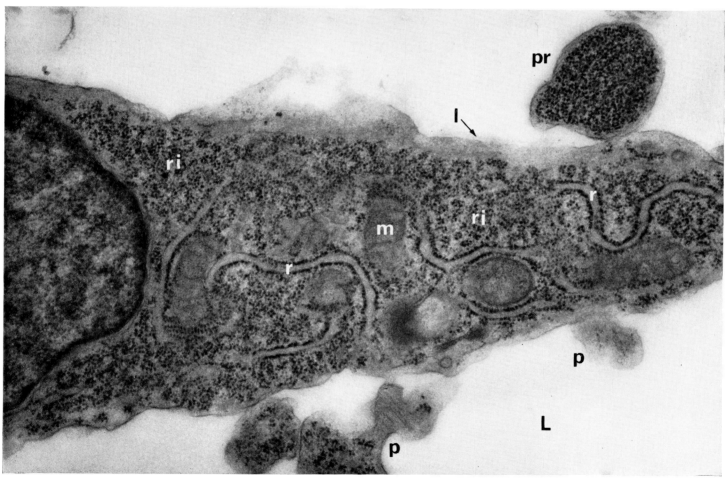

FIGURE 85

Further differentiation of endothelial cells beyond the condition illustrated in the previous micrograph involves a deepening of the cells whereby they appear less flattened on section, and the appearance within the cytoplasm of structures characteristic of endothelial cells of the post-natal microvasculature. These include micropinocytotic vesicles of the smooth (sv) and more specialized coated type (cv), as well as elongated rod-shaped organelles (r) which at high magnification are seen to consist of bundles of microtubules approximately 15 nm (150 Å) in diameter lying parallel to the long axis of the rod. The origin and function of these latter organelles is obscure.

A distinct basal lamina (l) is discernible in association with the outer plasma membrane of this cell, and projections (p) extend from the luminal surface.

FIGURE 86

This micrograph shows some other features of endothelial cells, in particular, the character of the intercellular junctions. Throughout the junction the plasma membranes are closely apposed, and over part of the area of contact (of varying length depending upon plane of section) the intercellular space is obliterated at a tight junction or zonula occludens (z). At the luminal end of the junction a thin marginal fold (mf) may be found projecting from one or both of the adjoining cells. The recurved ends of these folds may become adherent to and blend with the adjacent plasma membrane so as to entrap a droplet of fluid in a form of pinocytosis. Cyto-filaments (f) are just discernible in two of the cells.

Unlike those in previous illustrations, these endothelial cells are in contact externally with other cells (M) which are probably developing smooth muscle cells, though the special charac-ters by which these can be recognized are not yet apparent. Depending upon the size of the vessel and upon its distance from the epidermis, at this stage of development all variations from none at all to a complete cuff of such cells may be found external to the endothelial cells.

Fig. 85. Cytoplasm of endothelial cell lining vessel in dermis of arm of 215 mm C.R. (24 week) human fetus. Osmium fixation, lead staining. × 68,000.

Fig. 86. Endothelial cells lining vessel in dermis of arm of 215 mm C.R. (24 week) human fetus. Osmium fixation, lead staining. × 56,000.

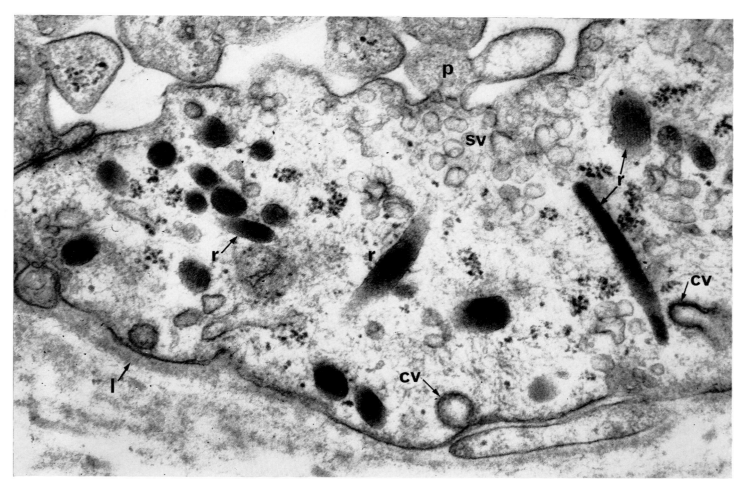

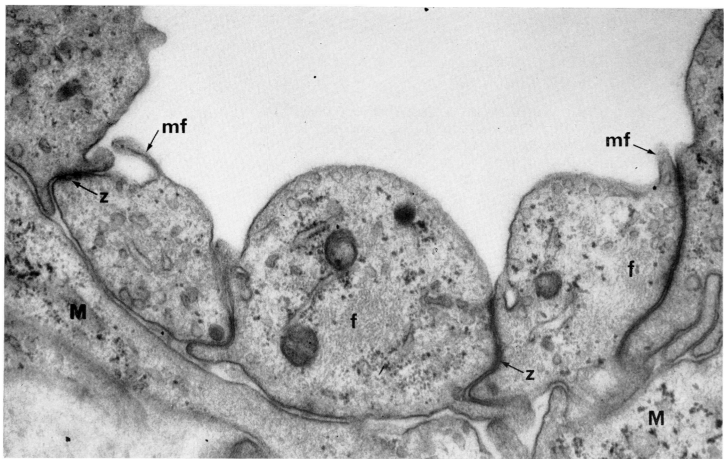

FIGURE 87

This presents a typical field from the dermis of a 24 week fetus in which many of the elements considered in previous micrographs are represented, and related to one another in a manner essentially similar to that obtaining in post-natal skin. A vessel with lumen (L) enclosed by endothelial cells (E) is seen, and external to these latter is an almost complete ring of cells (M) which are presumably developing smooth muscle cells. Close inspection will reveal that these have a basal lamina associated with the plasma membrane. It is not possible to say whether this vessel is an arteriole or a venule, and a similar difficulty in identifying elements of the micro-vasculature in isolated sections is encountered in post-natal skin since the basic structure of these small vessels is essentially similar, and the transition from one to the other is gradual.

Two Schwann cells (S) are present. The majority of the axons (a) related to the uppermost one are deeply placed within the cytoplasm, and it is reasonable to assume that they will persist into post-natal life as unmyelinated fibres. The Schwann cell in the lower part of the field is associated with a single large axon (a), and a group of smaller ones (a_1) which merely indent the plasma membrane, and are not isolated from one another or from the surrounding milieu. It might be assumed that these are in process of being cast off, and that the single large axon will remain to be further enveloped by concentric layers of plasma membrane and become a myelinated fibre.

Of the other cellular elements present, those labelled P, could be classed as perineurial cells, mainly because of their relation to the Schwann cells, and the cell marked F, with prominent rough endoplasmic reticulum is presumably a fibroblast. Collagen fibrils (C) are present in various situations.

Features of the dermis of post-natal skin are considered in Section 7.

Fig. 87. Typical field from dermis of arm of 215 mm C.R. (24 week) human fetus. Osmium fixation, lead staining. × 14,000.

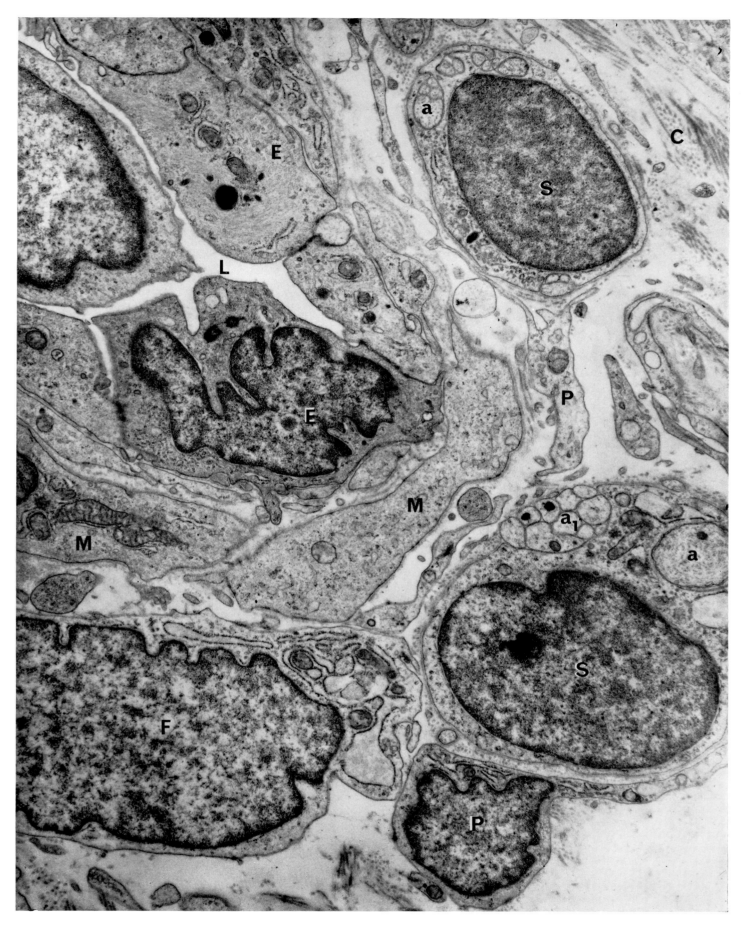

REFERENCES

MESODERM, FIBROBLASTS, AND COLLAGEN SYNTHESIS

Ashhurst, D. E. Fibroblasts, vertebrate and invertebrate. In: "Cell Structure and its Interpretation", eds. S. McGee-Russell and K. A. Ross. London, Edward Arnold, 1968.

Gould, B. S. Collagen biosynthesis. In: "Treatise on Collagen", Vol. 2, eds. G. M. Ramachandran and B. S. Gould. London, Academic Press, 1968.

Jackson, S. F. The morphogenesis of collagen. In: "Treatise on Collagen", Vol. 2, eds. G. M. Ramachandran and B. S. Gould. London, Academic Press, 1968.

Ross, R. The connective tissue fiber forming cell. In: "Treatise on Collagen", Vol. 2, eds. G. M. Ramachandran and B. S. Gould. London, Academic Press, 1968.

NERVE, SCHWANN CELLS

Bourland, A. "L'Innervation Cutanée". Paris, Masson, 1968.

Cravioto, H. The role of Schwann cells in the development of human peripheral nerves. *J. Ultrastruct. Res.*, **12**:634, 1965.

Gamble, H. J. Further electron microscope studies of human fetal peripheral nerves. *J. Anat.*, **100**: 487, 1966.

Gamble, H. J. and Breathnach, A. S. An electron microscope study of human fetal peripheral nerves. *J. Anat.*, **99**:573, 1965.

MICROVASCULATURE, ENDOTHELIUM

Florey, Lord. The endothelial cell. *Brit. med. J.*, **2**:487, 1966.

Rhodin, J. A. G. The ultrastructure of mammalian arterioles and precapillary sphincters. *J. Ultrastruct. Res.*, **18**:181, 1967.

Rhodin, J. A. G. Ultrastructure of mammalian venous capillaries, venules, and small collecting veins. *J. Ultrastruct. Res.*, **25**:452, 1968.

White, J. G. and Clausan, C. C. Blood cells and blood vessels. In: "Ultrastructure of Normal and Abnormal Skin", ed. A. S. Zelickson. London, Henry Kimpton, 1967.

5 Post-natal Interfollicular Epidermis-Keratinocytes

Basal layer — epidermal-dermal junction — stratum spinosum: tonofibrils — stratum granulosum: lamellar granules: keratohyalin — stratum corneum.

FIGURE 88

This micrograph surveys the various cell layers present in post-natal epidermis, and it may be compared with the late fetal stage illustrated in Fig. 59. Above the dermis (D) is the basal layer of cells (SB) with oval nuclei orientated perpendicular to the plane of the epidermal-dermal junction. The stratum spinosum (SS) comprises four to five layers of cells. The cells of the lowermost two layers, or so, are polyhedral in shape, and outlined by relatively electron-translucent areas which are interrupted by electron dense bands so as to present a coarsely striated appearance. The electron dense bands are in fact desmosomes with attached tono-filaments and correspond to the "nodes of Bizzozero" and "intercellular bridges" of light microscopy. There is, of course, no cytoplasmic continuity between the cells as the latter term suggests. In the upper part of the stratum spinosum the cells become more flattened and less clearly distinguishable, and superficial to them are two to three cell layers of the stratum granulosum (SG) overlain by the stratum corneum (SC). A non-keratinizing cell (nk) of the Langerhans type is present in the stratum spinosum, and stands out clearly by virtue of the absence of cytoplasmic tonofibrils.

Fig. 88. Epidermis from forearm of man aged 40. Osmium fixation, lead staining. × 5,600.

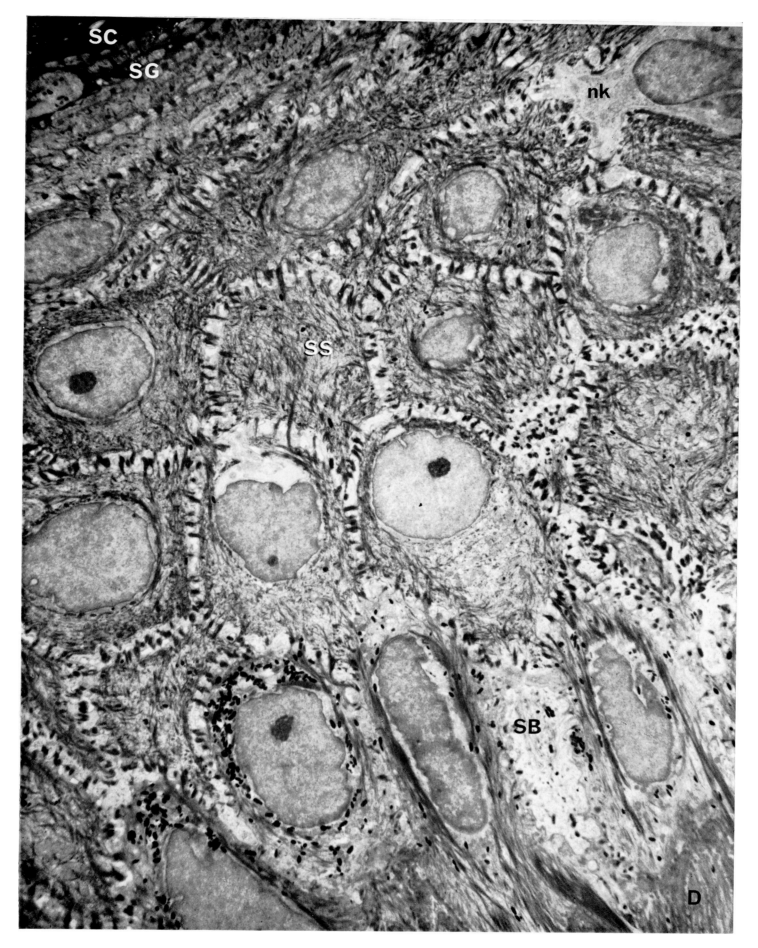

FIGURE 89

This shows general features of basal layer cells at low magnification. The tono-filamentous bundles (t) are orientated mainly perpendicular to the plane of the epidermal-dermal junction (j) and show a tendency to be concentrated in the juxta-nuclear region of the cytoplasm. One cell (F) stands out in marked contrast to the others. It has an elongated fusiform shape, its nucleus is likewise elongated and somewhat indented, the cytoplasm is more electron dense than that of neighbouring cells, and appears to have a higher concentration of melanin granules. That this cell is certainly a keratinocyte is clear from the presence of tono-filamentous bundles, and at higher magnification, desmosomes are seen to be present along the plasma membrane. The significance of these relatively electron-dense, or "dark" basal keratinocytes is at present unclear. They are encountered with reasonable frequency in most areas of normal epidermis, and their elongated appearance gives the impression that they are being compressed by neighbouring cells. Indentation of the nucleus and increase in cytoplasmic density are features of ageing or dying cells, and it may be that this is the nature of the cells in question. Morphogenetic cell death is a regular feature of developing and differentiating organs during embryonic life, and it would not be entirely surprising if it should occasionally occur post-natally in a situation such as the epidermis where turnover and renewal of cells is continually taking place. If these dark fusiform cells are in fact dying elements, their ultimate fate remains to be determined.

FIGURE 90

This micrograph illustrates melanin in basal layer cells. Fully melanized melanosomes—individual and compound—are randomly distributed within the general cytoplasm, but are concentrated to form "supra-nuclear caps" (me) above the nucleus (n). This localization is thought to be associated with a need to protect the nucleus against harmful effects of ultra-violet irradiation, and it is most marked in lightly pigmented skins with a low content of supra-basal melanin.

Fig. 89. Basal layer of epidermis from forearm of woman aged 45. Osmium fixation, lead staining. × 4,800.

Fig. 90. Supra-nuclear caps of melanin in basal epidermal cells from forearm of man aged 40. Osmium fixation, lead staining. × 8,000.

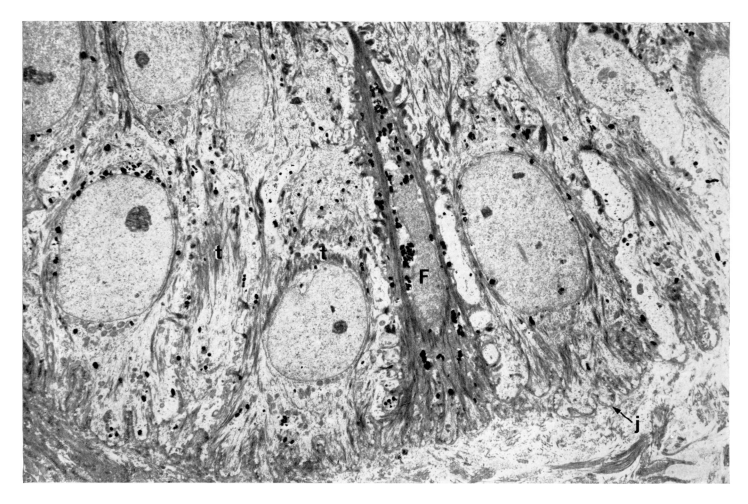

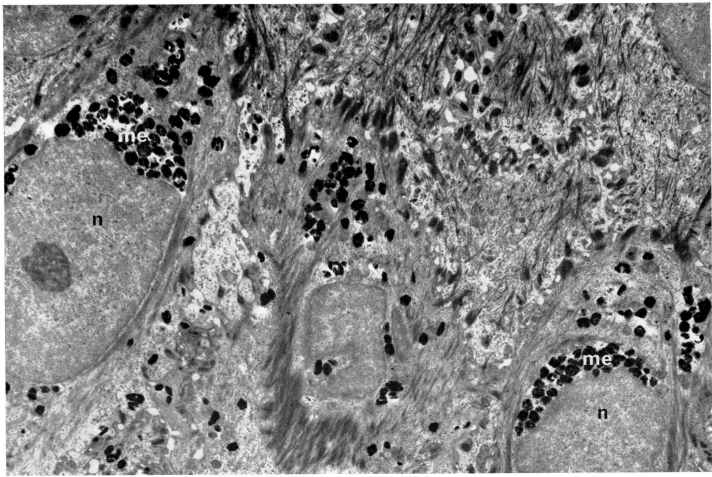

109

FIGURE 91

Development and differentiation of the main features of this region has already been considered in Section 1 (Figs. 19–24). One may note again the undulant character of the junction, the presence of hemi-desmosomes (h) at intervals along the basal plasma membrane, the basal lamina (la) with attached anchoring fibrils (a), and the reticular (r) and collagen (c) fibres of the superficial dermis. Small vesicles (v) attached to, or just within the plasma membrane of the basal cell are indicative of micropinocytotic activity at the interface between epidermis and dermis.

The tonofilaments of the basal cell are well seen in this micrograph, loosely aggregated into bundles coursing in different directions, and apparently attaching to the cytoplasmic aspect of the hemi-desmosomes. When sectioned transversely, as at t, the size of the filaments can be more accurately determined, and they have a diameter of 6–9 nm (60–90 Å). Whereas it is probable that ribosomes are concerned with initial stages in the production of tonofilaments, later stages are poorly understood, though currently under investigation by a number of workers. Observation of large numbers of sections from different regions of different individuals reveals considerable variations in the tonofilamentous content of basal cells and in the extent to which they may be aggregated into bundles to form tonofibrils. The prominence or otherwise of filaments and the ease with which they can be individually resolved within bundles, is to some extent dependent upon the staining technique employed. Accordingly, no single micrograph can be regarded as presenting an overall "typical" picture where these features are concerned.

Fig. 91. Epidermal-dermal junctional region from forearm of girl aged 18. Osmium fixation, combined lead and uranyl-acetate staining. × 60,200.

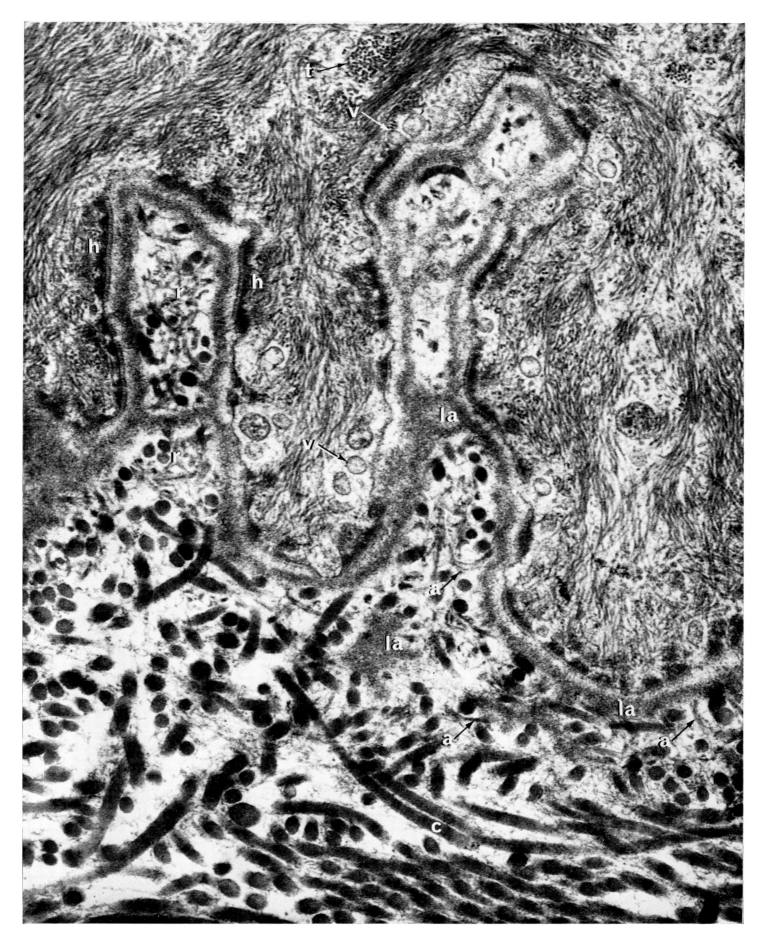

III

FIGURE 92

Parts of the cytoplasm of two basal layer cells from a new-born infant are shown here. Free ribosomal particles are abundant, but the rough endoplasmic reticulum (r) is poorly developed. Mitochondria, and tonofilaments aggregated to varying degrees are evident. One cell contains membrane-limited granules (g) with finely-particulate matrix, which have the morphological appearance of lysosomes. Until recently, it was generally accepted that lysosomes are absent from keratinocytes of normal human epidermis. However, their demonstration in normal mouse keratinocytes, and in cells of patients with infantile eczema, makes this appear less certain. The granules in question are identical in appearance with the membrane-limited organelles within which melanosomes are dispersed to form compound melanosomes (see Figs. 48 and 109) and these have recently been shown to exhibit acid phosphatase activity, which is characteristic of lysosomes. Accordingly, it is possible that the granules illustrated here are indeed lysosomes, though this identification must remain tentative in the absence of cytochemical evidence of acid phosphatase activity within them.

In addition to desmosomes (d), pinocytotic vesicles (v) are present along the lateral plasma membranes of the cells.

FIGURE 93

Centrioles (ce) though present, are rarely seen in basal layer cells, and the same applies to the Golgi apparatus which is, in general, poorly developed. Lipid droplets with circular or scalloped outline are occasionally seen, and a row of these (li) in characteristic position close to the nucleus (n) is shown in the inset. Glycogen is not normally found in the cytoplasm, but an occasional small deposit, or isolated single granules may be seen in cells of what appeared to be clinically normal epidermis.

Fig. 92. Cytoplasm of basal epidermal cells from forearm of 3-weeks infant. Osmium fixation, lead staining. × 51,000.

Fig. 93. Centriole in basal epidermal cell from forearm of man aged 40. Osmium fixation, lead staining. × 112,000. *Inset:* Lipid droplets. × 36,000.

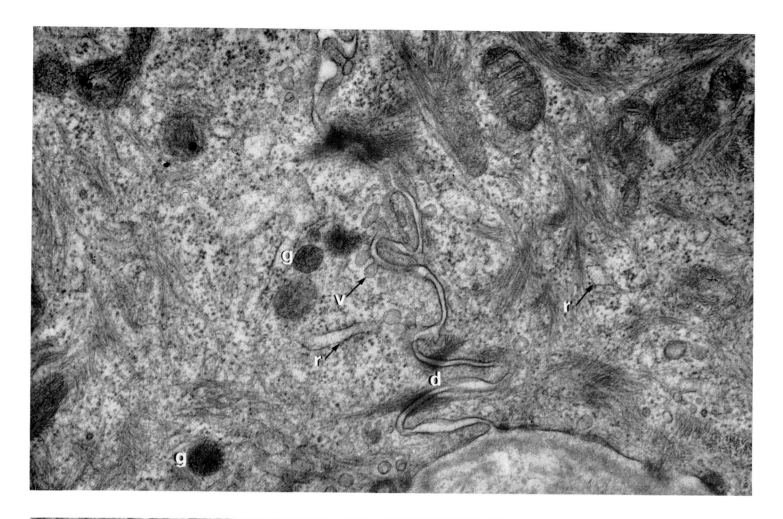

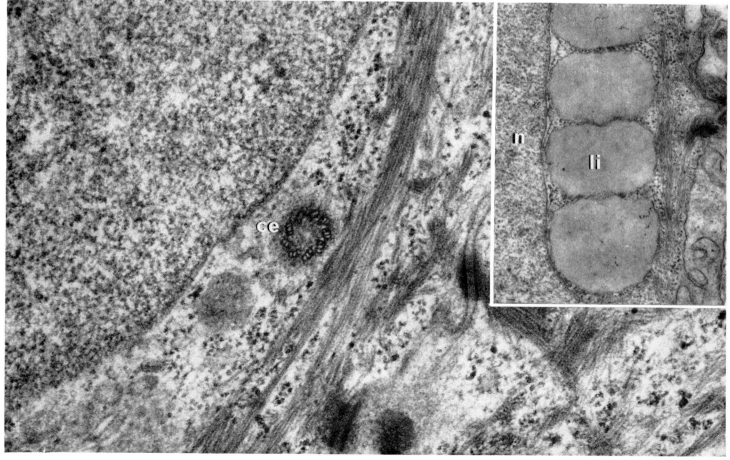

FIGURE 94

Two basal layer cells (B) are here seen in contact with the lowermost cells of the stratum spino-sum (S). The most obvious contrast between the differently situated cells relates to the tono-filaments. In the basal layer cells the filaments are rather loosely arranged to form more or less parallel bundles or tonofibrils, within which one can imagine that individual filaments would readily be distinguishable at higher magnification as in Fig. 91. In the spinous layer cells, tono-fibrils are much more prominent, possibly because they are more numerous, and they form an interlacing network which extends throughout the cytoplasm, apart from the region immedi-ately adjacent to the nucleus. The tonofibrils are more electron dense, or, to put it in another way, "stain" more intensely than those in the basal layer cells; they also appear more compact, and are less obviously made up of individual tonofilaments.

It is difficult to know what significance should be attached to this difference in electron den-sity or "stainability" of the tonofibrils of basal and spinous layer cells. The issue is further complicated by the fact that tonofibrils of the same cell display varying affinities to different stains. Thus, had the section opposite been stained with PTA, no significant difference in den-sity of tonofibrils in the two situations would have been apparent. The differences demon-strable have a chemical basis, but exactly what this is, is uncertain.

As regards other cytoplasmic components, there is not much difference between basal and lower spinous cells, though it is generally thought that centrioles are absent from the latter. Spinous cells are division products of basal cells which ascend to a higher level, and this move-ment must involve considerable alterations in intercellular attachments. The mechanisms involved do not appear to have been extensively investigated, or if so, with little result.

Fig. 94. Basal and lower spinous layer cells of epidermis from forearm of man aged 42. Osmium fixation, lead staining. × 11,700.

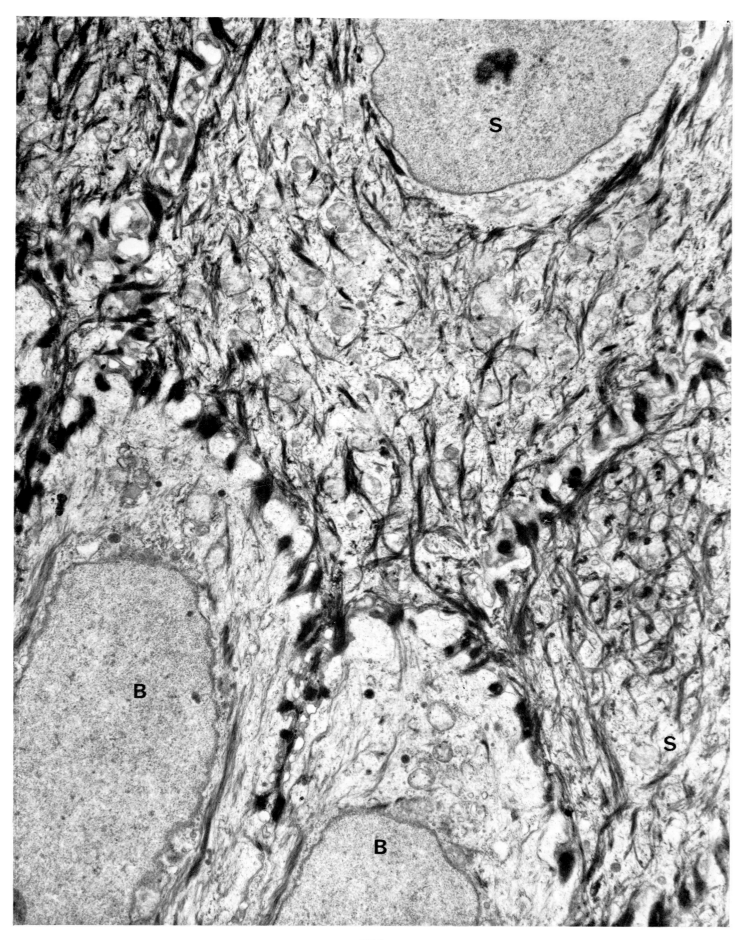

115

FIGURE 95

This is a very typical field and gives a good impression of the relationships between the cells and their main features at this level. The apposed plasma membranes are folded and interlocked in a most complicated fashion, and studded at intervals with desmosomes which appear sectioned in various planes. Tonofibrils are very prominent, and in some cells appear almost to envelop the nucleus.

The inset shows that in addition to desmosomes (d) junctional elements of the type known as a tight junction (t), or zonula occludens, may connect adjacent spinous layer cells. Along this type of junction the outer leaflets of the apposed cell membranes fuse, obliterating the intercellular space and form a central fusion line, separated on either side by a narrow relatively electron-translucent zone from the inner leaflet of the cell membrane. Since the intercellular space is occluded at these tight junctions, which in other epithelia are known to be continuous around each cell, they are thought to serve as "closing belts" or seals which can provide a barrier to diffusion of materials along the spaces between the cells. There is evidence that they are impermeable to macromolecules, water, certain ions and water-soluble molecules. It is generally accepted that the epidermal intercellular space is "open" towards the dermis, and in so far as these tight junctions serve as partial or complete barriers to diffusion of materials, they are probably concerned in the main with blocking flow inwards from the surface.

Fig. 95. Lower and intermediate layers of stratum spinosum of epidermis from forearm of girl aged 18. Osmium fixation, lead staining. ×6,600. *Inset:* Desmosome and tight junction from stratum spinosum of forearm epidermis of man aged 42. Osmium fixation, lead staining. ×186,000.

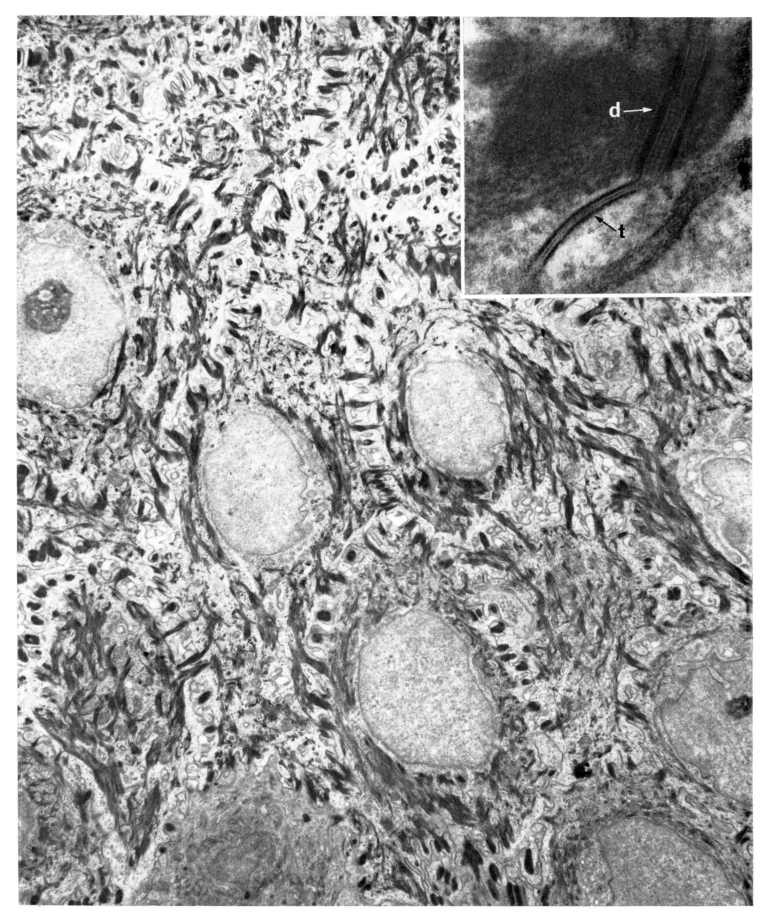

FIGURE 96

This micrograph is taken from an intermediate level of the stratum spinosum, and shows the interlacing meshwork of tonofibrils which is characteristic of this situation. Though much less apparent than in cells of the basal layer (cf. Fig. 91) it is evident in places (f) that the tonofibrils are made up of aggregations of individual tonofilaments. In some places also, the filaments exhibit a faint periodicity (p) along their length due to alternating dense and less dense regions, and it may be pointed out that tonofilaments present in the basal cell illustrated in Fig. 93 have a similar faintly beaded appearance. Where tonofibrils coursing in different directions meet and intermingle, they form somewhat more electron-dense zones (z), which, taken in isolation, could be described as areas exhibiting a "speckled" pattern, and within which the outlines of individual filaments are not discernible. It seems evident that such a speckled pattern and blurring of outline would naturally result from intermingling of bundles of filaments exhibiting individual periodicity. However, another interpretation has been given to the appearances illustrated here. Thus, Brody has suggested that the tonofibrils of the basal layer cells consist of two components—opaque filaments, and a less opaque interfilamentous substance in which they are embedded. At the transition to the stratum spinosum the ultrastructure of the tonofibrils, according to him, becomes completely changed, and neither individual filaments nor interfilamentous substance are seen. The tonofibrils appear as compact masses with a distinct speckled pattern. It is implied that some significant molecular change takes place to produce this pattern, though exactly of what nature is not made clear. It might be stressed that considerable caution should be exercised when drawing conclusions from purely morphological appearances in this general context, particularly, as already emphasized, since they may vary with different staining techniques. All one can do at present is point out that from micrographs presented here, and from others available, no evidence can be presented of a distinct interfilamentous substance within tonofibrils of basal layer cells. Furthermore, the "speckled pattern" of interlacing tonofibrillar bundles of the lower stratum spinosum seems to be capable of explanation without implying any profound molecular rearrangement at this level.

Fig. 96. Tonofibrils in spinous cell from forearm epidermis of man aged 40. Osmium fixation, lead staining. × 57,000.

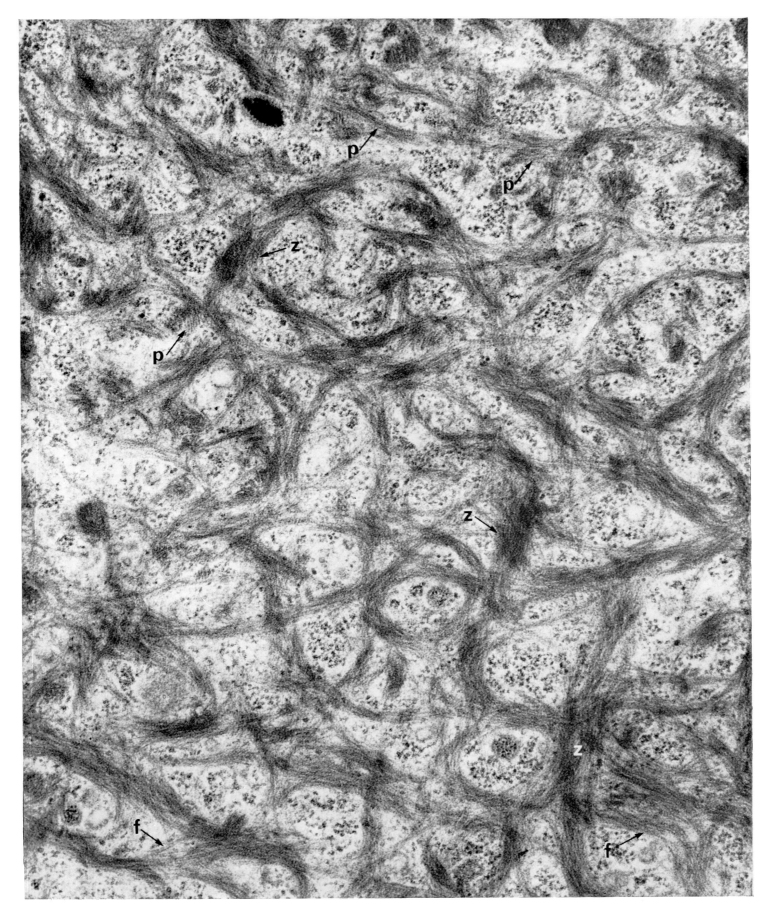

FIGURE 97

This field spans the upper part of the stratum spinosum (SS), the stratum granulosum (SG) and the lower part of the stratum corneum (SC). The flattening of the upper spinous cells is indicated by parallel linear arrays of desmosomes (d) along their boundaries, and the somewhat tigroid appearance of the cytoplasm is due to the tonofibrils. The stratum granulosum comprises two layers of cells, both containing irregular keratohyalin granules (k), which, as seen in the upper layer may almost completely envelop the nucleus. Within the lower granular cell, and also within the spinous cells, are small granules (g) not very prominent at this magnification. These granules are highly characteristic of this level of the epidermis and they are variously known as Odland bodies, membrane-coating granules, or lamellar granules. Their structure at higher magnification is shown in succeeding micrographs.

A picture such as this confronts one with the main problem of epidermal differentiation, i.e. what is involved in the transformation of a spinous cell into a granular one, and of this, in turn, into a flattened keratinized element of the stratum corneum. Tied up with this are questions of the origin and function of keratohyalin and lamellar granules, the fate of the tonofibrils, and finally the nature of keratin itself. Ultrastructural studies have contributed greatly towards defining and partially elucidating these problems, but their final solution cannot be achieved by purely morphological observations, the limitations of which must always be borne in mind when one is attempting to analyse a dynamic process involving complex structural and metabolic alterations.

Fig. 97. Upper layers of epidermis from forearm of man aged 40. Osmium fixation, lead staining. × 22,700.

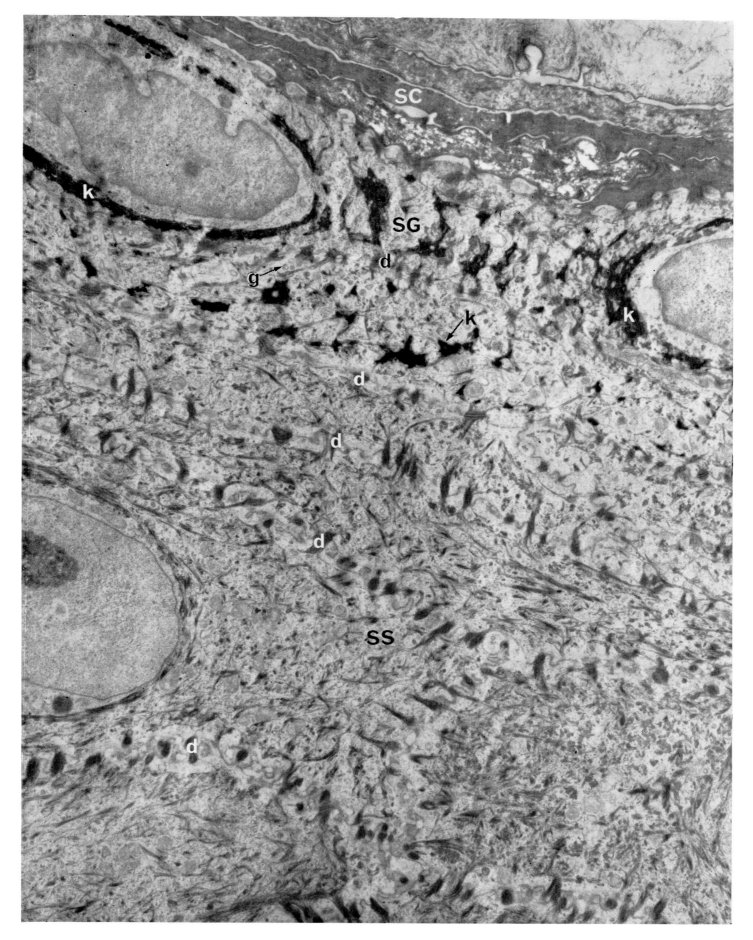

FIGURE 98

Lamellar granules (g) are round or ovoid bodies which are present in cells of the upper spinous and granular layers. Size alone (0·1–0·5 μm) allows them to be distinguished from mitochondria (m). Though distributed throughout the cytoplasm, they tend to be concentrated in the region close to the cell membrane, to which they may become attached in such a fashion that their contents are emptied into the intercellular space (see Figs. 100 and 102). Some authors believe that thereby they provide a coating for the outer surface of the cell membrane, and refer to them in consequence as "membrane-coating granules" (M.C.G.).

FIGURE 99

At high magnification the lamellar structure of the granules (g) becomes apparent. Parallel dense lamellae about 2·5 nm (25 Å) wide are separated by more translucent zones of 3–5 nm (30–50 Å), which in turn are bisected by a narrow dense line not always easily demonstrable in human skin. Depending upon plane of section of granules, several sectors exhibiting different main orientation of lamellae may be seen.

Lamellar granules are thought to contain a high content of phospholipid because their lamellar structure resembles that of synthetic phospholipid preparations. They also (*see inset*) show a particular affinity for stains such as osmium iodide which are of value in demonstrating phospholipid in other tissues. Nothing is known of their site of origin or mode of synthesis, and there is some doubt also concerning their function. One view states that on being discharged from the cell, the granules spread their contents over the outer surface of the plasma membrane coating it with an amorphous product which leads to it becoming thickened and resistant to keratinolytic agents. This coating may, also, by isolating the cell from its neighbours and the intercellular space, lead to a reduction in metabolic activity, and promote its transformation to the horny state. According to this viewpoint therefore, the granules play a key role in keratinization. An alternative suggestion is that the granules are actually derived by infolding and nipping off of segments of plasma membrane, and that they subsequently undergo disintegration within the cytoplasm. This theory would relate their formation to a need to reduce the surface area and folding of the plasma membrane as a preliminary to keratinization. A third view, based upon demonstration of acid phosphatase activity within the granules, is that they are specialized lysosomes. Whatever the merits of these different viewpoints, the appearance of the granules at a level in the epidermis where keratohyalin granules (k) are also forming certainly suggests that they are concerned in some way with the process of keratinization. Granules identical in structure are found in keratinizing oral epithelium, and in mouse oesophageal and gastric epithelium.

Fig. 98. Lamellar granules in spinous and granular cells of forearm epidermis of man aged 70. Osmium fixation, lead staining. × 31,500.

Fig. 99. Lamellar granules in granular layer cell of forearm epidermis of woman aged 42. Osmium fixation, lead staining. × 228,000. *Inset:* Lamellar granule stained with osmium iodide. × 200,000.

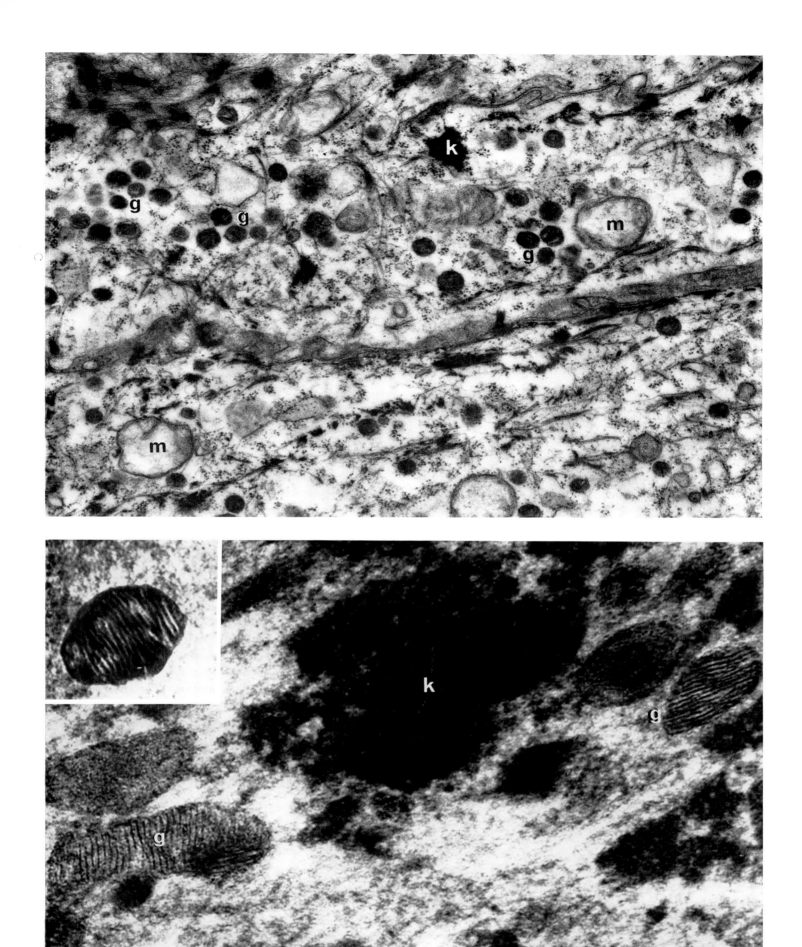

FIGURE 100

The most characteristic feature of the granulosa cell (G) is the presence of irregular kerato-hyalin granules (k). As in the fetus (see Figs. 53–56) this substance first appears in association with tonofibrils, and appears to extend along, or incorporate them, as it accumulates. In the most superficial granulosa cells (G) next to the stratum corneum (C) the tonofibrils (t) appear as compact slightly less dense ragged extensions from the periphery of the more opaque keratohyalin masses. Individual tonofilaments cannot be distinguished within the tonofibrils. The general cytoplasmic matrix appears less dense than that of underlying cells, and this is associated with a reduction in the number of organelles—mitochondria, lamellar granules, etc. The nucleus exhibits signs of degeneration, i.e. indentation, loss of uniform granularity, and in many cells may be almost completely disintegrated. At the junction between the stratum granulosum (G) and the stratum corneum (C) lamellar granules (g, *inset*) may be seen discharging their contents into the intracellular space.

FIGURE 101

In the majority of sections, the transition between stratum granulosum (G) and stratum corneum (C) is abrupt, with granulosa cells of the type figured above (Fig. 100) directly succeeded by frankly keratinized elements. In some sections, however, cells with some features regarded as characteristic of both layers may be encountered, and are labelled "transition cells" (T). These cells contain only remnants of nuclei, or lack them entirely, but occasional mitochondria (m) may be seen. Keratohyalin (k) and less densely staining compact tonofibrillar masses (t) are present, the latter particularly evident in the neighbourhood of desmosomes (d). In these respects the transition cells resemble granulosa cells. However, the plasma membrane (p) is thickened in comparison with that of the underlying more typical granulosa cell (G), and thereby resembles the plasma membrane of the stratum corneum cell (C). Thickening of the plasma membrane is considered to be an essential feature of keratinization and in this respect the transition cell can be regarded as having progressed further in that direction than the underlying cell. Its flattened outline and general lack of folding of the plasma membrane are other features by which it resembles more a stratum corneum cell.

Exhaustive examination of micrographs of transition cells has failed to clarify what is involved in the final transformation of granulosa type cells into fully keratinized elements. Fetal studies to date have likewise contributed little to the solution of this problem.

Fig. 100. Granulosa cell from forearm epidermis of man aged 72. Osmium fixation, lead staining. ×27,600. *Inset:* Lamellar granule at junction of stratum granulosum and stratum corneum. ×79,500.

Fig. 101. Transition cell from forearm epidermis of woman aged 42. Osmium fixation, lead staining. ×60,000.

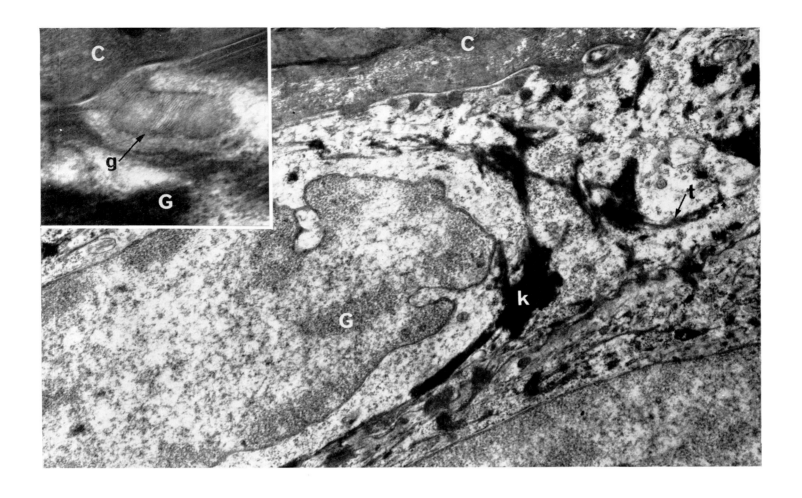

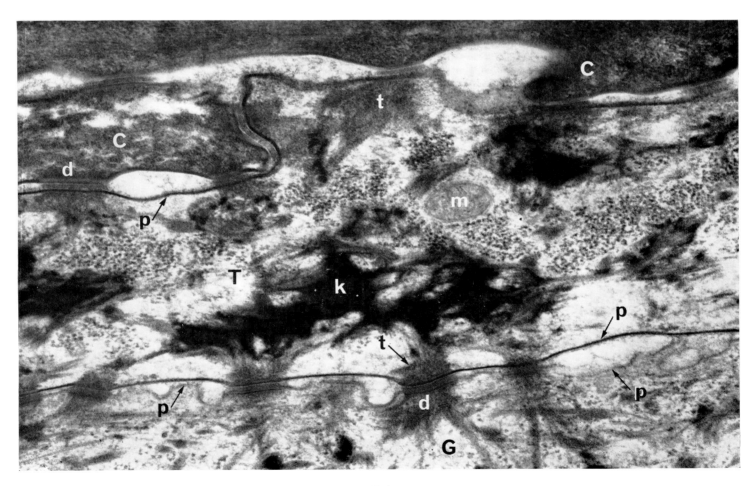

FIGURE 102

In both fetal (Figs. 54 and 55) and post-natal epidermis, keratohyalin first appears as an amorphous highly electron-dense substance within or about tonofibrils. Whether or not it is a specific new product synthesized by the granulosa cells and deposited upon pre-existing tonofibrils, or merely a more intensely staining region indicative of chemical and molecular alteration of tonofibrillar substance, without other addition, is currently being argued. Micrographs of fetal epidermis (Fig. 54) might appear to favour the former view, and with post-natal epidermis either can be made to appear more or less likely depending upon the fixative and staining method employed. It is clear that this problem will not be solved by inspection, however prolonged of routine micrographs. Recent electron autoradiographic studies have indicated that synthesis of histidine-rich protein is involved in the formation of keratohyalin in granulosa cells, and it has since been shown that an amorphous electron-dense component can be selectively extracted from keratohyalin granules leaving intact a fine fibrillar substance. These studies certainly support the view that keratohyalin is a distinct entity, and that the "keratohyalin granules" of routine micrographs consist of two components, a tonofibrillar one, and another the source and chemical nature of which remains to be determined.

Depending upon fixation and staining, a "speckled" pattern may be demonstrable within keratohyalin granules (k). This appearance could be interpreted as due to low-density filaments embedded in denser amorphous matrix, and could well fit in with the results of the extraction experiments mentioned above.

Lamellar granules (g) are present in the cytoplasm of the lower of the two cells illustrated here, and at the lower left-hand corner of the field, one is seen in an intercellular position.

FIGURE 103

This micrograph, obtained from the granular layer of characteristically thick sole of foot epidermis, is of interest in that it appears to show segregation of dense (d) and more translucent areas (t) within keratohyalin granules. However, it is more likely that the denser masses correspond to the keratohyalin granules of previous micrographs (made up of two components) and that the less dense areas represent compacted tonofibrillar substance not associated with an amorphous component. They are very similar in appearance to tonofibrils (f) located elsewhere in the cytoplasm.

The tonofilament is the characteristic product of the basal epidermal keratinocyte and it may be of value at this stage to attempt a summary of its fate as it progresses to higher levels below the stratum corneum. In the basal and lower spinous layers, tonofilaments become aggregated into bundles of tonofibrils within which they can still be individually resolved. In the upper spinous layers, tonofibrils become more compacted, and their basic filamentous substructure becomes progressively obscured; whether this is due to some fundamental molecular reorganization is unclear. In the stratum granulosum a new substance, i.e. the dense amorphous component of keratohyalin granules, is deposited upon some, but not all, of the tonofibrils, a variable proportion of which therefore pass to the stratum corneum unaffected by infiltration with this material.

Fig. 102. Keratohyalin and lamellar granules in granular cells of forearm epidermis of woman aged 42. Glutaraldehyde-osmium fixation, lead staining. × 102,700.

Fig. 103. Keratohyalin in granular cell from sole of foot of child aged 3. Osmium fixation, lead staining. × 57,700.

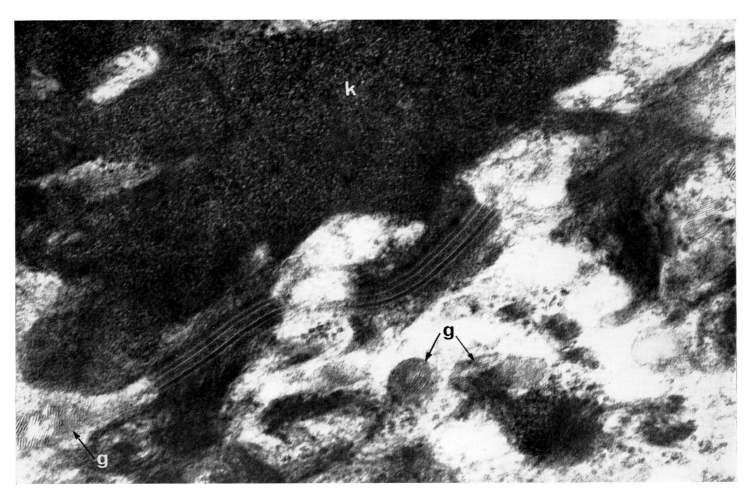

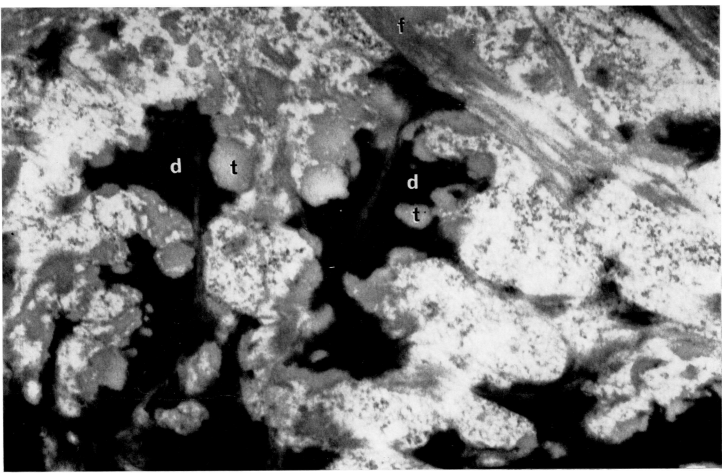

FIGURE 104

The final product of epidermal differentiation is the stratum corneum, which consists of layers of flattened keratinized cells, each approximately 0·5 to 0·8 μm thick, and about 30 μm in diameter. The number of layers varies with body region, ranging from 15 to 20 on the abdomen and back to several hundreds on the palm and soles. Upwards of 45 layers may be counted superficial to the stratum granulosum (SG) in the micrograph opposite, which is from the skin of the arm. The cells are closely bound together, and large spaces frequently seen within the stratum are artefactual, being due to processing. This tightly-knit construction of the stratum corneum is indicative of its important function as a barrier to the passage of materials in either direction across it.

In electron micrographs, the structure of cells at all levels of the stratum corneum is rarely uniform, and variations in density and other features are frequently encountered. This can be seen in the micrograph opposite, and particular attention may be drawn to the cells marked f, which are significantly less dense in appearance than their neighbours. This is apparently due, at this magnification, to the contrast between the loose fibrillar character of the matrix of the former and its more compact homogeneous arrangement in the majority of cells. Some of these variations have been attributed to fixation or other processing artifacts, but this is probably not the complete story, and they may in fact have some significance in relation to differences in structure or degrees of keratinization. The appearance of stratum corneum cells also varies with the staining technique employed, all of which makes it difficult to decide what is the morphological equivalent of a fully keratinized cell, using this term in a strictly chemical sense.

Fig. 104. Stratum corneum from epidermis of arm of man aged 72. Osmium fixation, lead staining. × 5,100.

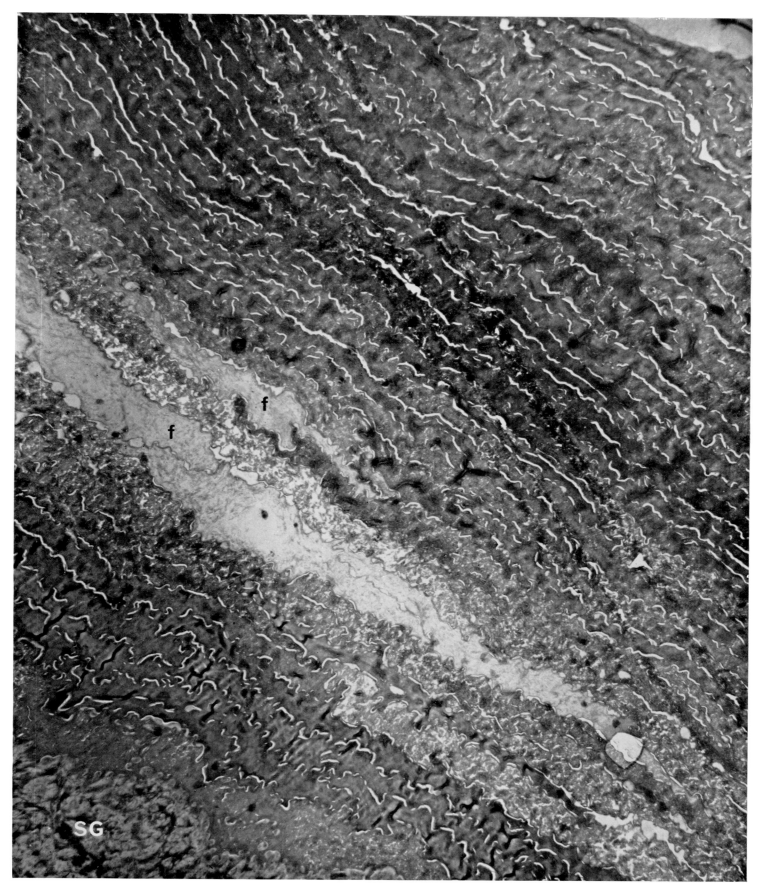

FIGURE 105

Portions of four stratum corneum cells can be seen here. The one adjacent to the stratum granulosum (SG) has a homogeneous matrix which at higher magnification can be resolved into a so-called "keratin pattern" of low density filaments embedded in a denser substance (Figs. 106 and 107). The other three have a distinctly fibrillar matrix (f), and the question arises how to account for this difference. A view receiving support in some quarters would suggest that the lowermost cell more closely typifies the keratinized state, and that the appearance of the others is an artifact of processing, due either to poor fixation or to the extraction of material from the matrix at this or some later stage of preparation. The occurrence of structurally empty areas in various situations could support this view. Also, recent experiments have shown that extraction by alkali of an amorphous protein substance from stratum corneum cells with more homogeneous appearing matrix, leaves them looking not unlike the other type of cell illustrated here. However, in many micrographs, cells of the two different types may be found lying immediately adjacent at practically all levels of the stratum corneum, and to attribute their dissimilar appearances solely to local fixation defects, is something which some workers find difficult to accept. They would rather be inclined to say that filaments in stratum corneum cells may be either tightly or loosely packed, depending upon relative amounts of amorphous interfilamentous substance, and that cells of more homogeneous appearance exhibiting keratin pattern contain a larger amount of this substance than others. This view is not incompatible with the results of the extraction experiments mentioned above. In so far as tonofibrils and keratohyalin can be regarded as the filamentous and amorphous components concerned, it seems not entirely unlikely that cells entering the stratum corneum from the stratum granulosum might from time to time contain variable or disproportionate amounts of one or other, and that the differences observed may be due to this. It will be recalled that appearances in fetal epidermis (Fig. 57) could be explained on a similar basis.

Whatever the general quality of fixation in the above connection, this micrograph adequately illustrates some other features of the stratum corneum. In the intercellular spaces, variable amounts of granular or reticular material (i) may be seen. This is thought to represent the contents of lamellar granules discharged at a lower level. This seems to be borne out by the fact that, as shown in the inset, characteristic lamellation (l) is sometimes seen in this situation. Denser areas (d) occurring at regular intervals represent the intercellular component of desmosomes, which, in the stratum corneum lack the dense attachment plaque associated with the inner aspect of the plasma membrane. This is well seen in relation to the desmosomes (de) connecting granular and stratum corneum cells. An attachment plaque (P) is present on one side, but not on the other. The thickened plasma membrane of the stratum corneum cell is evident, and interestingly, shows varying degrees of stainability.

Fig. 105. Innermost cells of stratum corneum from forearm epidermis of girl aged 18. Osmium fixation, lead staining. × 61,200. *Inset:* lamellated material in space between stratum corneum cells from forearm epidermis of woman aged 42. Osmium fixation, lead staining. × 148,000.

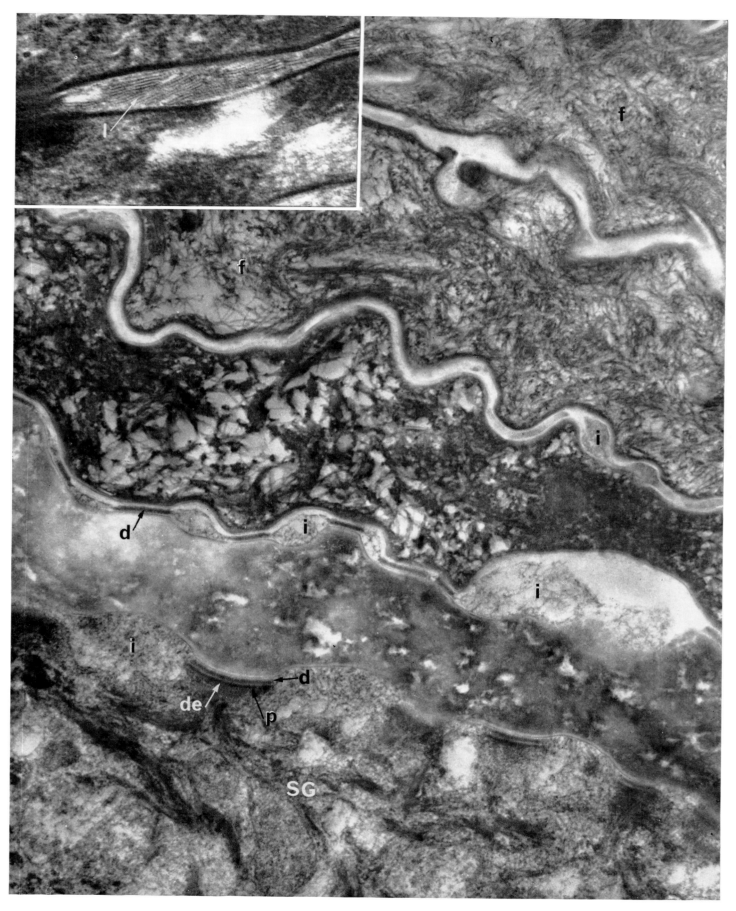

FIGURES 106 and 107

The section from which the upper of these two micrographs (Fig. 106) was obtained was stained with lead hydroxide. The matrix of the stratum corneum cells presents a faintly tigroid appearance suggesting an ordered pattern, which, however is nowhere clearly evident. It becomes more apparent following additional staining with uranyl acetate as in Fig. 107. This "keratin pattern" has been interpreted as being produced by packed low-density filaments (f) set in an amorphous substance of greater density, and is thought to represent the final stage of differentiation of the epidermal keratinocyte. It has been suggested that the filaments are derived from tonofibrils, and the amorphous substance from keratohyalin granules, but this is by no means certain, since the chemical nature of the two components has not been established. Besides, the chemical constitution of the suggested precursors themselves—tonofibrils and keratohyalin—remains to be worked out. It is not possible therefore, at present, to interpret the morphological appearances in chemical terms, or vice versa.

In Fig. 106 the intercellular material (i) thought to be derived from lamellar granules is particularly dense, and certainly, appearances in the centre of the field suggest its function may be to provide a thin coating for the outer aspect of the plasma membrane (p) of the stratum corneum cell. The thickened character of this latter in comparison with lower levels has already been mentioned, though exactly what is involved in the transformation is not clear. The plasma membrane is the part of the cell most resistant to keratinolytic agents.

Fig. 106. Stratum corneum cells from forearm epidermis of man aged 42. Osmium fixation, lead staining. × 111,600.

Fig. 107. Stratum corneum cells from forearm epidermis of man aged 42. Osmium fixation, combined lead and uranyl acetate staining. × 120,000. *Inset:* Keratin pattern at higher magnification. × 168,000.

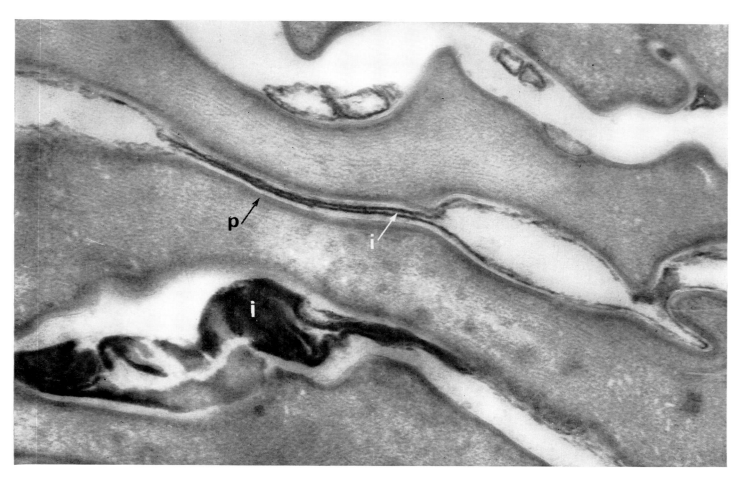

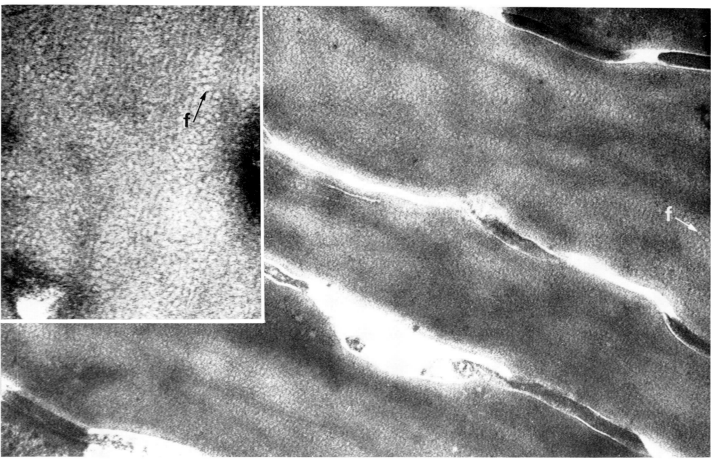

133

REFERENCES

Brody, I. Different staining methods for the electron microscope elucidation of the tonofibrillar differentiation in normal epidermis. In: "The Epidermis", W. Montagna and W. C. Lobitz, eds. New York, Academic Press, 1964.

Farquhar, M. G. and Palade, G. E. Cell junctions in amphibian skin. *J. Cell Biol.*, **26**:263, 1965.

Frithiof, F. and Wersääl, J. A highly ordered structure in keratinizing human oral epithelium. *J. Ultrastruct. Res.*, **12**:371, 1965.

Fukuyama, K., Burman, M. M. and Epstein, W. L. The preferential extraction of keratohyalin granules and interfilamentous substances of the horny cell. *J. Invest. Derm.*, **51**:355, 1968.

Matoltsy, A. G. and Parakkal, P. F. Keratinization. In: "Ultrastructure of normal and abnormal skin". A. S. Zelickson, ed. London, Henry Kimpton, 1967.

Mercer, E. H. "Keratin and keratinization". Oxford, Pergamon, 1961.

Odland, G. F. Tonofilaments and keratohyalin. In: "The Epidermis", W. Montagna and W. C. Lobitz, eds. New York, Academic Press, 1964.

Wolff, K. and Holubar, K. Odland-Körper (membrane coating granules, keratinosomen) als epidermale Lysosomen. *Arch. klin. exp. Derm.*, **231**:1, 1967.

6 Intra-Epidermal Non-Keratinocytes

Melanocyte: melanogenesis — Merkel cell — Langerhans cell.

FIGURE 108

As already mentioned (p. 28) melanocytes are derived from the neural crest, and begin to enter the epidermis at about the eleventh week of fetal life. In post-natal epidermis they are confined to the basal layer, where the incidence of melanocytes in relation to keratinocytes has been estimated to vary between 1:4 in some situations (cheek) to 1:11 in others (arm and thigh). Recent observations, however, indicate that these regional differences in population density are not as great as previously thought. In electron micrographs the melanocyte (M) is readily distinguishable from surrounding keratinocytes (K) by virtue of a mere translucent cytoplasm which contains the common organelles, but no tonofibrils (f), as such, though some cyto-filaments may be present (see Fig. 109). Desmosomes are not associated with the lateral plasma membrane, nor hemi-desmosomes with the basal part in contact with the dermis (D). Due to the thinness of sections, the dendritic nature of individual melanocytes is rarely fully apparent, but in addition to the basal perikaryon, seemingly unattached dendritic processes (d) are commonly present interspersed among neighbouring keratinocytes.

The most characteristic feature of the melanocyte is the presence of cytoplasmic granules—melanosomes (m), exhibiting varying degrees of electron density and internal structure. These are formative and mature stages of melanin granules as seen in light microscopy. Melanosomes are also present in the cytoplasm of keratinocytes, which are thought to receive the mature, fully melanized granules from melanocytes by a process akin to phagocytosis. That is to say, penetrant dendrites containing granules are "nipped off" and engulfed by the keratinocyte, and following absorption of the limiting dendritic membrane, the granules become freely dispersed within the cytoplasm. Here they may remain individually discrete, or become aggregated within membrane limited organelles to form compound melanosomes. Compound melanosomes are not found in melanocytes.

It is commonly believed that individual melanocytes have a limited period of survival as functionally active elements, and that as they become worn out they are replaced by division products of neighbouring melanocytes. The ultimate fate of these defunct melanocytes is unclear. At one time it was thought that they were passed through the supra-basal layers as Langerhans cells and eventually exfoliated. However, it is now almost certain that the two cell types are of different lineage, so the Langerhans cell can no longer serve as "effete melanocyte" in this scheme. In the absence of a mitotic balance sheet for melanocytes, it is impossible to estimate their normal rate of turnover. It seems probable now that this may be very slow, and that it is only occasionally that one becomes worn out and requires replacing. If this be so, it will be a matter of luck to find one and try to determine its fate. This might be disintegration, with the remnants either being engulfed by keratinocytes or Langerhans cells, or passed into the dermis to be dealt with by macrophages.

Fig. 108. Basal epidermal melanocyte from forearm skin of woman aged 40. Osmium fixation, lead staining. × 17,000.

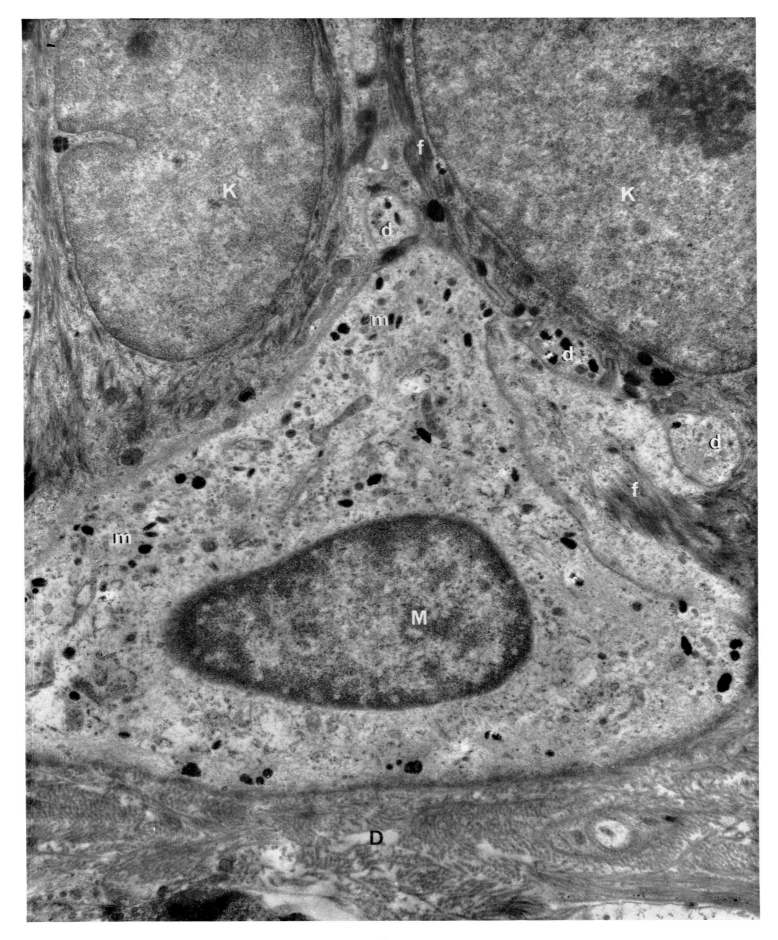

137

FIGURE 109

Absence of tonofilaments is usually quoted as a main feature whereby the melanocyte can be distinguished from the keratinocyte. However, it does contain some cytoplasmic filaments. These are not very apparent in active melanocytes, but in relatively inactive cells, such as the melanocytes of pale epidermis of freckled subjects, they are quite evident. They are particularly prominent (f) within the cytoplasm of the albino melanocyte (M) as figured here. The diameter of the individual filaments is about the same as that of tonofilaments (t) present in keratinocytes (K), but they show little or no tendency to be aggregated into bundles. The significance of the cytofilaments is unknown, and whether or not there is any fundamental difference between them and tonofilaments is unclear. Similar filaments are found within a variety of different cell types such as the fibrocyte (Fig. 130), the vascular endothelial cell (Fig. 162), and the Schwann cell (Fig. 142).

Within the keratinocyte (K) are membrane-limited granules (g) of the type previously noted (Fig. 92) as possibly being lysosomal in nature. A well-melanized melanosome (m) is present within one of these. This shows that the albino melanocyte is capable of producing some melanin, and that it transfers melanosomes to keratinocytes. The basic defect in albinism is thought to be a genetically determined failure of melanocytes to produce a sufficient amount of the enzyme tyrosinase which is concerned with the synthesis of melanin from the precursor, the amino-acid tyrosine. Albinism is not a condition in which there is a complete failure of melanogenesis, but the level of such activity may be so low that it is not apparent clinically.

Fig. 109. Basal epidermal melanocyte and keratinocyte from forearm skin of albino girl aged 20. Osmium fixation, lead staining. × 75,600.

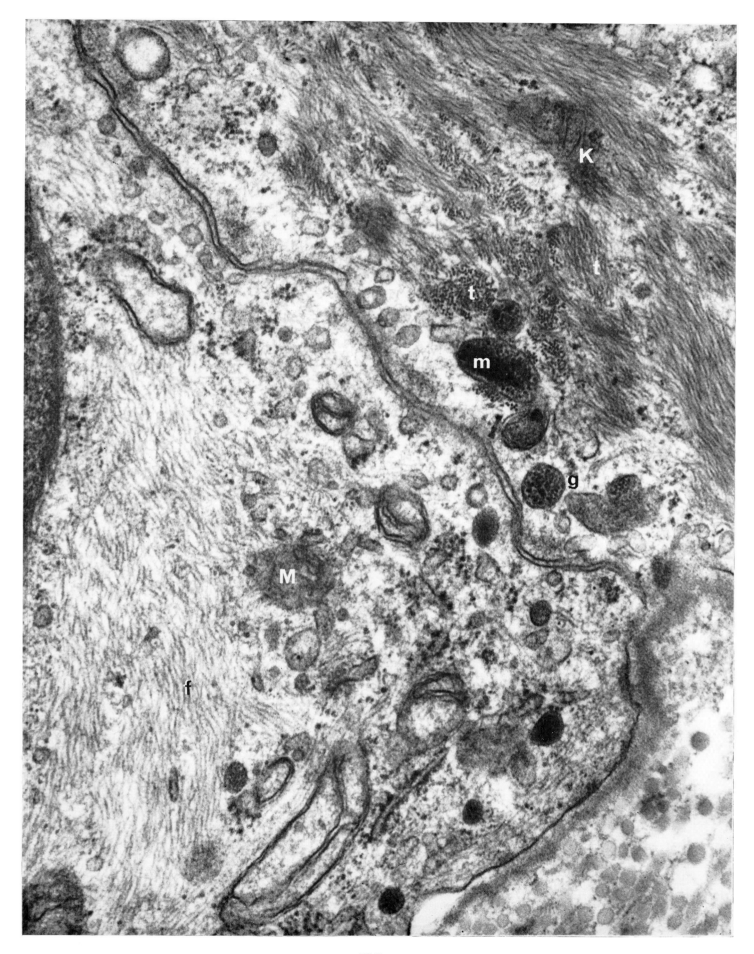

FIGURES 110 and 111

The characteristic product of the melanocyte is a pigmented granule, the melanosome, the ontogeny and organization of which are now well understood as a result of ultrastructural observations combined with autoradiography and density gradient enzyme assays. All melanocytes, whether of the interfollicular epidermis, the hair bulb, or the retinal pigmented epithelium produce melanosomes, which, though they vary in size, appear to be developed in a similar fashion, and to have the same basic structure. Current interpretation of the process of melanogenesis can be briefly stated as follows: The enzyme tyrosinase is synthesized on ribosomes and conveyed via the endoplasmic reticulum to the Golgi area where it accumulates in membrane limited "formative vesicles" of Golgi origin. These vesicles gradually increase in size developing a characteristically patterned matrix in the process, at which stage they are known as "premelanosomes". As melanin—produced by interaction of tyrosinase with the substrate tyrosine—is deposited within the premelanosome, the internal structure gradually becomes less apparent until a mature, uniformly electron-opaque granule results. Partially and fully melanized granules are termed "melanosomes". Tyrosinase activity is demonstrable in ribosomes and endoplasmic reticulum, but the premelanosome is thought to be the sole site of actual melanin synthesis *in vivo*. It was once thought that the melanosome might be a modified mitochondrion, but there is very little support for this view nowadays.

Golgi membranes (go), formative vesicles (v) of varying size, and premelanosomes (p) are present in the cytoplasm of the melanocyte illustrated in Fig. 110. This is an albino melanocyte, and it has been chosen to illustrate the early stages of melanosome ontogeny since these are rarely satisfactorily demonstrable in interfollicular epidermal melanocytes of normally pigmented skin. Mitochondria (mi) have a totally different appearance and structure. Fig. 111 shows part of the cytoplasm of a melanocyte from fetal hair-bulb. Rough endoplasmic reticulum (r) and melanosomes (m) at various stages of melanization are seen. It is evident that these latter have a highly ordered internal structure, which can more conveniently be described in connection with the larger melanosomes present in the retinal melanocytes as illustrated overleaf.

Fig. 110. Cytoplasm of epidermal melanocyte from forearm skin of albino girl aged 20. Osmium fixation, lead staining. × 48,000.

Fig. 111. Cytoplasm of hair-bulb melanocyte from forearm skin of 215 mm C.R. (24 week) human fetus. Osmium fixation, lead staining. × 54,000.

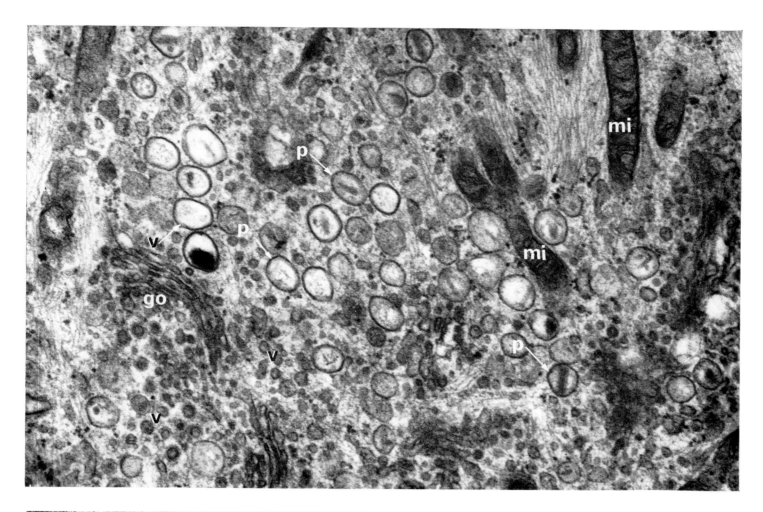

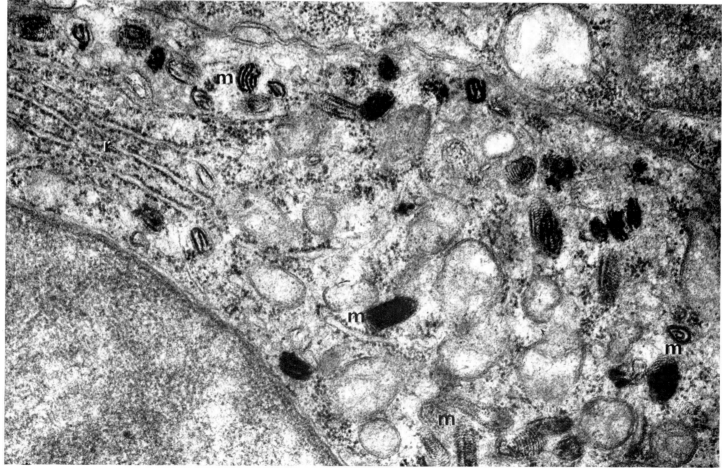

MELANOSOME

FIGURES 112 and 113

Melanosomes have an elongated oval shape, and in interfollicular epidermal melanocytes measure about 0·37 by 0·15 μm. Those of hair-bulb melanocytes are larger (0·7 by 0·3 μm), while the melanosomes of the retinal pigment epithelium may measure up to 1·9 μm in length and 1·4 μm in width. Partially melanized melanosomes on cross section, as in Fig. 112, exhibit an internal structure which has been interpreted as consisting of a series of concentrically arranged sheets, or of a single sheet arranged in a spiral manner. On longitudinal section, as in Fig. 113, the sheets when cut normally present as parallel lines with 6–8 μm (60–80 Å) periodicity (p) and often apparently helically coiled (h). Segments of sheets included in the plane of section (s) exhibit similar periodicity, or in minimally melanized granules (see inset), a lattice-like appearance due to an orthogonal array of particles with a spacing of 6–8 μm (60–80 Å) along the length of the granules, and of about 4·5 μm (45 Å) in the direction at right angles. The minor spacing becomes obscured with increasing melanization, leading to the more frequently encountered "cross striated" appearance. When melanization is completed, no definite internal structure can be seen within the melanosome, and it no longer exhibits tyrosinase activity.

Attempts to extend interpretation of the fine structure of the melanosome to the molecular level, have not proved very successful to date. It is still not known if the matrix of the granule is made up of a protein scaffold on which tyrosinase is deposited, or if tyrosinase serves both as active enzyme and sole structural protein. Besides, the arrangement of the matrix as it appears in micrographs has had different interpretations. The apparent helical-coil arrangement seen on longitudinal section is a case in point. Some authors believe this is due to the presence of individual longitudinally oriented "fibres", which are in fact helically coiled. Others have suggested that the appearance may be due to deposition of melanin at sites located alternately on either side of a sheet which when sectioned normally gives an apparent helical appearance. The latter explanation would seem to fit better the appearances presented here, but the final word on this matter must await further investigations. Melanosomes of red hair and of poorly pigmented interfollicular epidermis of freckled subjects are more rounded in shape than those of the darker-skinned, and the matrix appears to be organized differently.

Melanocytes in fetal interfollicular epidermis are illustrated in Figs. 47 and 48.

Fig. 112. Transverse section of melanosome from retinal pigment epithelium of 20 mm C.R. (9 week) human fetus. Osmium fixation, lead staining. × 132,000.

Fig. 113. Longitudinal section of melanosome from retinal pigment epithelium of 20 mm C.R. (9 week) human fetus. Osmium fixation, lead staining. × 126,000. *Inset:* lattice-like arrangement of particles on matrix sheet of melanosome. × 120,000.

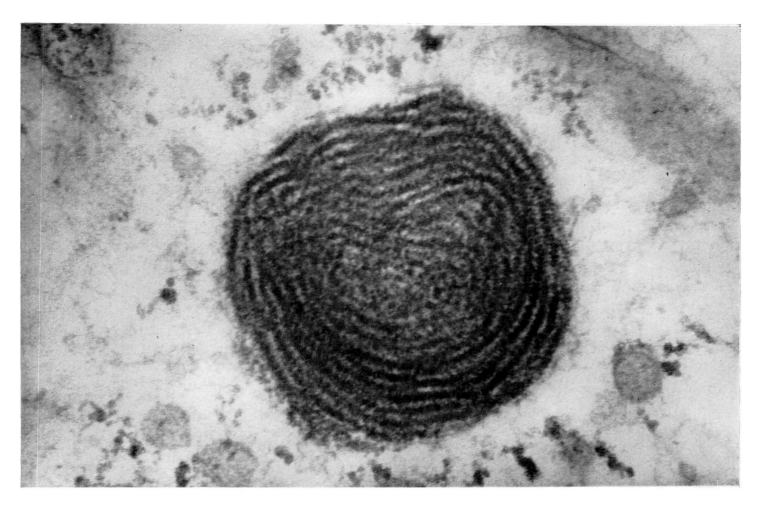

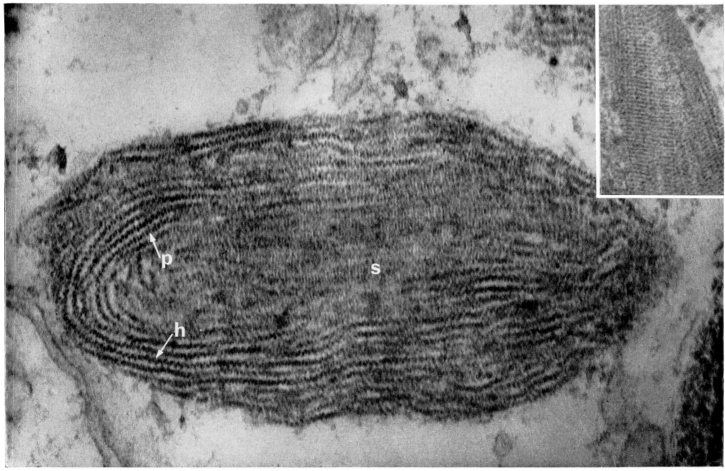

FIGURE 114

Merkel cells are specialized non-keratinocytes present in the basal layer of the epidermis, mainly of distal non-hairy skin, but occasionally, they may also be found in hairy skin. As already mentioned (pp. 74–77) they are usually closely associated with terminal neurites in the former situation. The most characteristic feature of the cell is the presence of round electron-dense granules (g), located mainly on the opposite side of the nucleus to the Golgi apparatus (go). These granules allow one to distinguish the Merkel cell with certainty from the other non-keratinocytes, i.e. melanocytes and Langerhans cells, each of which contains a specific cytoplasmic organelle by means of which it can, in turn, be identified. Membrane-limited vesicles (v), mitochondria (m) and electron-dense granules (l), larger than the specific granules, are also seen in the cytoplasm.

The Merkel cell, unlike the melanocyte and the Langerhans cell, is connected to surrounding keratinocytes by desmosomes (d). Since the presence of desmosomes along the plasma membrane is usually regarded as a typical keratinocyte feature, it might seem questionable therefore to label the Merkel cell a non-keratinocyte. However, there is no evidence that it ever leaves the basal layer to become keratinized at higher levels, and as already mentioned (p. 76) there is some suggestion that it may be an immigrant of Schwann-cell lineage; desmosome-like structures are found associated with Schwann-cell plasma membrane in certain circumstances. None the less, the remote possibility remains that it is a highly specialized keratinocyte, which, unlike neighbouring cells, and because of a particular function, remains fixed in the basal layer.

In digital skin, the Merkel cell and associated neurites are thought to form a complex which serves as a touch receptor—the Merkel disc of light microscopy—and there is much evidence to support this view. In non-digital skin, such as that in which the cell opposite was found, the two elements are not invariably associated together. It is difficult to know what to make of this. Presumably a Merkel cell unrelated to neurites could not serve as a touch receptor, and it may be that it is capable of serving some other function as well.

Fig. 114. Merkel cell in basal layer of arm epidermis of 3 week infant. Osmium fixation, lead staining. × 18,500.

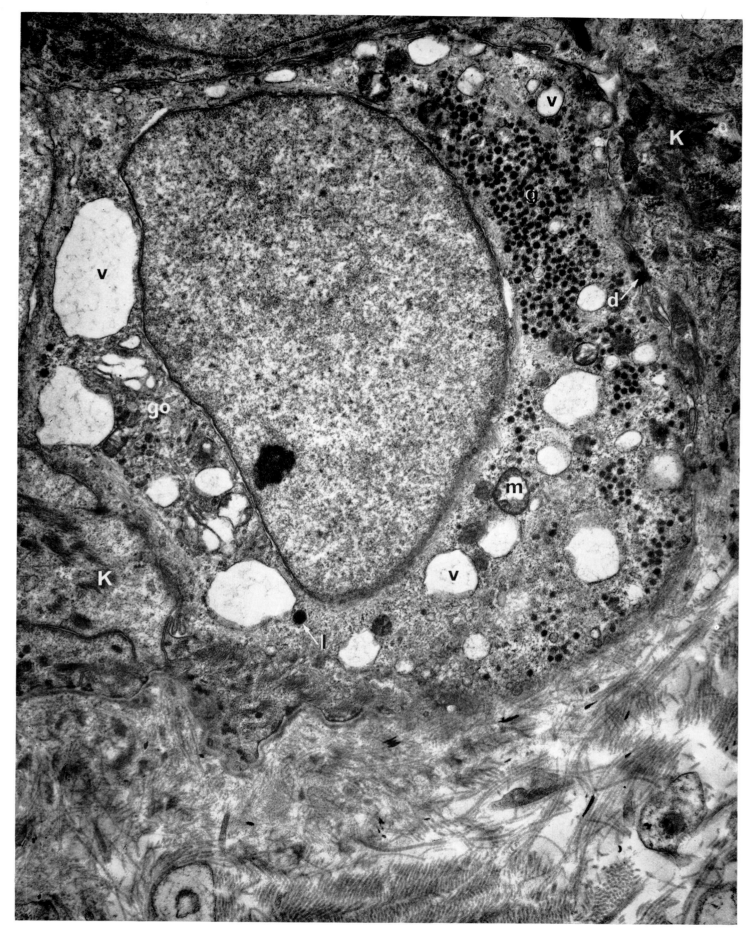

FIGURES 115 and 116

These two micrographs illustrate features of the Merkel cell at higher magnification. The specific granules have a diameter of 100 nm (1,000 Å) or less, and are membrane limited, with a core of variable density. Fine filaments (f) are present in the cytoplasm, and associated with the inner aspect of desmosomes (d) connecting the cell to adjacent keratinocytes (K). Hemi-desmosomes are absent from the basal plasma membrane (p) in contradistinction to keratino-cytes which exhibit them (h) in this situation.

Some of the vesicles (v) present in the cytoplasm have well-defined limiting membranes, but others (V_1 in lower micrograph) appear to lack this feature. In some cases this could be attri-buted to oblique sectioning of the membrane, but in other cases a membrane does appear to be entirely lacking. The significance of these vesicles is unknown. Some may be located at the periphery of the cell so close to the plasma membrane as to suggest that their contents might be discharged into the intercellular space. Vesicles apparently lacking a limiting membrane may represent globules of lipid or some other substance lying free in the cytoplasm and lost during processing.

Fig. 115. Cytoplasm of Merkel cell from basal layer of arm epidermis of 3 week infant. Osmium fixation, lead staining. × 42,500.

Fig. 116. Cytoplasm of Merkel cell from basal layer of arm epidermis of 3 week infant. Osmium fixation, lead staining. × 42,500.

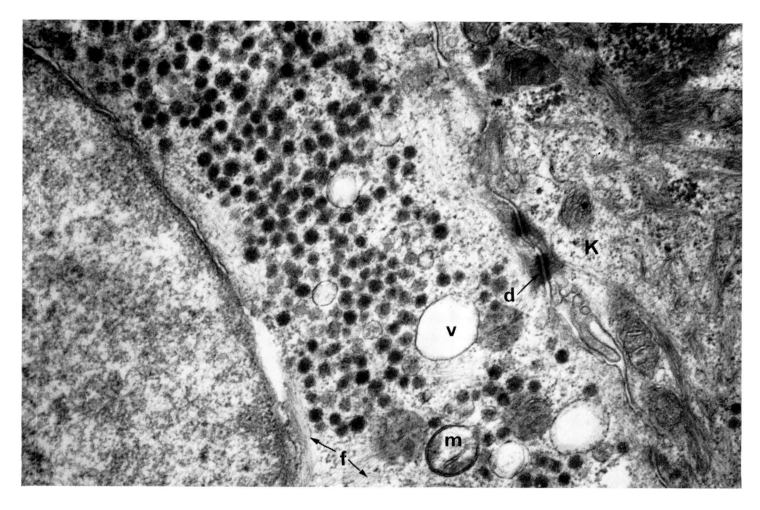

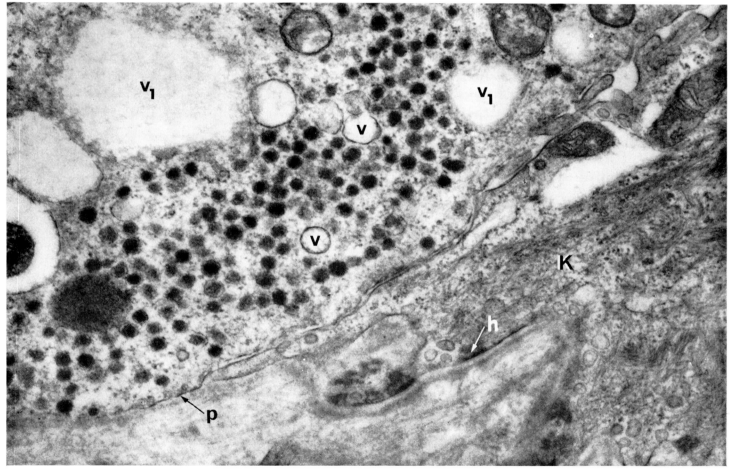

147

FIGURE 117

The characteristic granule of the Merkel cell has a distinct limiting membrane (m) which is separated by a narrow translucent zone from the more electron-dense core. To date, it has not been possible to define any definite structural arrangement within the central core, but in some instances one gets the impression of a lattice-like arrangement of fine particles. Some of the membrane-limited vesicles (v) are not much larger than the typical granules, and it is possible they may be derived from them.

The nature of these granules is unknown. Morphologically, they closely resemble mono-amine-storing granules of neural cells, but so far, histochemical studies have failed to reveal the presence of catechol-amines in Merkel cells.

FIGURE 118

The source and mode of formation of Merkel granules have yet to be established. Since they are regarded as secretory in nature it has been suggested they may be derived from the Golgi apparatus. In this section of the juxta-Golgi region of a fetal Merkel cell, vesicles (ve) and tubules which are either of Golgi origin, or possibly belonging to the agranular endoplasmic reticulum, are seen close to profiles (f) which could represent formative stages of the granules. A single mature granule (g) is present in the lower part of the field. However, while suggestive, appearances such as this cannot be said to throw much light on the source or ontogeny of the granules, which, as mentioned already, are usually concentrated in an area remote from the Golgi region. Histochemical, electron-histochemical, and electron-autoradiographic techniques must be brought to bear on the problem.

Fig. 117. Granules in cytoplasm of Merkel cell from basal layer of arm epidermis of 3 week infant. Osmium fixation, lead staining. × 105,500.

Fig. 118. Juxta-Golgi region of cytoplasm of Merkel cell from interfollicular arm epidermis of 215 C.R. (24 week) human fetus. Osmium fixation, lead staining. × 52,500.

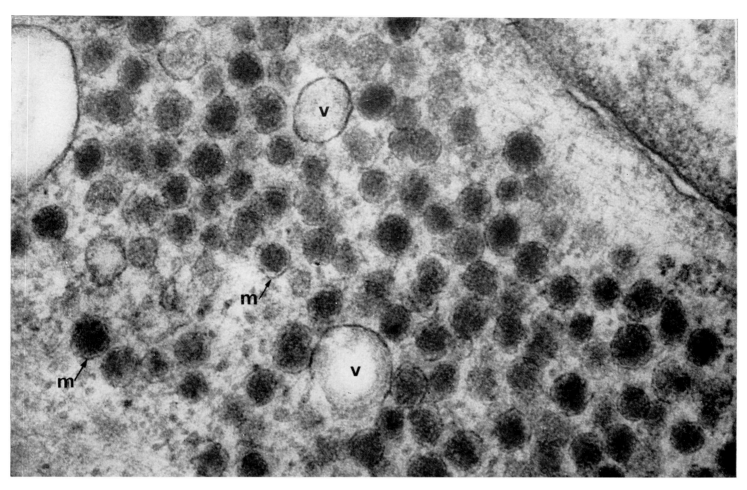

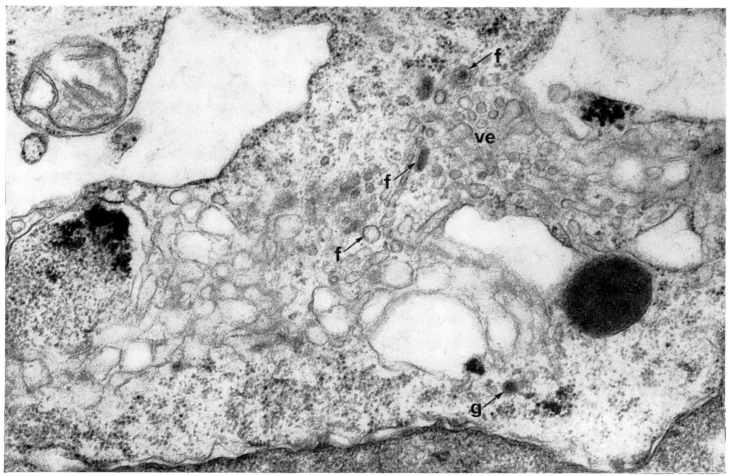

FIGURE 119

Langerhans cells (L) are dendritic (d) non-keratinocytes present in the supra-basal layers of the epidermis, and occasionally also, in the basal layer. As already mentioned (p. 72) they can be distinguished from keratinocytes by an absence of desmosomes and tonofilaments, and from melanocytes because premelanosomes or individual melanosomes are not found in the cytoplasm. The nucleus is usually very indented and in addition, the cells contain a highly characteristic organelle, the Langerhans granule, which provides the best criterion for their identification, though, being of small dimensions it is not very prominent at lower magnifications. The concentration of characteristic granules varies considerably from cell to cell, and when not very numerous, it is evident they may be absent from a number of sections through the same cell. This may present a problem in identification, and indeed it has been suggested on the basis of interpretation of single sections, that cells exhibiting all the features of Langerhans cells apart from the characteristic granules, represent another type of intra-epidermal non-keratinocyte. However, there is really no evidence to support this, and almost invariably, serial, or closely spaced sections through the cells in question, reveal some granules. Only one such granule can be seen within the cell figured here, and it may amuse the experienced reader to try and locate it.

Langerhans cells were first observed over 100 years ago, and there has been much argument concerning their origin, nature and function. Ultrastructural studies have contributed greatly towards solution of these problems, but some uncertainties still remain.

Fig. 119. Langerhans cell in spinous layer of forearm epidermis of woman aged 40. Osmium fixation, lead staining. × 10,200.

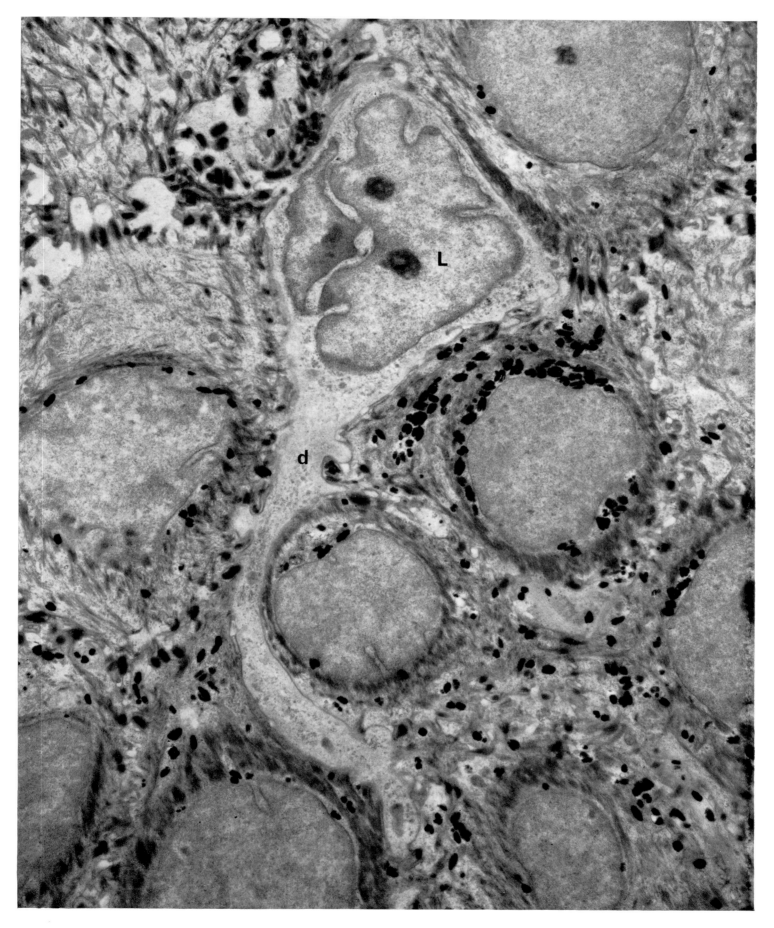

FIGURE 120

Langerhans cells were originally revealed in light microscopy by treating epidermis with an acid solution of gold chloride. As this technique is also used to reveal neural elements, it seemed not unreasonable to suggest that Langerhans cells might be intra-epidermal neuro-sensory or neuro-hormonal cells, and a few workers are still inclined to this view. The fact that they can also be stained supra-vitally with quinone-imine dyes, such as methylene-blue, could be quoted in support. However, over the years the alternative opinion began to emerge that the cells are "effete" or worn-out melanocytes, which traverse the supra-basal layers of the epidermis to be ultimately cast off, and this was supported by an almost overwhelming body of circumstantial evidence derived from comparative and experimental investigations. Early studies on the ultrastructure of the Langerhans cell lent support to this view that it is related to the melanocyte, but it soon became clear that the relationship could not be of the nature postulated. Subsequent histochemical, electron-histochemical, fetal and pathological studies reinforced a growing suspicion that the two cells might not be related at all, and this seems finally to be established by clear-cut experimental evidence that Langerhans cells are not derived from the neural crest, from which the melanocytes stem. Current opinion is that the Langerhans cell is a functionally active element of probable mesodermal origin, and some of the evidence which has led to the emergence of this view will be outlined in the following pages.

This micrograph presents a Langerhans cell from epidermis which was impregnated with gold chloride before processing for electron microscopy. Tissue preservation in general is poor with this type of preparation, but the presence of tonofibrils (t) in keratinocytes (K) and their absence in the Langerhans cell is evident. Particles of dense gold-chloride deposit are randomly scattered throughout the cytoplasm of the Langerhans cell, but are absent from the characteristically indented nucleus; they do not appear to be localized in relation to any specific cytoplasmic organelles. Preparations of this type reveal little concerning the possible lineage or function of the cell, but they were of value in establishing the fact that the supra-basal non-keratinocytes of electron microscopy correspond with the gold-positive dendritic cells of light microscopy, thereby allowing comparison and correlation of evidence arising out of application of the two different techniques.

Fig. 120. Langerhans cell from gold-impregnated forearm epidermis of man aged 42. Osmium fixation, lead staining. × 31,200.

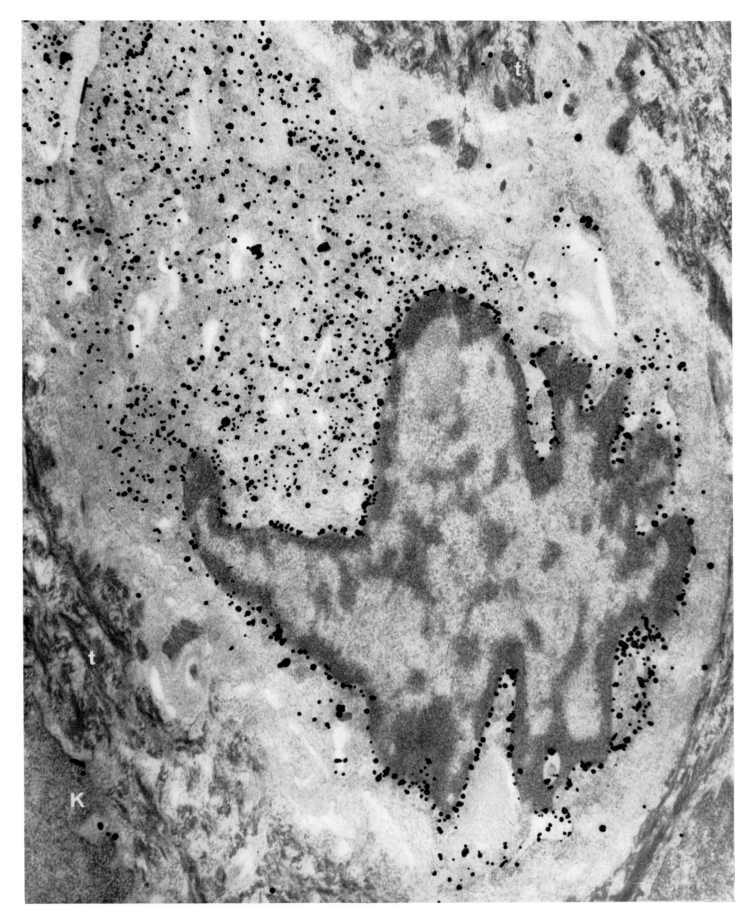

FIGURE 121

At this magnification all the characteristic features of the Langerhans cell are apparent. One can note the absence of desmosomes and tonofibrils, the indentation of the nucleus, and the specific cytoplasmic organelles—the Langerhans granules. These appear on section as rod (r) or racquet (ra) shaped structures, variable in number, and not localized to any particular region of the cytoplasm. In many sections, membrane-limited organelles with morphologic features of lysosomes are seen, and one such (l) is present here. That these are in fact lysosomes, has been established by demonstration of acid phosphatase activity within them.

One of the reasons which led earlier investigators to question the postulated relation between Langerhans cell and melanocyte, was failure to demonstrate melanosomes within the cytoplasm of the former. Were the Langerhans cell a worn-out melanocyte, one might expect their occasional occurrence. In the event, melanosomes were subsequently found within Langerhans cells, and on the basis that this was evidence the cell was capable of synthesizing melanin, it was classed as a "transitional" type of melanocyte. However, melanosomes, when present, are disposed in a manner characteristic more of cells which receive extraneous melanin than of those which synthesize it. They (m, *inset*) are fully melanized, and invariably contained within membrane-limited organelles (l) similar in appearance to the compound granules of keratinocytes. Individual melanosomes are not seen free in the cytoplasm, nor have formative stages (premelanosomes) been demonstrated. One is led to conclude, therefore, that there is no real evidence the Langerhans cell is capable of synthesizing melanin, and that the presence of melanosomes need not necessarily imply it is some form of melanocyte.

Fig. 121. Langerhans cell from forearm epidermis of girl aged 18. Osmium fixation, lead staining. ×31,500. *Inset:* melanosomes in cytoplasm of Langerhans cell. ×34,000.

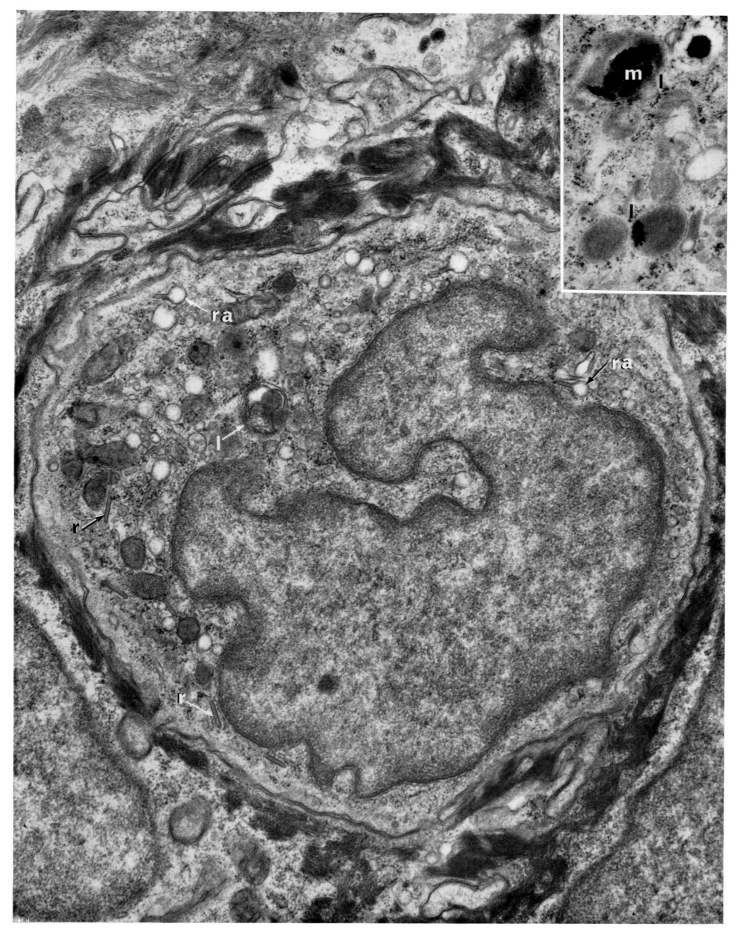

FIGURE 122

The general appearance of the cytoplasm of this cell, with a well-defined Golgi apparatus (go), mitochondria, and numerous ribosomes, is difficult to reconcile with the view that it is "effete" or worn-out. In fact, the Langerhans cell appears as an actively functioning element, capable of, and engaged in, protein synthesis. There is nothing about it to support the suggestion that it is a defunct melanocyte—a view which it became increasingly difficult to maintain as pictures such as this accumulated.

The rod-shaped sectional profiles (r) of Langerhans granules are seen to present an outer limiting membrane and a central lamella which may appear as a continuous line, or as a row of particles with a spacing of 6–7 nm (60–70 Å). Racquet-shaped profiles (ra) have a similar structure, except that the limiting membrane is expanded at one end, and the vesicular structures (v) almost certainly represent sections of these expanded portions. The more sac-like profiles (s) also result from sectioning of similar expanded segments, and it has now been established that expansion of the membrane is not confined to the ends, but can occur at any point along the granule. Obliquely-sectioned granules (p) exhibit periodicity of the same order as that of the central lamella. Analysis of variable images in different planes of section, and of serial sections of individual organelles has led to the conclusion that the Langerhans granule is a disc- or plate-like structure, 40–50 nm (400–500 Å) thick, which may be bent, curved (*see inset*) or even invaginated so as to resemble a cup.

A lysosome (l) is also present within this cell. At the lower end of the field is portion of a keratinocyte containing tonofilaments (t).

Fig. 122. Cytoplasm of Langerhans cell from forearm epidermis of girl aged 20. Osmium fixation, lead staining. × 68,400. *Inset:* curved Langerhans granules. × 69,000.

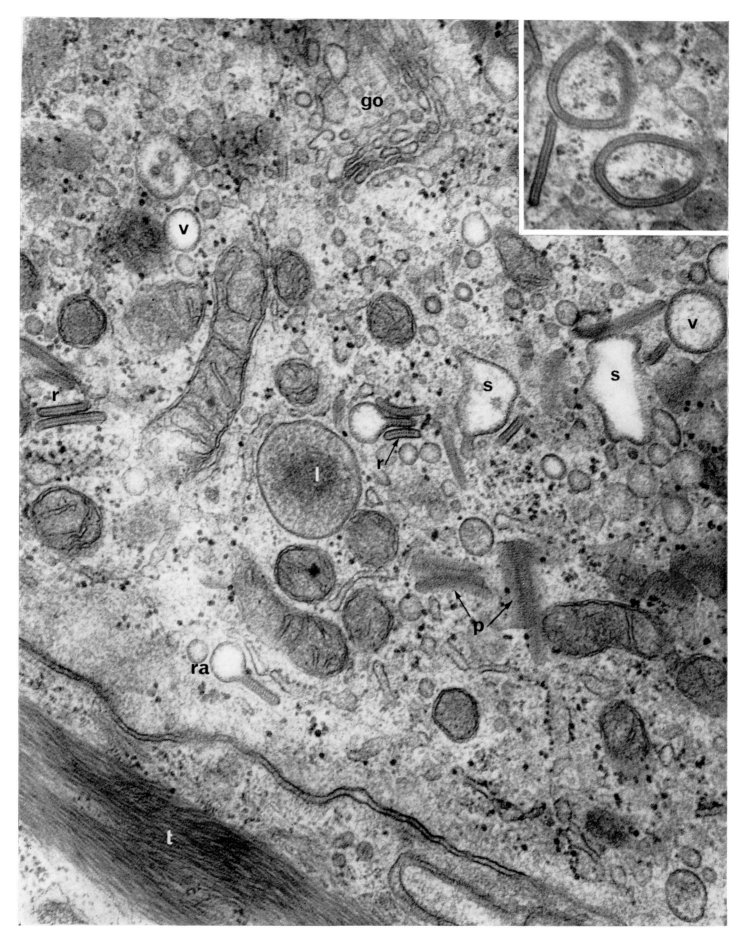

FIGURE 123

Further details of the structure of the Langerhans granule become apparent at higher magnification. The limiting membrane (l) is lined on its inner aspect by a row of dense particles (d) with a spacing of 5–6 nm (50–60 Å); this arrangement is often clearest in the expanded portion of the granule. In this situation also, the central lamella may be seen to split (s), indicating that it consists of two sheets of particles, and K. Wolff has succeeded in resolving these in the non-expanded portion of the granule. Four sheets of particles therefore are contained within the limiting membrane, and when granules are cut tangentially or face-on (t, *and inset*) these present a two-dimensional square lattice of particles.

The source and mode of formation of Langerhans granules is unknown. A Golgi origin was originally proposed, but there is no real evidence for this, besides which, it is not easy to reconcile with the appearances illustrated in the lower micrograph.

FIGURE 124

Here, Langerhans granules (g) are shown with limiting membrane directly continuous with the plasma membrane (p) of the cell, and the interior opening into the intercellular space between it and an adjacent keratinocyte (K). This appearance could be explained in two ways. Firstly, if the granules are produced from the Golgi apparatus or elsewhere within the cell, it could be that they migrate towards the periphery, become attached to the plasma membrane as here, and liberate their contents into the surrounding milieu. This would imply they are secretory, or excretory in function. Alternatively, it may be that the granules are formed by infoldings of the plasma membrane, which are subsequently "nipped off" to form plate-like structures lying free in the cytoplasm, and that what is seen here is a formative stage. This would suggest an absorptive function for the granules. In this connection, it may be noted that they bear some resemblance to absorptive vesicles of certain cells of lower animals, and the more one studies them, the more one feels they are a manifestation of some sort of surface membrane activity, rather than secretory elements.

Fig. 123. Langerhans granules. Osmium fixation, lead staining. ×102,600. *Inset:* square-lattice arrangement of particles within tangentially-sectioned granule. ×145,600.

Fig. 124. Langerhans granule attached to plasma membrane of cell. From forearm epidermis of man aged 42. Osmium fixation, lead staining. ×62,500. *Inset:* granule attached to plasma membrane. ×75,400.

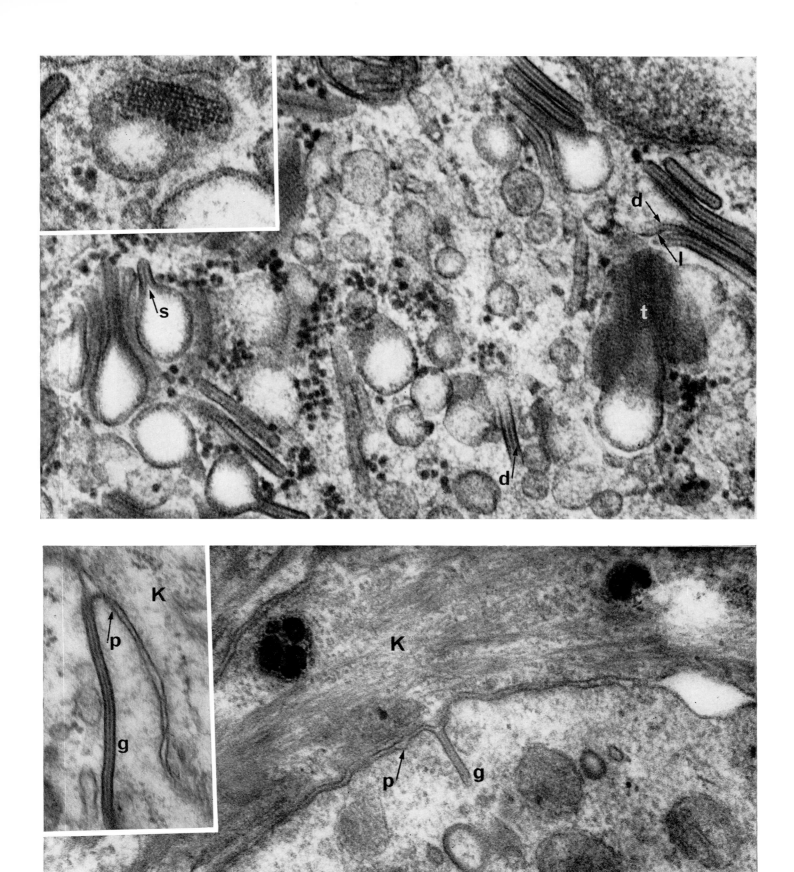

FIGURE 125

A variety of membrane-limited organelles (ly) with morphological characteristics of lysosomes, and exhibiting acid phosphatase activity, may be found in Langerhans cells. One type with concentrically arranged internal membranes, and known as a "myelin body" (my) is of interest in that their number becomes greatly increased following painting of skin (of experimental animals) with carcinogenic hydrocarbons. Multi-vesicular bodies are also frequently seen, but whether the structure labelled, v, belongs to this class of organelle is doubtful. It may well represent a sectional profile of the expanded part of a Langerhans granule.

Langerhans cells contain hydrolytic enzymes, some of which have been demonstrated by electron histochemical techniques. The enzymes concerned are, nucleoside triphosphatase (man, monkey, guinea-pig), aliesterase (mouse, rat), cholinesterase (sheep and bat), alkaline phosphatase (African Lorisidae) and aminopeptidase (guinea-pig). The significance of these observations, or of the species differences indicated, is unclear. However, they do confirm the impression gained from purely morphological observations that the Langerhans cell is in no sense moribund, and that it performs some important function within the epidermis. This is underlined by the fact that fully differentiated Langerhans cells are present within fetal epidermis as early as the 12th week.

Fig. 125. Lysosomes in cytoplasm of Langerhans cell from forearm epidermis of girl aged 20. Osmium fixation, lead staining. ×67,500.

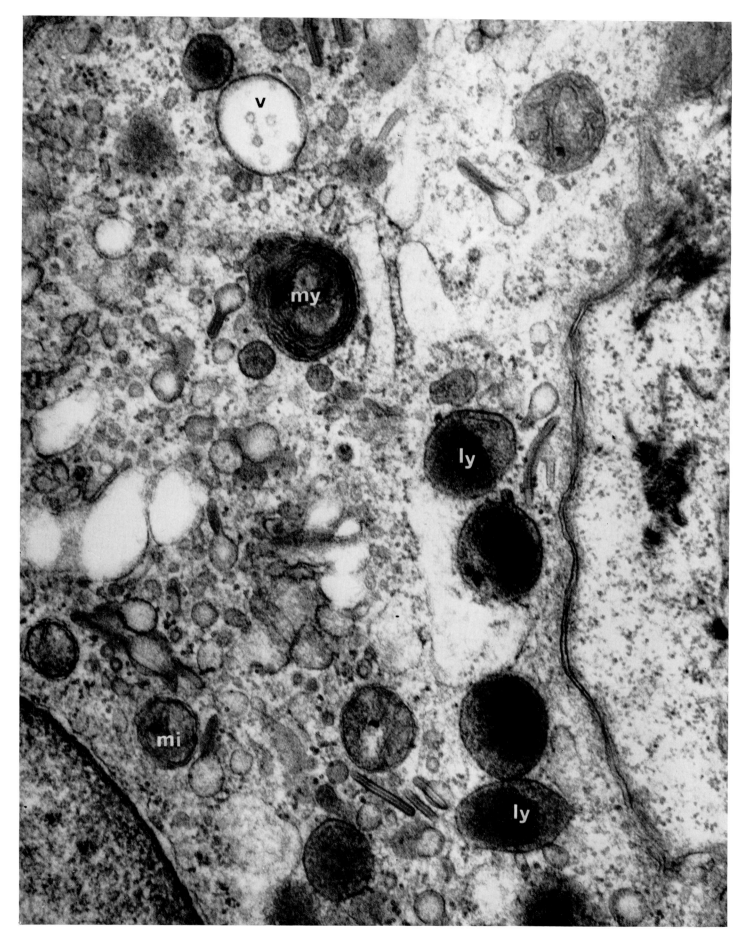

FIGURE 126

Langerhans cells are situated within a keratinizing squamous epithelium, and their function is most probably related to this particular type of environment. There is no evidence that they are involved in the process of keratinization as such, but that they can influence the keratinocytes is strongly suggested by pictures such as that opposite. Here, immediately adjacent to the Langerhans cell (LC), is an area of fine granularity (g), evidently part of the cytoplasm of the keratinocyte (K) which elsewhere presents a normal appearance with tonofibrils (t) etc. The absence of normal structure within the area (g) suggests that it has been affected by some cytolytic influence, and its situation, right up against the Langerhans cell, could further suggest that the latter is primarily responsible. An alternative explanation would be that lysis of the keratinocyte cytoplasm is the primary event, and that the Langerhans cell has been attracted towards it. As the succeeding micrograph (Fig. 127) shows, similar areas of apparently disintegrating keratinocyte cytoplasm may be enveloped by, and even incorporated within, Langerhans cells. Appearances such as this, coupled with the presence of lysosomes and hydrolytic enzymic activity, have naturally led to the suggestion that the Langerhans cell may function primarily as an intra-epidermal macrophage or phagocyte. The suggestion previously made that the specific granule may be a type of absorptive vesicle would tend to support this. A side effect of this type of function might be a loosening of interkeratinocyte attachments which could aid the general mechanism of cell movement towards the surface. All of this is of course, highly speculative, but these are the lines along which a majority of workers nowadays are thinking.

Fig. 126. Langerhans cell and keratinocyte from forearm epidermis of man aged 40. Osmium fixation, lead staining. × 22,500.

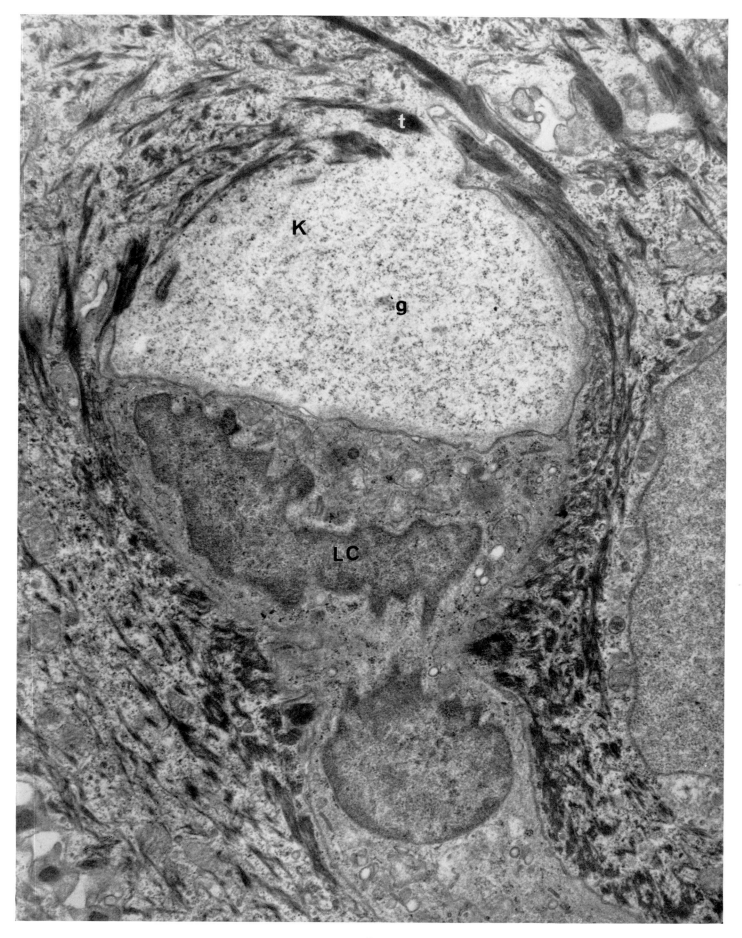

163

FIGURE 127

In this micrograph, a Langerhans cell (LC) is seen apparently enveloping disintegrating cyto-plasm (g) of a neighbouring keratinocyte (K). The tips of the enveloping processes are indi-cated at p. This would seem to represent a further stage of the process illustrated in the previous Fig. 126, and provides further evidence for the view that the Langerhans cell has a phagocytic function.

Until recently, the characteristic rod- or racquet-shaped granule was thought to be specific to the Langerhans cell, and it was believed that the cells themselves were not present in any tissue other than epidermis. However, A. Zelickson showed that they may occasionally occur in the dermis and this can be confirmed for normal skin (Fig. 134). More recently, French workers have shown that cells identical in every respect with epidermal Langerhans cells are characteristic of lesions of Histiocytosis-X, both cutaneous and extra-cutaneous, so much so, that their presence has become accepted as a main diagnostic feature of this condition. These cells are classed as "histiocytes", and are almost certainly mesodermal elements. Their mor-phological identity with Langerhans cells certainly suggests that the latter are immigrant cells of histiocyte-lineage which serve as epidermal macrophages. Should this prove to be the final answer to the problem of the origin and function of the Langerhans cells, it will be necessary to establish if their migration into the epidermis takes place over a limited period (possibly confined to fetal life) subsequent to which they become reproductively self-maintaining, or if their numbers are maintained by continuous recruitment from a reservoir of cells in the der-mis. The sparsity of these cells in normal dermis, and the fact that those already present in the epidermis are known to be capable of dividing, makes the former possibility seem more likely.

Fig. 127. Langerhans cell and keratinocyte from forearm epidermis of man aged 40. Osmium fixation, lead staining. × 22,700.

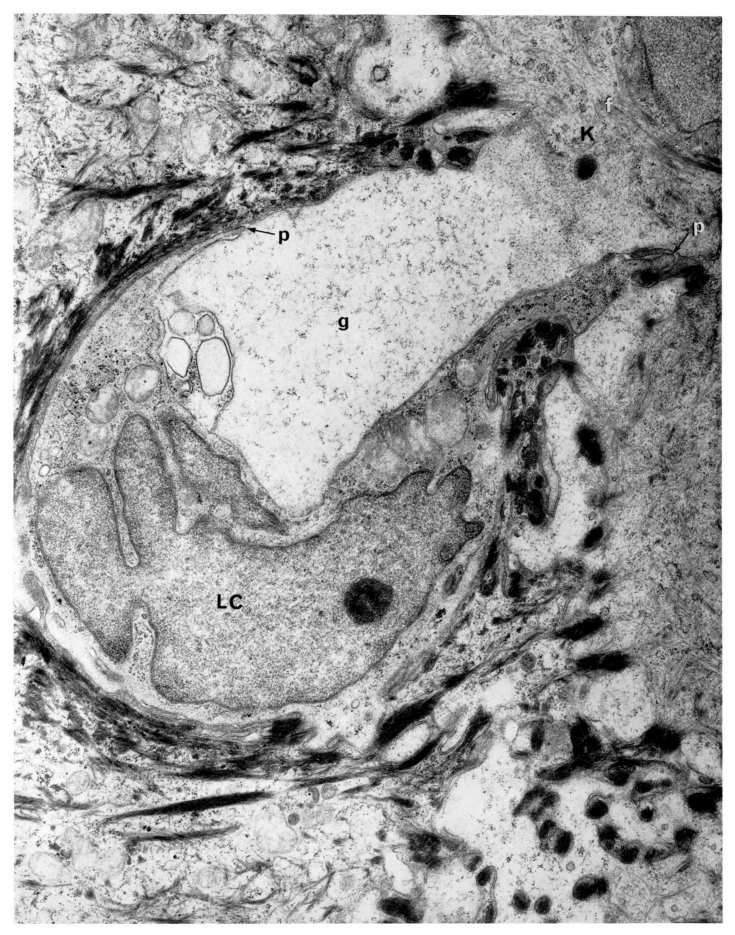

165

REFERENCES

MELANOCYTE AND MELANOGENESIS

Breathnach, A. S. Normal and abnormal melanin pigmentation of the skin. In: "Pigments in Pathology", ed. M. Wolman, New York, Academic Press, 1969.

Della Porta, G. and Mühlbock, O., eds. "Structure and Control of the Melanocyte". Berlin, Springer, 1966.

Fitzpatrick, T. B. Mammalian melanin biosynthesis. *Trans. St. John's Hosp. Derm. Soc.*, **51**:1, 1965.

Fitzpatrick, T. B., Myomoto, M. and Ishikawa, K. The evolution of concepts of melanin biology. In: "Advances in Biology of Skin, Vol. VIII, The Pigmentary System". Eds. W. Montagna and Funan Hu. Oxford, Pergamon, 1967.

Moyer, F. H. Genetic variations in the fine structure and ontogeny of mouse melanin granules. *American Zoologist*, **6**:43, 1966.

Seiji, M. Melanogenesis. In: "Ultrastructure of Normal and Abnormal Skin". Ed. A. S. Zelickson. London, Henry Kimpton, 1967.

MERKEL CELL

Kenshalo, D. R., ed. "The Skin Senses". Springfield, Thomas, 1968.

Munger, B. L. The intra-epidermal innervation of the snout skin of the opossum. *J. Cell Biol.*, **26**:79, 1965.

Mustakallio, K. K. and Kiistala, U. Electron microscopy of Merkel's "Tastcelle", a potential monoamine staining cell of human epidermis. *Acta derm.-venereol.*, **47**:323, 1967.

LANGERHANS CELL

Basset, F. and Nezelof, C. Présence en microscopie électronique de structures filamenteuses originales dans les lésions pulmonaires et osseuses de l'histiocytose X. Etat actuel de la question. *Bull. Soc. Méd. Hôp. Paris*, **117**:413, 1966.

Breathnach, A. S. The cell of Langerhans. *Int. Rev. Cytol.*, **18**:1, 1965.

Breathnach, A. S. and Wyllie, L. M.-A. The problem of the Langerhans cells. In: "Advances in Biology of Skin, Vol. VIII, The Pigmentary System". Eds. W. Montagna and Funan Hu. Oxford, Pergamon, 1967.

Sagebiel, R. W. and Reed, T. H. Serial reconstruction of the characteristic granule of the Langerhans cell. *J. Cell Biol.*, **36**:595, 1968.

Wolff, K. Die Langerhans-Zelle. Ergebnisse neuerer experimenteller Untersuchungen. *Arch. klin. exp. Derm.*, **229**:54, 1967.

Wolff, K. The fine structure of the Langerhans cell granule. *J. Cell Biol.*, **35**:468, 1967.

Zelickson, A. S. The Langerhans cell. *J. Invest. Derm.*, **44**:201, 1965.

7 Dermis — Connective Tissue and Individual Cells

Collagen and fibroblasts — elastic fibre — histiocyte — dermal Langerhans cell — macrophage — mast cell.

FIGURE 128

In light microscopy it is customary to describe the dermis as consisting of a more superficial papillary layer in contact with the under surface of the epidermis, and a deeper reticular layer which merges without any clear-cut boundary with the underlying hypodermis. These regional distinctions are not very evident in most electron micrographs—except in very low-power pictures—because fields available for examination are so much more restricted. Another result of this is that one cannot present a single micrograph as being "typical" of dermis as a whole; the different elements of which it is constituted—collagen and elastic fibres, individual cells of various types, nerves, vessels—are not uniformly distributed, and it is very rarely that all are represented in an individual field of view.

This micrograph illustrates the basal layer of the epidermis (E), the epidermal-dermal junction (j), and the papillary region of the dermis. There are quite a number of cells present in the latter situation, but their concentration cannot be regarded as typical of this region in general; immediately adjacent fields of similar area might contain fewer, or none at all. Of the cells present, two can certainly be identified as Schwann cells (S) because of their association with neuraxons (a), but the others have no such clear-cut distinguishing characteristics, and therefore present a problem. The cell with electron-dense indented nucleus (L) bears some resemblance to a lymphocyte, but the remainder defy any attempt at classification. They are certainly not mast-cells (Figs. 134, 139 and 140), probably not fibroblasts, and there seems little justification for regarding them as "macrophages" (Fig. 136). Some observers might label them as "histiocytes", a suitably non-committal term which can serve for the moment to designate such dermal cells of doubtful lineage. They will be considered in greater detail later (p. 176).

The epidermal-dermal junction has already been dealt with in previous sections (Figs. 24 and 91) and requires no further comment, apart from drawing attention to the lack of organization of the collagen fibres in the region immediately subjacent to the basal lamina of the epidermis. This contrasts with fibres at deeper levels (C) which are arranged in bundles running in various directions. Elastic fibres are frequently present among these bundles at levels deeper than that illustrated here.

Fig. 128. Epidermal dermal junction and papillary region of dermis from forearm skin of man aged 43. Osmium fixation, PTA staining. × 7,600.

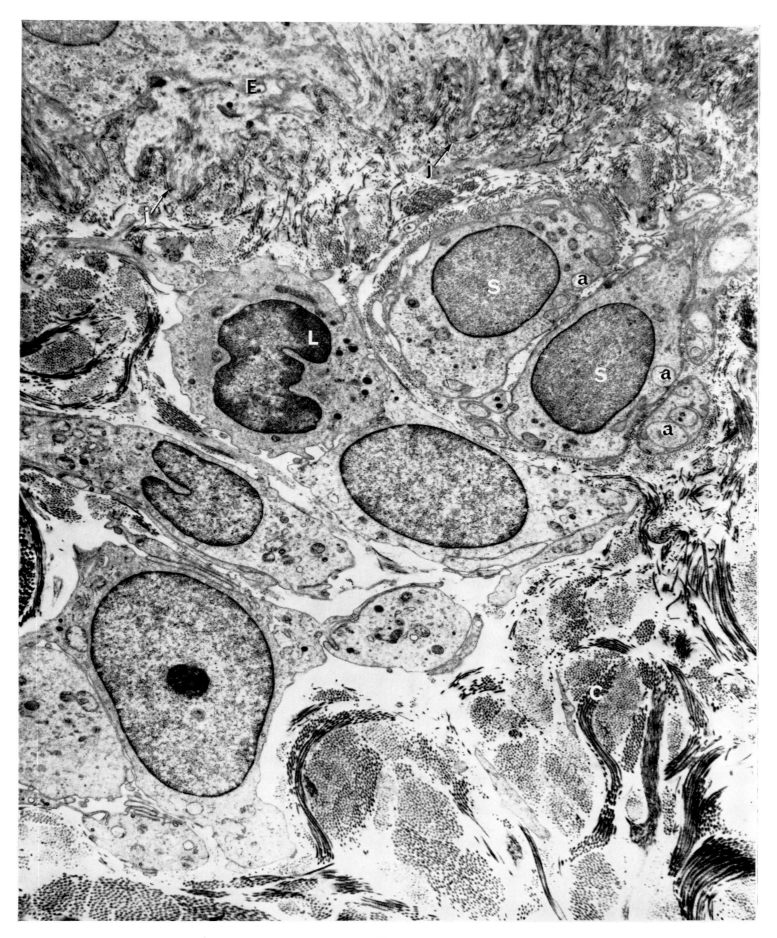

FIGURE 129

This micrograph of the reticular region of the dermis shows bundles of collagen fibres cut transversely, apart from one in the centre of the field which has been sectioned obliquely. The spaces between the bundles are probably largely produced by shrinkage or other artifacts of processing, and cannot therefore be taken to give a true representation of the extent of the "tissue space", or of areas occupied by "ground substance". This latter is an amorphous matrix in which the formed elements of connective tissue are embedded, and it has a high content of muco- or protein-polysaccharide. The ground substance does not show up with routine stains, but some components of it are demonstrable with special techniques such as colloidal iron or ruthenium red. It is not to be regarded simply as inert packing material filling spaces between bundles or individual fibres. In fact, it has an important influence on collagen synthesis and stabilization. A fibroblast (F) with moderately developed rough endoplasmic reticulum is also present. The plasma membrane is poorly defined—a common occurrence in sections stained with PTA, and one which has led to the probably erroneous suggestion that precursor collagen fibres are released from the cell through deficiencies in the plasma membrane.

FIGURE 130

This shows portion of a fibroblast and adjacent collagen fibres from a section doubly stained with lead and uranyl acetate. One may note the clearly defined and intact plasma membrane of the cell, and the absence of large spaces between it and the surrounding collagen, a truer representation of the condition *in vivo* than that seen in the upper micrograph.

   Fibroblasts of fetal skin, in a more active state than those presented here, are illustrated in Figs. 67–70.

Fig. 129. Collagen bundles and fibroblast from forearm skin of girl aged 8. Osmium fixation, PTA staining. × 12,000.

Fig. 130. Fibroblast and collagen from forearm skin of girl aged 20. Osmium fixation, lead hydroxide and uranyl acetate staining. × 61,200.

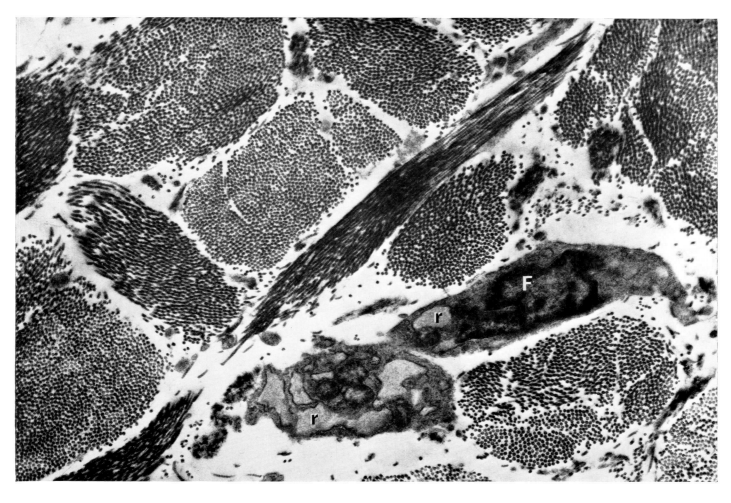

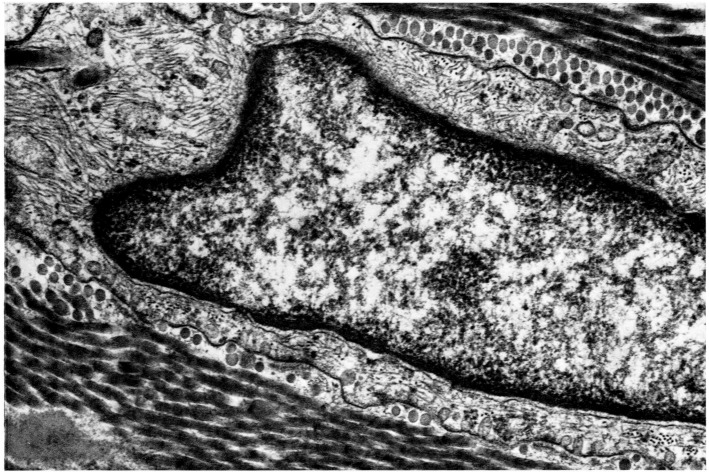

FIGURE 131

Collagen of post-natal skin exists in the form of fibres varying in diameter from about 20–100 nm (200–1,000 Å). In longitudinal section the fibres appear striated, exhibiting an axial period which, on the basis of measurements of animal fibres, and of fibres reconstituted from solutions of collagen, is usually given as 64 nm (640 Å). In the micrograph opposite, the band pattern is seen to repeat every 55 nm (550 Å) along the length of the fibres, and this somewhat closer spacing has also been quoted by other observers of ultra-thin sections of human dermal collagen. The discrepancy may well be due to effects of fixation and imbedding. At high magnification, up to 12 or 14 sub-bands per period may be detected, and it is customary to label these with letters of the alphabet; the sub-band chosen to indicate the major period in this micrograph is the *d* band. In shadowed preparations of teased collagen, the fibres have a characteristically corrugated appearance, with each period exhibiting a raised region. A degree of corrugation is evident with some of the fibres illustrated here, the raised region being located about mid-way between repeating *d* bands.

As mentioned previously (p. 84), collagen fibres are formed by aggregation and polymerization of helically-coiled macromolecules of tropocollagen which are estimated to be about 280 nm (2,800 Å) in length, and to have a diameter of 1·4 nm (14 Å). The characteristic period and band pattern of the mature collagen fibre, which represents a molecular map of the distribution of basic side chains along the length of its component tropocollagen molecules, is thought to be produced by the manner of packing of the latter, though views differ as to the exact arrangement. According to the "quarter-stagger" theory, neighbouring molecules, or linear arrays thereof are displaced longitudinally with respect to each other by a distance equal to a quarter of their length. An alternative suggestion is that the tropocollagen molecule has specific bonding regions occurring at one-fifth intervals along its length, and that the band pattern is produced by bonding of adjacent molecules in a side to side fashion. It has been reported by Braun-Falco that an inverse sequence of cross bands in adjacent fibres is frequently observed in human skin collagen, and he suggests that this anti-parallel orientation may play an important role in relation to the cohesion of fibres within bundles.

Fig. 131. Collagen fibres from forearm skin of woman aged 40. Osmium fixation, PTA staining. × 180,000.

FIGURE 132

In sections of the dermis stained with PTA, electron-dense areas of mottled appearance (e) may be seen among the collagen bundles or closely associated with fibroblasts (F) and their processes. These are elastic fibres which, like collagen fibres, are produced by fibroblasts. They consist of two components, microfibrils and amorphous substance. In the fetus, the micro-fibrils appear first, but as development proceeds, increasing amounts of amorphous substance are deposited upon them, so that in the mature state the microfibrils are largely obscured. This is particularly the case with preparations stained with PTA, which has a particular affinity for the amorphous component constituting over 90 per cent of the fibre. An elastic fibre so stained is shown in the inset, where it appears as an amorphous mass (a) within which microfibrils cannot be detected, though these (f) are evident at the periphery, where they form a ragged envelope giving the fibre a characteristically frayed appearance.

FIGURE 133

An elastic fibre (E) sectioned longitudinally is shown in this micrograph taken from a section stained with lead and uranyl acetate. The frayed edge due to peripheral microfibrils (f) is well seen, and within the mainly amorphous part, some skeins of microfibrils (s) are just evident. Selective removal of the amorphous component with elastase renders these more apparent. Between the elastic fibre and the fibroblast (F) are free microfibrils (f_1) of a type which are ubiquitous in the connective tissue, and which in certain situations, e.g. close to the basal lamina of the epidermis, are referred to as reticular fibres (Fig. 91). They have been variously regarded as collagen or elastin precursors, or as protein-polysaccharides which do not become further organized, but their true identity and significance remain to be established.

Separation of the two components of the elastic fibre has established that the amino-acid composition of the amorphous component is identical with that described for elastin. This resembles collagen in its high contents of glycine, alanine and proline, and low content of tyro-sine, but differs in its high content of valine and low content of hydroxyproline, and in particular in containing two new amino-acids, desmosine and isodesmosine. The microfibrillar component is apparently a protein which is neither collagen nor elastin, but its exact amino-acid composition has not been worked out yet.

Fig. 132. Collagen bundles and elastic fibres from forearm skin of girl aged 8. Osmium fixation, PTA staining. × 11,200. *Inset:* elastic fibre at higher magnification. × 72,600.

Fig. 133. Elastic fibre, fibroblast and collagen from forearm skin of girl aged 20. Osmium fixation, lead hydroxide and uranyl acetate staining. × 40,200.

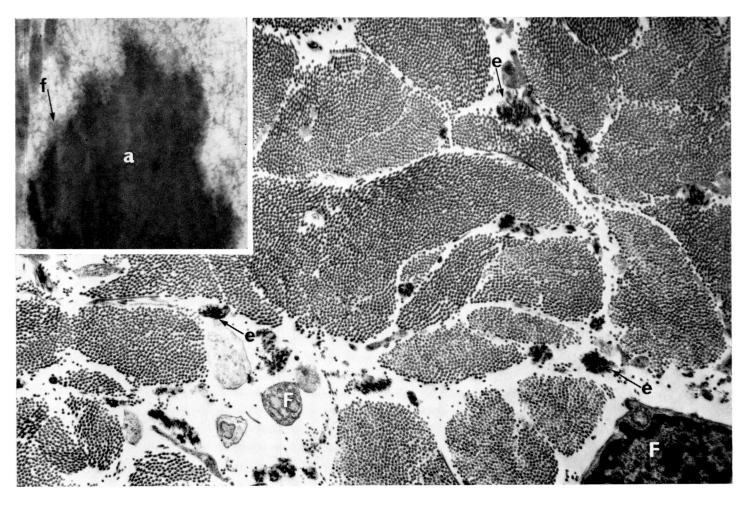

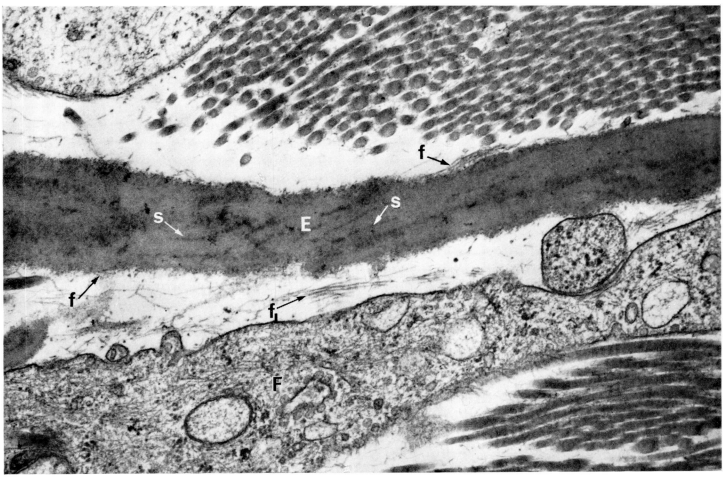

FIGURE 134

The dermis contains a variety of free cells, two types of which are represented in this micrograph. The first type is the mast-cell (M) which has a cytoplasm packed with granules of highly characteristic structure, and villous folds projecting from the plasma membrane. Mast cells occur most frequently in the neighbourhood of small vessels (V) and nerves (S), and are further illustrated in Figs. 139 and 140. The other type of cell (H) is identified mainly on the basis of negative features, i.e. it lacks the distinguishing characters of other cells such as fibroblasts, mast cells, Schwann cells etc. This is the type of cell which it was previously suggested (p. 168) might tentatively be labelled a "histiocyte". The nucleus is commonly indented, and the somewhat granular cytoplasm contains many small vesicles as well as membrane-limited organelles with the characteristics of lysosomes. Mitochondria are not very numerous, and the rough-surfaced endoplasmic reticulum is poorly developed.

The term "histiocyte" is used in light microscopy to specify fixed connective-tissue cells which in certain circumstances become actively motile and engage in phagocytosis. In these circumstances they are referred to as "macrophages". It may well be that the cells seen here represent histiocytes at the ultrastructural level, and that in this sense they can be regarded as inactive or potential macrophages. However, in the absence of any definite evidence of phagocytotic activity this might not seem justified; the more so, since, as discussed on the following page, there is a definite possibility that the cells in question are in fact undifferentiated Langerhans cells. A major difficulty in labelling these cells is the unsatisfactory nature of the terms "histiocyte" and "macrophage", which are interchangeable in one sense, but not entirely so in another. Perhaps the best thing to do would be to refer to the cells as "relatively undifferentiated dermal cells of doubtful lineage and function" and leave it at that. Whatever their nature, they constitute a significant proportion of the population of free dermal cells.

Fig. 134. Cells in reticular region of forearm dermis of woman aged 40. Osmium fixation, lead staining. × 11,100.

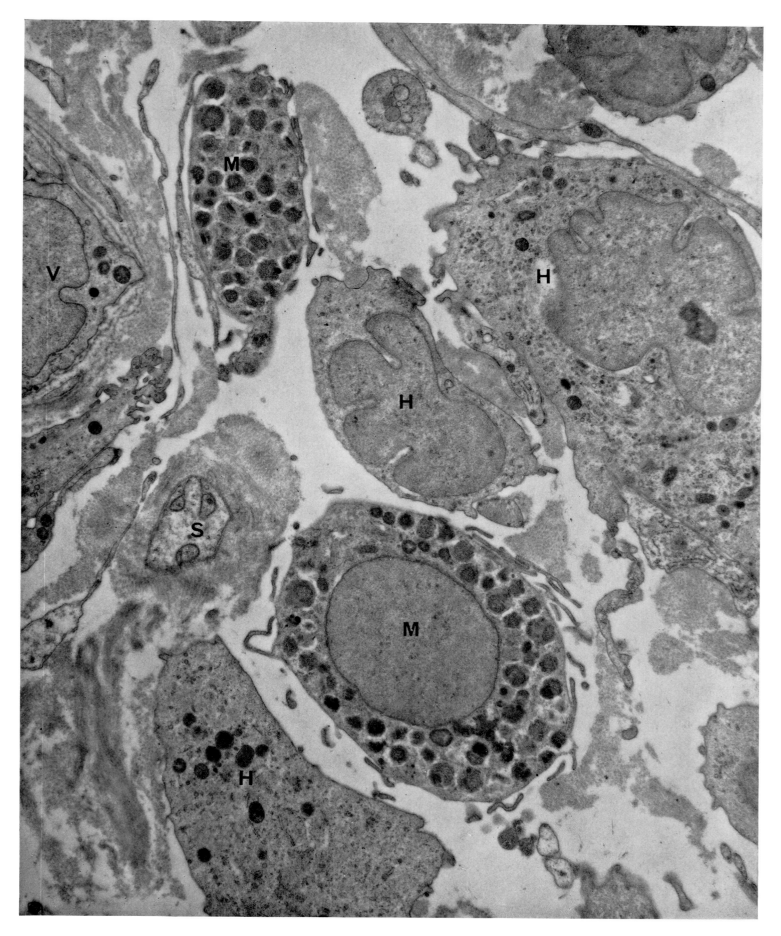

FIGURE 135

This dermal cell contains rod (r) and racquet-shaped (ra) profiles already described as characteristic of Langerhans cells (see Figs. 121–124). Until recently, it was generally thought that Langerhans cells are confined to the epidermis, but A. Zelickson demonstrated their occasional presence in the dermis, and they have subsequently been observed in this situation by other workers. They also occur in large numbers in cutaneous and extra-cutaneous lesions of Histiocytosis-X, and in this condition have been referred to by histopathologists as "abnormal histiocytes". These observations have led to the emerging view that the Langerhans cell is primarily of mesodermal origin, and that those present in the epidermis are immigrant elements which cross the epidermal-dermal junction at a certain stage of fetal life, after which they become reproductively self-maintaining without further, or only occasional, recruitment from the underlying dermis. Some circumstantial evidence can be presented to support this view:

In the previous micrograph (Fig. 134) cells (H) were presented with the suggestion that they may be "histiocytes", or at any rate relatively undifferentiated cells of probable mesodermal origin. The cell figured opposite is very similar to these (it also contains lysosomes, (ly)), and indeed, were it not for the presence of Langerhans granules in the cytoplasm of the former, it would be difficult to draw any distinction between them. This could suggest that the Langerhans cell is a variant, or perhaps more mature or more active form of the presumed histiocyte, maturity or increased activity being manifested by the presence of the characteristic granules. In Histiocytosis-X, large numbers of Langerhans-type cells are present in the lesions, and the question of their source must arise. According to the present argument they could represent more active forms of "histiocytes" already present. There is abundant evidence from experimental studies on epidermal Langerhans cells that the presence and concentration of granules is related to the functional state of the cell, an observation which could fit in with this. Taking the evidence as a whole, one might advance the following proposition: There is present in normal mesenchyme and dermis a population of cells of the type illustrated in Fig. 134, which for the moment may be classed as "histiocytes". The ability to produce "Langerhans granules" is latent in these cells, but in normal circumstances is manifest in only a few, such as the one opposite. In other circumstances, e.g. when involved in a pathological process (Histiocytosis-X), or following migration into an epithelial environment (epidermis) the cells react by producing large numbers of granules and are classed as Langerhans cells. Granule production indicates a specific functional response of the cell. While this hypothesis could string together a number of apparently irreconcilable observations, it is to be regarded at present as very tentative.

Fig. 135. Langerhans cell in dermis of forearm skin of man aged 42. Osmium fixation, lead staining. × 23,750.

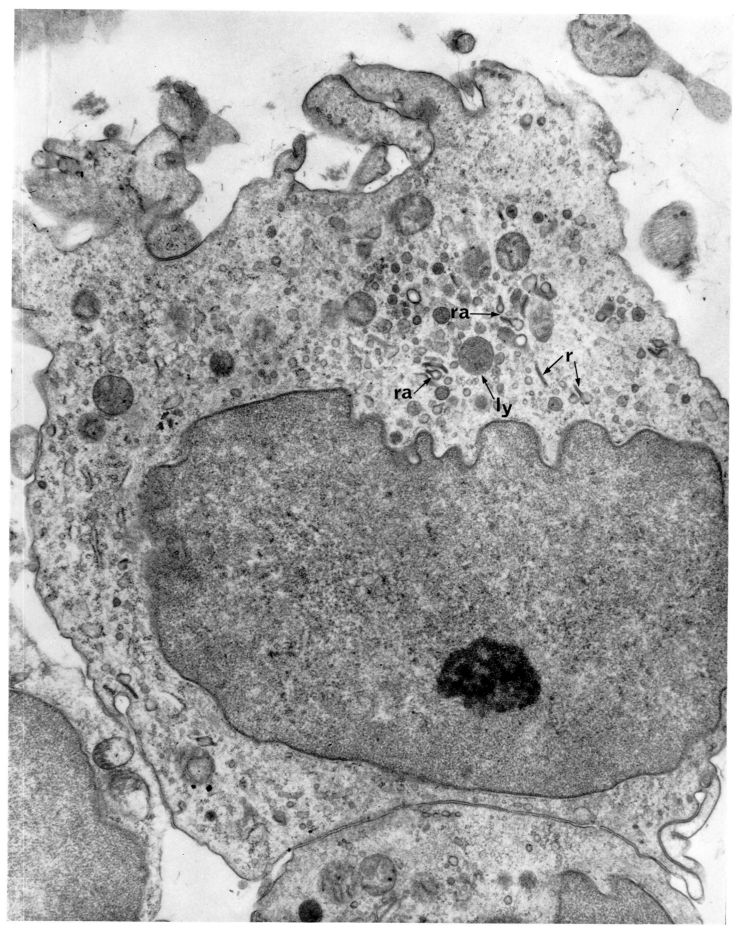

179

FIGURE 136

Cells which are capable of phagocytosing particulate matter and degrading or digesting it within membrane-limited organelles known as lysosomes, are classed as macrophages. Such cells are widely distributed among tissues, and are important in freeing the internal milieu of foreign material. They are encountered with reasonable frequency in normal dermis.

Lysosomes are membrane-limited organelles containing a variety of hydrolytic enzymes, the demonstration of which (e.g. acid phosphatase) within them is the only certain criterion for their identification. Cytochemical studies combined with straightforward morphological observations have revealed the remarkable structural heterogenicity of these cytoplasmic bodies, examples of which are seen here. They have a single limiting membrane (m), but their shape, size, and internal structure vary enormously. The simplest form appears as a round electron dense body of finely granular internal structure (St) which is often referred to as a storage granule or primary lysosome. These may sometimes be confused with electron-dense mitochondria (Mi) but the presence of cristae within the latter, and the double limiting membrane usually allows them to be distinguished. Some lysosomes contain myelin-like concentric systems of membranes, which has led to them being referred to as "myelin bodies" (My), while others (Mo) may present a mottled appearance due to irregular disposition of dense flocculent material within them. Larger bodies with areas of differing density, vesicles, remnants of cell organelles or obviously extraneous material, are referred to as "digestive vacuoles" (Di).

The term "macrophage" derives from a particular activity of the cell, and gives no indication of its lineage. Many cells present in skin, such as Schwann cells, fibroblasts, Langerhans cells, and even the epidermal keratinocytes, contain lysosomes, and in certain circumstances are known to engulf extraneous particles. In this connection therefore they might also be referred to as macrophages. However, the term is commonly restricted to connective tissue cells of the type shown whose primary function is evidently phagocytosis, and which lack the more specialized features which identify cells of the other classes mentioned.

Portion of the cell nucleus (n) is within the field.

Fig. 136. Macrophage from dermis of forearm skin of woman aged 40. Osmium fixation, lead staining. × 30,400.

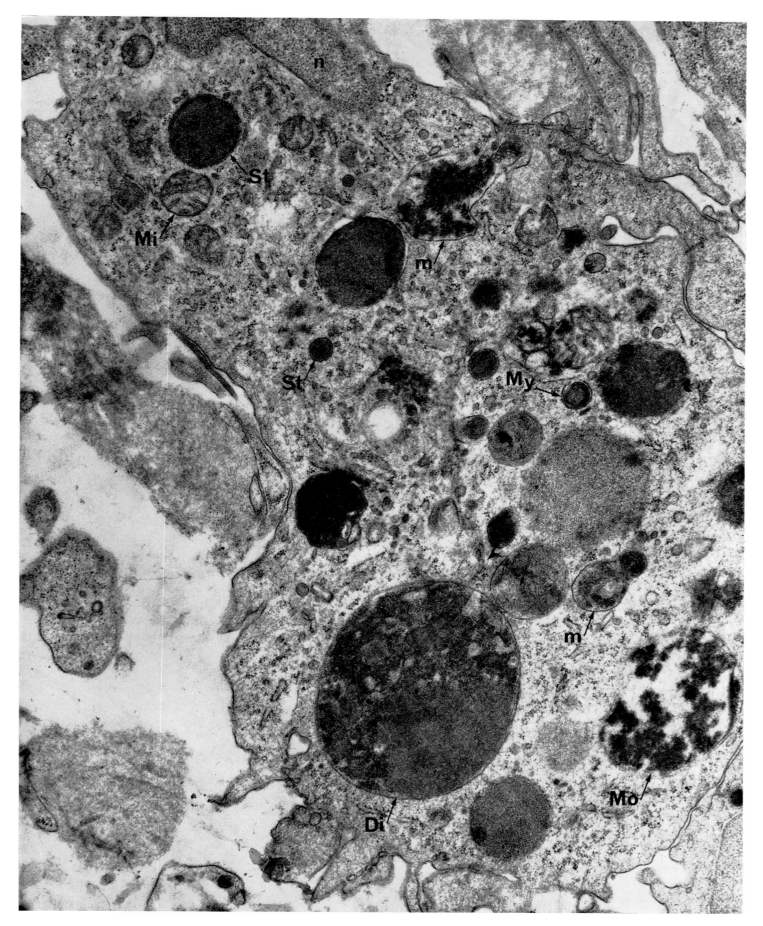

FIGURE 137

This cell is a dermal macrophage with cytoplasm packed with melanosomes which it has ingested. It is not a melanocyte, or melanin-synthesising cell, because formative stages or premelanosomes (p. 140) are not present in the cytoplasm, besides which, the fully melanized melanosomes are aggregated together within membrane-limited phagasomes (p) preparatory to being broken down. Melanocytes are not present in normal dermis, so melanosomes ingested by dermal macrophages must have originated in the epidermis. It is not clear if they come from melanocytes or keratinocytes, or both, nor has it been established exactly how they enter the dermis. All one can say is, that melanosomes are never seen lying free in the dermis. An experimental study conducted recently by E. Frenk may hold the key to this problem. He showed that painting skin of guinea-pigs with monoethyl ether of hydroquinone resulted in degeneration of the epidermal melanocytes and their subsequent engulfment by dermal macrophages. As pointed out previously (p. 136) it is generally held that epidermal melanocytes eventually become worn-out, and removal of the Langerhans cell from its role of "effete melanocyte" presents a problem concerning the fate of these latter. It may be they are engulfed entire, or in fragmental form, by dermal macrophages, and that this is how they leave the epidermis. The fact that this process has not yet been seen in normal human skin may be due to the fact that it is a comparatively rare occurrence, and that the turnover rate of melanocytes is not as rapid as previously thought.

FIGURE 138

This micrograph illustrates a further stage in the degradation of melanosomes within a dermal macrophage. Some relatively intact melanosomes (m) are still evident within membrane-limited structures (lysosomes), but within others, characterized by internal lamellation (l), the process of breakdown has reached a stage that all that remains is what might be described as "melanin dust". It is not known what enzyme is involved in the final breakdown of melanin, which is particularly resistant to destruction *in vitro*.

Fig. 137. Melanosome-containing macrophage from forearm skin of man aged 28. Osmium fixation, lead staining. × 18,000.

Fig. 138. Degradation of melanosomes within macrophage from forearm skin of man aged 42. Osmium fixation, lead staining. × 27,000.

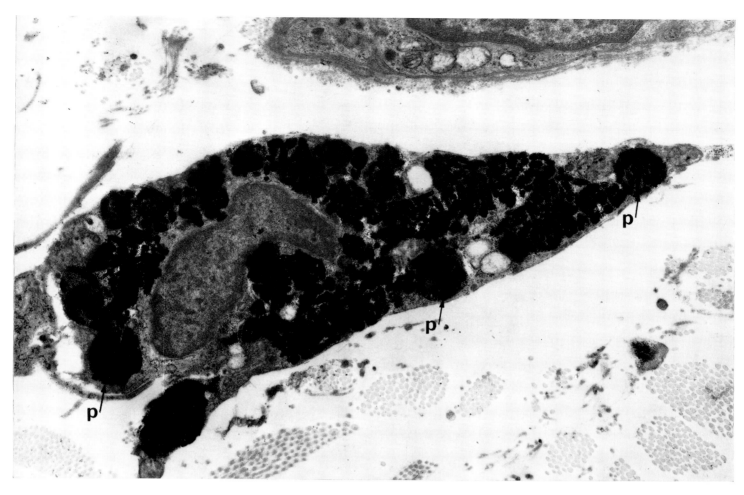

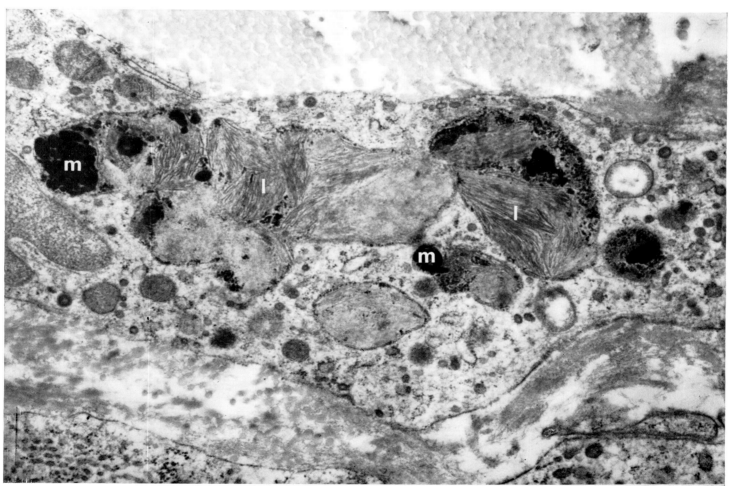

Figure 139

Mast cells are frequently encountered in normal human skin, particularly in the vicinity of small vessels and nerves (Fig. 134), and the presence of large numbers of cytoplasmic granules makes them easily identifiable in electron micrographs. Apart from the granules, the cytoplasm also contains the common organelles such as mitochondria (mi), Golgi apparatus (go) etc., and occasionally, lipid droplets. Slender villous processes (pr) projecting from the plasma membrane are also characteristic of the mast cell. It is often stated that mast cells exist in two different forms, the round and the elongated, but it is doubtful if this distinction has either validity or functional significance.

On section, the granules present a variety of appearances. Some (d) appear almost uniformly dense in low-power micrographs, but at higher magnification (*see inset*) the internal structure appears finely granular, and a crystalline arrangement may be seen. Other granules (c) exhibit a central dense core, and a less dense peripheral zone, while others (t) contain relatively translucent areas of hyaline appearance. Finally, many granules (see following Fig. 140) are seen to have a partially lamellar internal structure, the lamella being straight, curved, or arranged in whorls. Individual granules may exhibit varying combinations of the above features, and the actual appearance presented by any one, will depend upon their localization within it, and upon the plane in which it was sectioned. Some workers claim to be able to make a distinction between immature and mature granules on the basis of such sectional appearances, but their conclusions are inevitably speculative since the site of origin of the granules remains unknown, and studies to date on fetal mast cells (Figs. 75 and 76) have shed little light on this problem.

Fig. 139. Dermal mast cell from forearm skin of girl aged 20. Osmium fixation, combined lead and uranyl acetate staining. ×20,800. *Inset:* granule with internal crystalline arrangement. ×112,000.

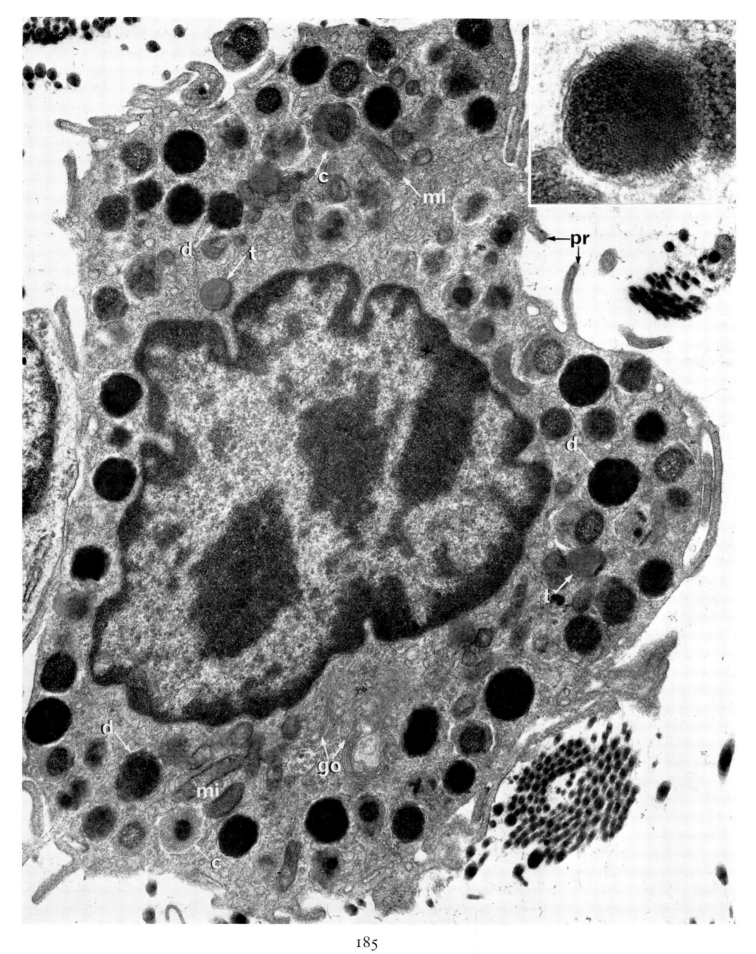

FIGURE 140

Most of the granules seen in this section of a mast cell exhibit the typical bent or whorled lamellar sub-structure, and the one shown in inset has a more regular arrangement of parallel lamellae. Many granules show evidence of a limiting membrane (m) which at times may be difficult to distinguish from the outermost of the internal lamellae. With granules of fetal mast cells the limiting membrane is more clearly defined (Fig. 76). Mitochondria (mi) are also seen in this micrograph, and though bearing a superficial resemblance to the granules, are readily distinguishable on closer inspection.

Mast cells are known to contain histamine, heparin, and in some species, serotonin (5-hydroxytriptamine) and there is good evidence that these substances are located within the cytoplasmic granules. There is no information available, however, as to their individual disposition in relation to the lamellar, granular or crystalline sub-components. Mast cells can be induced to release their contents of histamine, heparin and serotonin under a variety of experimental conditions, with appropriate effects on the vascular system and blood coagulation, and this is associated with extrusion and disruption of the granules. It is doubtful if degranulation occurs under normal physiological conditions, and the mast cell is thought to function primarily as an element of the emergency defence and reparative mechanisms of the body.

It has been suggested, on the basis of some structural similarity and acid phosphatase activity, that the mast cell granule represents a special type of lysosome. It has also been suggested that the granules are very similar to melanosomes in structure, and that the mast cell and the melanocyte belong to the same cell lineage. Neither of these views has received general support.

Fig. 140. Dermal mast cell from forearm skin of girl aged 20. Osmium fixation, lead staining. × 76,000. *Inset:* granule showing parallel arrangement of lamellae. × 234,000.

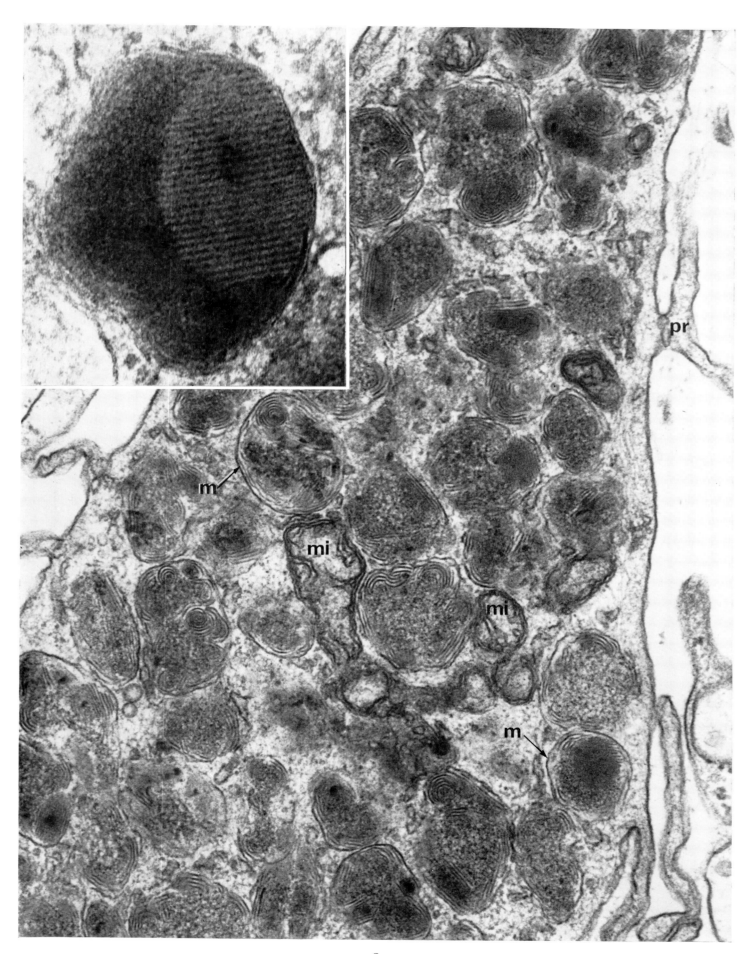

REFERENCES

COLLAGEN, FIBROBLAST AND ELASTIC FIBRE

Braun-Falco, O. and Rupec, M. Some observations on dermal collagen fibrils in ultra-thin sections. *J. Invest. Derm.*, **42**:15, 1964.

Ramachandran, G. N. (ed.). "Treatise on Collagen", 3 vols. New York, Academic Press Inc., 1967.

Ross, R. and Bornstein, P. The elastic fiber. 1. The separation and partial characterization of its macromolecular components. *J. Cell Biol.*, **40**:366, 1969.

LANGERHANS CELL AND HISTIOCYTE

Basset, F. and Nezelof, C. Présence en microscopie électronique de structures filamenteuses originales dans les lésions pulmonaires et osseuses de l'histiocytose X. Etat actuel de la question. *Bull. Soc. Méd. Hôp. Paris*, **117**:413, 1966.

Breathnach, A. S. and Wyllie, L. M. The problem of the Langerhans cells. In: "Advances in Biology of Skin, Vol. VIII, The Pigmentary System". Eds., W. Montagna and Funan Hu. Oxford, Pergamon, 1967.

Wolff, K. Die Langerhans-Zelle. Ergebnisse neuerer experimenteller Untersuchungen. *Arch. klin. exp. Derm.*, **229**:54, 1967.

Zelickson, A. S. The Langerhans cell. *J. Invest. Derm.*, **44**:201, 1965.

MACROPHAGE, LYSOSOMES, MELANIN DEGRADATION

De Reuck, A. V. S. and Cameron, M. P. (eds.). "Lysosomes". London, J. & A. Churchill, 1963.

Frenk, E. Experimentelle Depigmentierung der Meerschweinchenhaut durch selektiv toxische Wirkung von Hydrochinon-monoäthyläther auf die Melanocyten. *Arch. klin. exp. Derm.*, **235**:16, 1969.

MAST CELL

Hashimoto, K., Gross, B. G. and Lever, W. F. An electron microscopic study of the degranulation of mast cell granules in urticaria pigmentosa. *J. Invest. Derm.*, **46**:139, 1966.

Kobayasi, T., Midtgård, K. and Asboe-Hansen, G. Ultrastructure of human mast-cell granules. *J. Ultrastruct. Res.*, **23**:153, 1968.

Smith, D. E. The tissue mast cell. *Int. Rev. Cytol.*, **14**:328, 1963.

8 Preterminal and Terminal Cutaneous Nerves

Schwann cell: unmyelinated and myelinated axons: myelin — fibrous sheaths of nerve: perineurium and endoneurium — pre-terminal dermal nerves — nerve terminals — Meissner corpuscle.

FIGURE 141

This micrograph, taken from a section of sural nerve, illustrates the basic components of peripheral nervous tissue. Four Schwann cells (S) with nuclei included in the plane of section are seen, as well as processes (Pr) thereof, or of others, which have been sectioned at some distance from the nucleus. Intimately associated with the Schwann cells and their processes are neuraxons (a), some of which are surrounded by an electron-dense closely laminated myelin sheath (m). This is produced by a spiral wrapping of the Schwann cell plasma membrane around the axon. Neuraxons lacking a myelin sheath, and having a simpler relation with the Schwann cell, i.e. merely indenting the plasma membrane, or being suspended from it by a "mesaxon" (me), are unmyelinated axons, several of which are usually associated with a single Schwann cell. Associated with the plasma membrane of the Schwann cell is a well-defined basal lamina (b).

The Schwann cells and their associated axons are embedded in endoneurial collagen (En), which also contains fibroblasts or their processes (f). Much discussion has centred around the question of the source of the endoneurial collagen; some authors maintain it is produced exclusively by fibroblasts, while others believe the Schwann cells contribute to it, especially during regeneration following nerve section or other injury. Small bundles of collagen fibres (co) are sometimes seen indenting, or being enveloped by Schwann cell plasma membrane in a manner similar to unmyelinated fibres. This appearance cannot be taken to be indicative of collagen synthesis on the part of the Schwann cell. It is more likely a manifestation of a tendency for Schwann cells to envelop not only axons, but other elongated structures of suitable dimensions.

Peripheral nerve trunks have two connective tissue sheaths the perineurium and the epineurium, neither of which is represented in this field from a central region of the nerve. The smaller intra-dermal branches under consideration here generally lack an organized epineurium, but the perineurium (Figs. 147 and 148) persists as they traverse the reticular region of the dermis and finally terminates as they approach the papillary region. In this latter situation (Figs. 152 and 153) Schwann cells and associated axons lie freely in contact with the general connective tissue.

Fig. 141. Sural nerve of woman aged 27. Osmium fixation, lead staining. × 20,400.

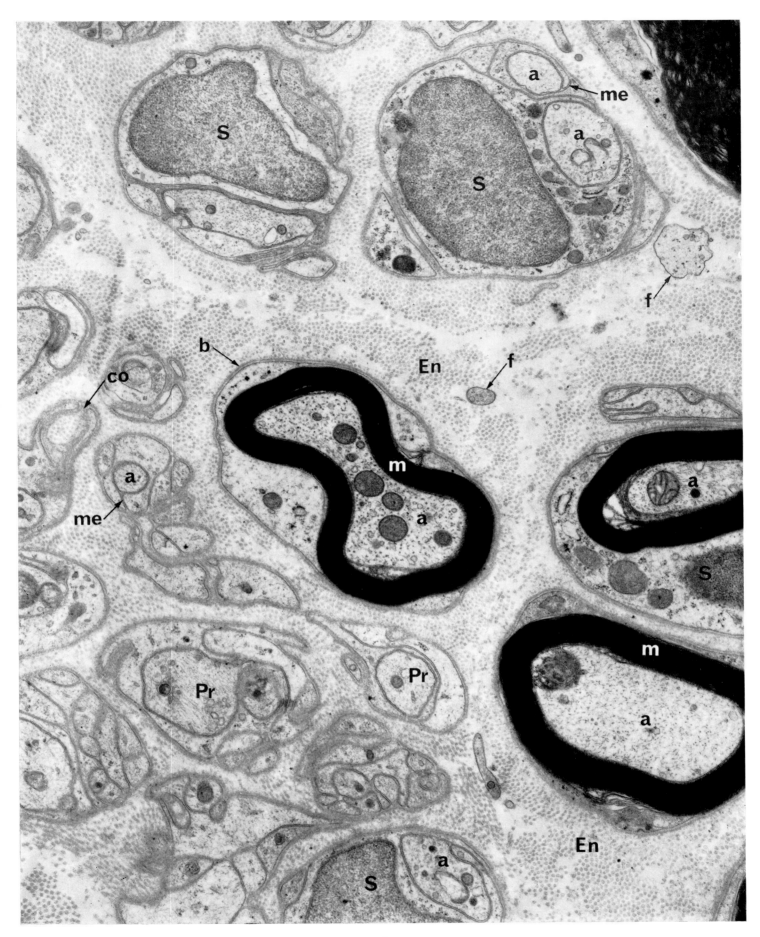

FIGURE 142

At an early stage of fetal life nerves consist of bundles of axons loosely enveloped by Schwann cells (Fig. 77), but as development proceeds, processes of the cells invade the axonal bundles so that eventually the individual axons are segregated from one another. They then appear in cross sections as indenting the surface of the Schwann cell, or lying in grooves of varying depth which are in communication with the extracellular space through a narrow channel bounded by two closely apposed layers of invaginated plasma membrane, which together constitute the mesaxon. Axons which in post-natal life retain this relatively simple relationship with the Schwann cell are known as unmyelinated axons. Some mesaxons become greatly elongated and spirally wrapped around the axon to form a multi-layered sheath—the myelin sheath—and axons so ensheathed are known as myelinated axons.

The cytoplasm of the Schwann cell contains the common organelles, mitochondria (mi), Golgi apparatus (go) etc., as well as filamentous bundles (f), lysosomes (ly), and occasionally lipid droplets. It can almost invariably be distinguished from other dermal cells because of the presence of axons (a) and of a basal lamina (b). The axons associated with this cell are of the unmyelinated variety, enclosed, or suspended by mesaxons (m) whose continuity with the plasma membrane is evident. In the left lower part of the field two axons enclosed in a common mesaxon are seen; these presumably are branches of a common stem. It may perhaps be emphasized that though the axons appear to lie within the Schwann cell, they are, in fact, separated from the cytoplasm by the infolded plasma membrane.

FIGURE 143

The Schwann cell is an irregular cell with finger-like processes extending proximally and distally from the main part containing the nucleus. Accordingly in transverse sections passing through the cell at some distance from the nuclear region, apparently isolated processes (Pr) with associated axons (a) and surrounded by basal lamina (b) are seen. In any one section, most of these processes probably belong to the same cell, though some may be interdigitating processes of adjacent cells. As seen here, there is considerable variation in the extent to which individual axons are enveloped by the Schwann cell processes. Some merely indent the surface, and over part of their extent are separated from the external milieu only by basal lamina. Others have distinct mesaxons of varying length. In general, it is not legitimate to conclude from a single section that the less completely invested axons are approaching termination, because serial sections reveal that as it traverses the territory of an individual Schwann cell the degree of envelopment of the axon may vary. Also, as the tip of the Schwann cell process is approached, its sectional area is diminished and the associated axons become less completely invested; as they become related to the succeeding Schwann cell, they may again be more deeply placed.

Fig. 142. Cytoplasm of Schwann cell from forearm dermis of girl aged 18. Osmium fixation, uranyl acetate and lead staining. × 48,000.

Fig. 143. Schwann cell processes and unmyelinated axons from forearm dermis of girl aged 18. Osmium fixation, lead staining. × 40,600.

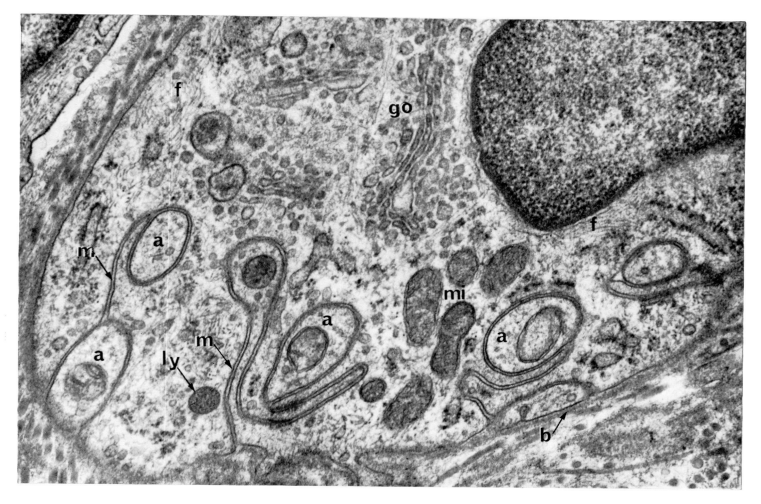

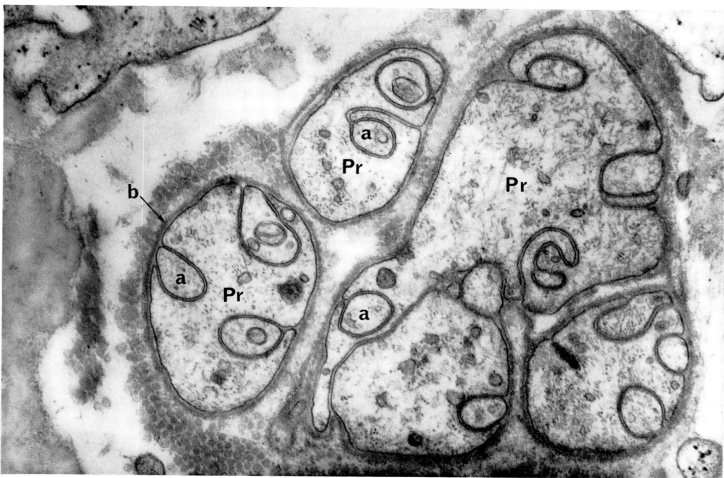

FIGURE 144

The myelinated axon (A) differs from the unmyelinated type in that the mesaxon (me) is greatly lengthened and wrapped around it to form a multi-layered sheath (M) of varying thickness. The concentrically arranged lamellae of the myelin sheath are not very evident in low-power micrographs, or with moderately thick sections, but they are clearly seen at higher magnifications (Figs. 145 and 146). Myelinated and unmyelinated fibres are never associated together in relation to the same Schwann cell, and individual Schwann cells (S) never contain more than a single myelinated axon.

Exactly how the myelin sheath is formed, remains to be established. It is generally accepted that it is not formed by rotation of the axon, nor by a rotation of the Schwann cell as a whole around the axon. Formation of the extra membrane substance seems to be confined to the mesaxon, though how this comes to be disposed in the form of a tight spiral around the axon, is poorly understood.

Fig. 144. Myelinated axon from sural nerve of woman aged 27. Osmium fixation, lead staining. ×66,600.

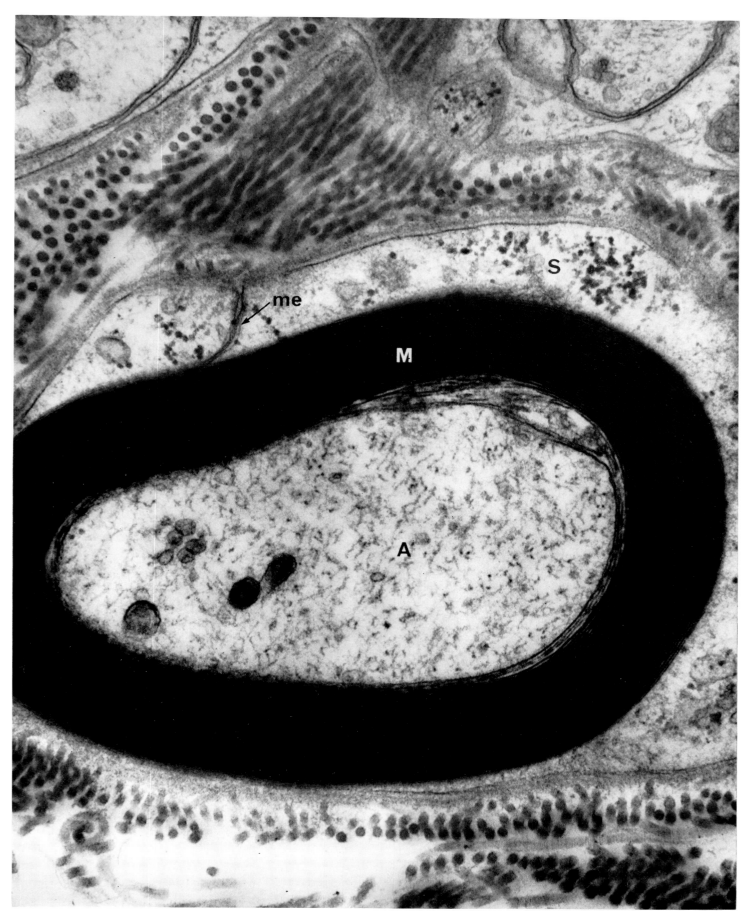

FIGURE 145

The concentric arrangement of the lamellae of the myelin sheath of the axon (A) is clearly seen in this micrograph, which also includes segments of the basal lamina (b), plasma membrane (p), and cytoplasm of the Schwann cell (S). There is a regular alternation of dense lines and less dense slightly wider areas across the cut surface of the sheath, and from what has been said concerning its mode of formation, it might be thought that the dense lines represent the tightly-wrapped mesaxon, and that the less dense intervening areas are layers of Schwann cell cytoplasm sandwiched between its lamellae. This, however, is not the case, as explained below.

FIGURE 146

At higher magnification the less dense layers of the myelin sheath are seen to contain a faint intermediate line (i) called the intraperiod line because it lies mid-way between the thicker and more obvious dense lines of the major myelin period. The major dense line is about 3 nm (30 Å) thick, the intraperiod line about 2 nm (20 Å) and the less dense area, including the latter is about 9 nm (90 Å). The major dense line and the intraperiod line are produced as follows: The plasma membrane of the cell consists of two leaflets, outer and inner, though these are not always apparent in micrographs unless the tissue has been fixed with potassium permanganate. The mesaxon therefore, consisting as it does of two layers of plasma membrane really comprises four leaflets, and these can just be discerned at the tip of the arrow in Fig. 144. In the formation of the myelin sheath, the invaginated outer leaflets come together to form the thinner intraperiod line, thereby excluding the extracellular space from the sheath, and the cytoplasmic aspects of adjacent inner leaflets likewise come together to form the major dense line. The less dense areas on either side of the intraperiod line, therefore, represent not cytoplasm, but the interval between inner and outer leaflets of Schwann cell plasma membrane.

Fig. 145. Myelinated axon from sural nerve of woman aged 27. Osmium fixation, lead staining. × 122,000.

Fig. 146. Myelin sheath of axon from sural nerve of woman aged 27. Osmium fixation, lead staining. × 265,200.

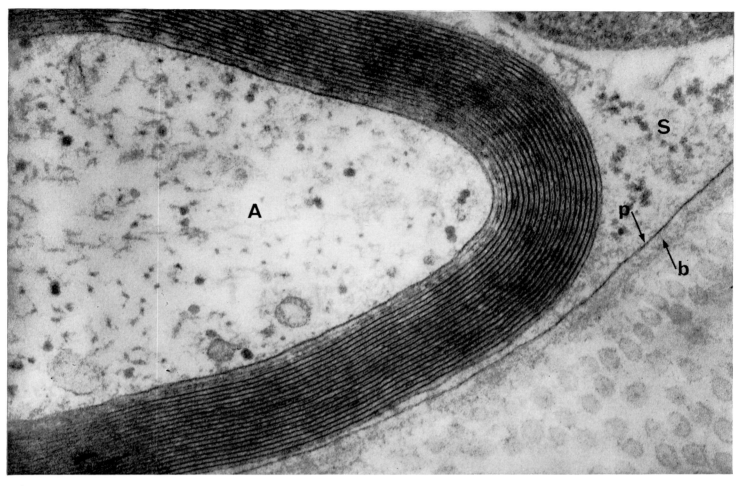

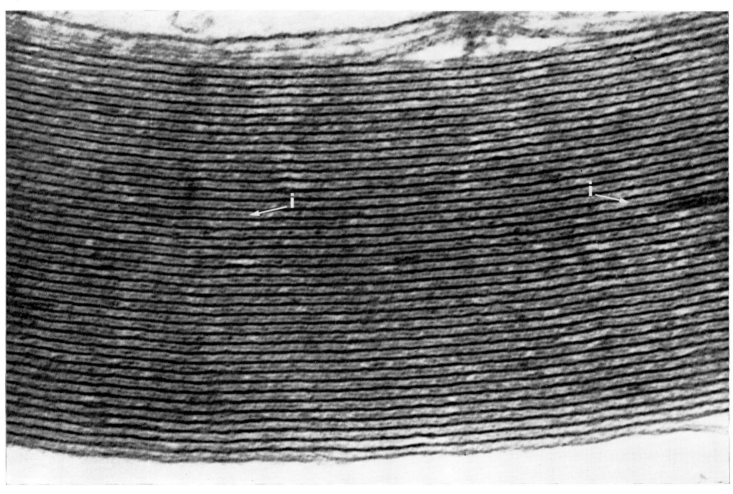

FIGURE 147

The perineurium consists of concentric layers of flattened cells separated by collagen fibres. In large nerves, up to nine layers of cells may be present, but with smaller branches the number is reduced. In this section of a segment of a nerve from the reticular region of the dermis, two layers of perineurial cells (P) are seen enclosing Schwann cells (S) with unmyelinated and myelinated (M) axons, as well as endoneurial collagen and fibroblasts (F). The cells are flattened, even in the nuclear region, from which slender processes (Pr) extend to establish contact with neighbouring cells of the same layer (outside the field). A basal lamina (b) is associated with the plasma membrane, and collagen fibres (c) are present between cells of the two layers.

FIGURE 148

The basal lamina (b) associated with perineurial cells (P) is clearly seen in this micrograph. It will be observed however that it is not continuous in relation to that aspect of the plasma membrane of the outer cell which faces the inner one. Myelinated (M) and unmyelinated axons (U) are present in the endoneurium.

The question of the developmental origin of perineurial cells remains unsettled. Some workers believe they are derived from mesenchymal cells which also give rise to fibroblasts, while others claim they stem from the neural crest, like Schwann cells. The presence of a basal lamina might seem to favour the latter view. Much of the tensile strength of peripheral nerves is provided by the perineurium, and it also forms an effective barrier between the nerve fibres and substances present in the surrounding tissue fluid, e.g. certain ions, drugs and infective agents.

Fig. 147. Perineurial sheath of nerve from reticular region of arm dermis of man aged 24. Osmium fixation, uranyl acetate and lead staining. × 9,600.

Fig. 148. Perineurium and endoneurium of nerve from reticular region of arm dermis of man aged 24. Osmium fixation, uranyl acetate and lead staining. × 39,000.

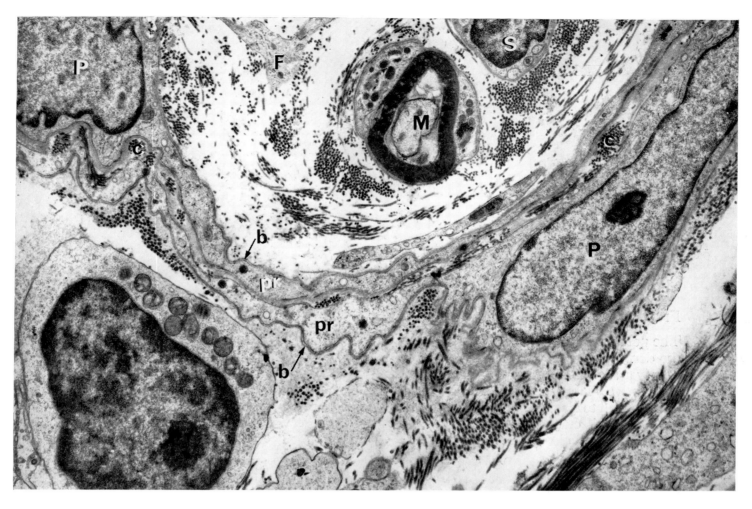

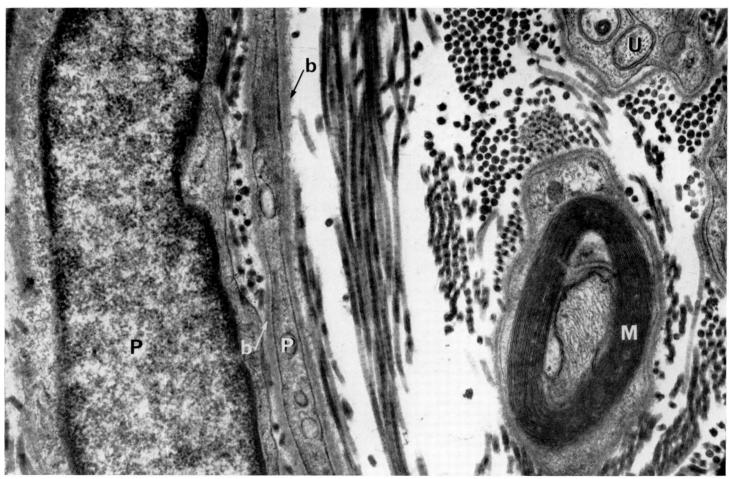

FIGURE 149

The perineurium (P) of this small nerve lying alongside a vessel (V) in the reticular region of the dermis, consists of a single layer of cells. It encloses several Schwann cell processes (Pr) mostly associated with unmyelinated axons (a) but one (M) contains a myelinated axon. Note the relatively large area occupied by endoneurial collagen (En). The quantity of this is thought to be related to elasticity and tensile strength, and it is not surprising therefore that it should be large in small cutaneous nerves, which, owing to the mobility of skin, may be exposed to stretch in many circumstances.

FIGURE 150

In the papillary region of the dermis, myelinated fibres are rarely seen, and this nerve is constituted of two Schwann cell processes (S) with associated unmyelinated axons (a). The relatively large amount of endoneurial collagen (En) within the perineurial sheath may again be noted. The perineurium (P) is one layer thick, and in fact, appears to consist of a single cell, enveloping processes of which meet and overlap at O. The basal lamina (b) is deficient over the greater extent of the endoneurial aspect of the plasma membrane of this cell, a feature frequently observed, but the significance of which is not apparent. The Schwann cell processes, however, are completely invested by a continuous basal lamina (b).

Fig. 149. Sheathed nerve and vessel from reticular region of forearm dermis of man aged 46. Osmium fixation, lead staining. × 11,000.

Fig. 150. Small sheathed nerve from papillary region of forearm dermis of man aged 46. Osmium fixation, lead staining. × 37,000.

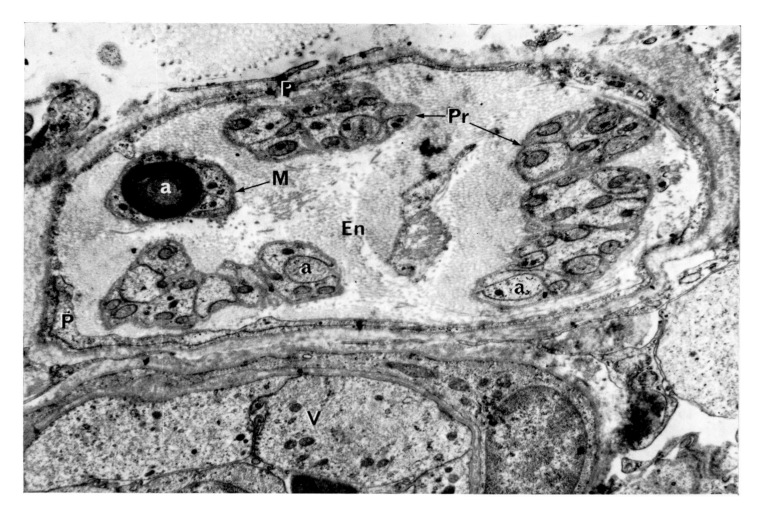

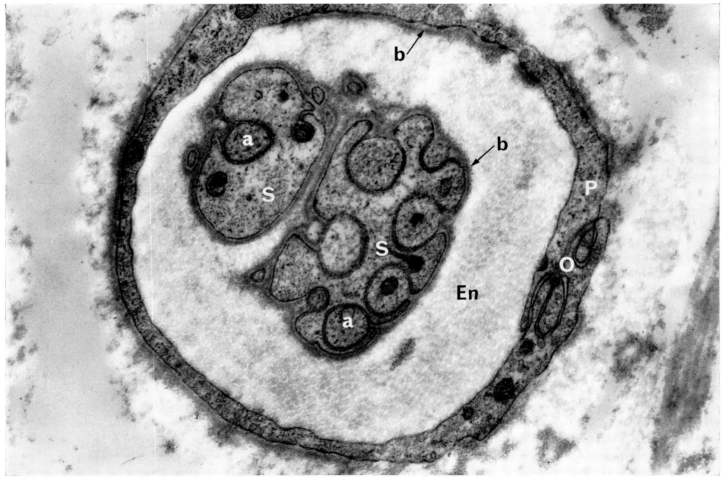

FIGURE 151

In the upper reticular and papillary regions of the dermis myelinated fibres are very rarely seen, and the great majority of the neural elements consist of Schwann cell processes with un-myelinated axons (a). These axons may be either somatic sensory fibres which remain un-myelinated all the way back to their origin from cells of the posterior root ganglia, somatic sensory fibres which if followed centrally prove to be terminal branches of fine myelinated fibres, or, post-ganglionic autonomic fibres. There is no morphological basis for distinguishing these different types of fibres in micrographs of individual sections, and fibre diameter is no absolute guide in this connection. Axons varying in diameter between o·1 and o·6 μm are seen here.

The diameter of endoneurial collagen fibres (En) is significantly less than that of epineurial fibres (Ep) lying outside the perineurium (P). This difference is seen in all peripheral nerves, but its significance is obscure. As far as can be determined, there is no information available concerning possible differences in type or period of banding of fibres in the two situations. One may note here again the incomplete basal lamina (b) on the endoneurial aspect of the plasma membrane of the perineurial cell, and the small pocket (p) of endoneurial collagen which has been enveloped by one of the Schwann cell processes.

Fig. 151. Sheathed nerve from upper reticular region of forearm dermis of man aged 46. Osmium fixation, lead staining. × 28,300.

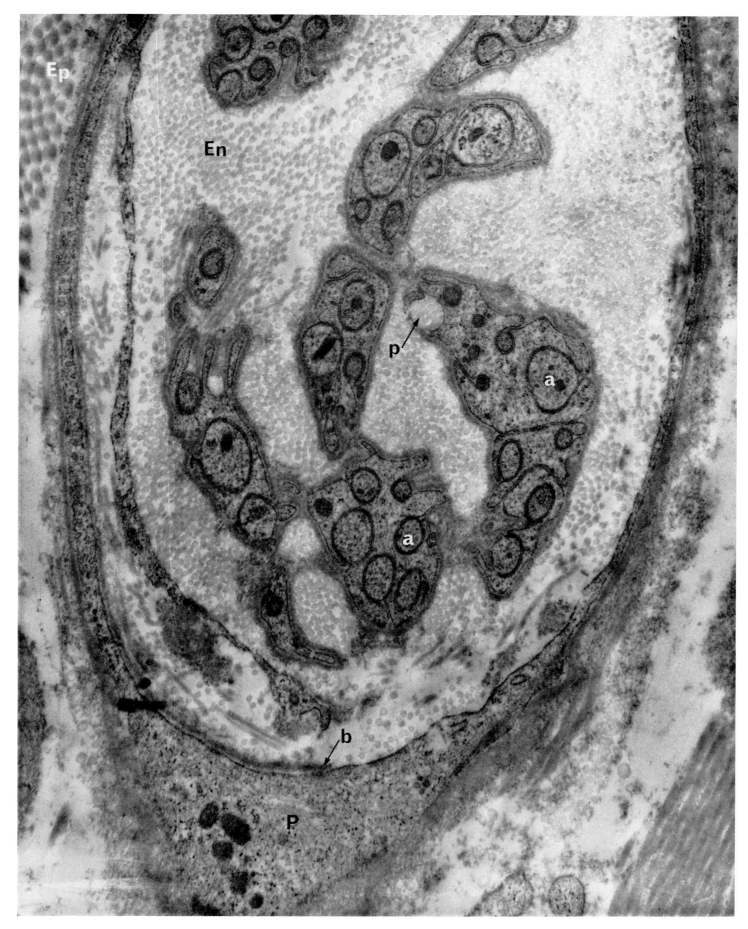

FIGURE 152

In the sub-epidermal region of the papillary dermis the nerves lack a perineurial sheath, and appear as Schwann cell processes (S) with accompanying axons (a) lying free in the general connective tissue at variable distances from the basal lamina (b) of the epidermis, and usually running parallel with it and the surface. Schwann cells sectioned through the nuclear region are frequently seen in this situation (Fig. 128). The cells (F) lying close to the nerve illustrated here are probably fibroblasts fortuitously associated with it. They lack any evidence of the basal lamina which is characteristic of perineurial cells, though it is remotely possible that they belong to this class, since, as previously mentioned the perineurial basal lamina tends to become discontinuous as the surface is approached, and it would not be entirely surprising if the most peripheral cells were completely devoid of it.

   Some light microscopists maintain that there is present in the sub-epidermal region a "neuro-vegetative syncytial terminal network" of autonomic fibres and "intercalated cells", the whole constituting a peripheral "neuro-hormonal" system. Ultrastructural studies have consistently failed to provide any evidence for the existence of this allegedly important system. Certainly, a syncytial arrangement of nerve fibres cannot be demonstrated in this situation (or anywhere else for that matter), and none of the cells commonly encountered could justifiably be labelled "neuro-hormonal".

Fig. 152. Unsheathed Schwann cell processes and unmyelinated axons from papillary region of forearm dermis of woman aged 20. Osmium fixation, lead staining. × 28,800.

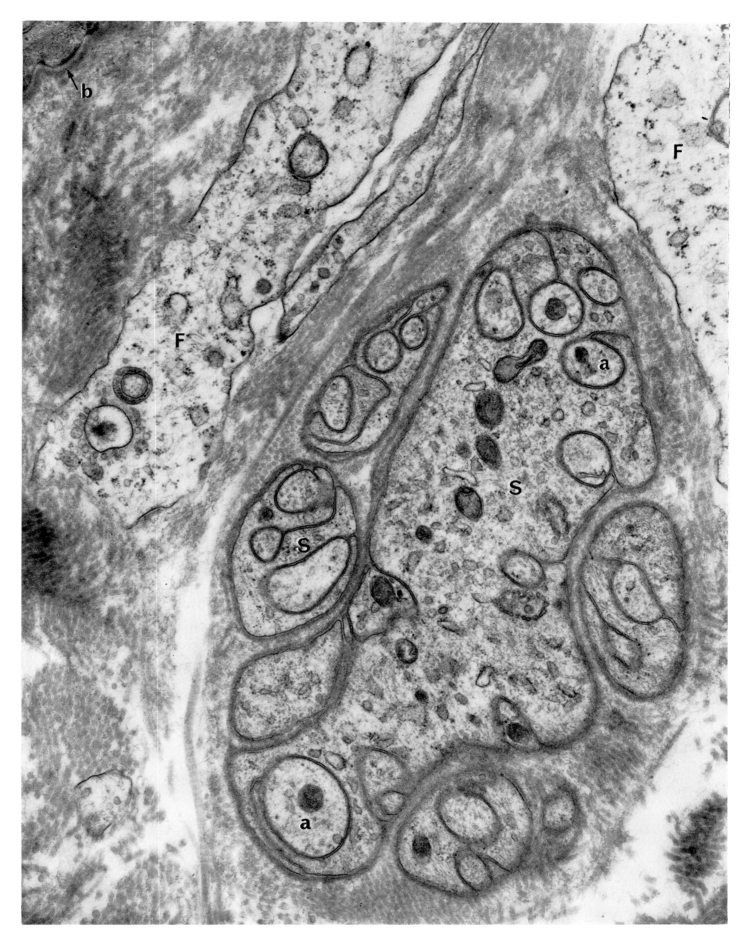

205

FIGURE 153

Cutaneous nerves terminate either as "free nerve endings" just beneath the basal lamina (b) of the epidermis (E), or in association with specialized receptor organs such as the Merkel cell (Fig. 114) or the Meissner corpuscle (Figs. 155–157). The free endings are not naked axons, but small Schwann cell processes (S), surrounded by basal lamina (b), and containing one or more axons (a). The axoplasm of these axonal terminals often contains an accumulation of mitochondria, vesicles, or small granules. Very rarely, as shown in Fig. 154 below, a terminal axon may be seen to establish direct contact with a basal epidermal cell. Light microscopists claim to be able to demonstrate intra-epidermal nerve fibres in interfollicular regions of human hairy skin, but as far as can be determined, no electron micrograph has ever been published which convincingly demonstrates this. Rounded profiles of membrane-limited cytoplasm frequently seen among the epidermal keratinocytes have been regarded as axons, but these could equally well represent dendritic processes of melanocytes or Langerhans cells, and it it impossible to distinguish one from the other on purely morphological grounds. Intra-epidermal nerve fibres are however present in human distal non-hairy skin, but they invariably enter the epidermis in association with Merkel cells.

FIGURE 154

This micrograph illustrates a feature observed only once during five years almost daily examination of the epidermal-dermal junction of interfollicular regions of human hairy skin. An obliquely-sectioned axonal terminal (ax) with ensheathing Schwann cell process (S) is seen approaching a basal epidermal cell (E) and establishing direct contact (between arrows a, e) with it. The apposed membranes are not clearly defined at the point of contact, since they have been sectioned obliquely. The Schwann cell sheath also extends as far as the epidermis and its terminal tips (t) are indicated. There is direct continuity (b) between the Schwann cell basal lamina, and the basal lamina of the epidermis. Within the axoplasm are granular bodies usually associated with nerve terminals, and it is interesting to observe similar granules (g) within a membrane-limited structure lying free in the adjacent dermis. This could also by virtue of this, be a nerve terminal, but if so, it is a true "naked" axon, since it appears to lack either a Schwann sheath or a basal lamina.

Fig. 153. Sub-epidermal nerve terminal from forearm skin of man aged 46. Osmium fixation, lead staining. × 46,200.

Fig. 154. Nerve terminal establishing direct contact with basal epidermal cell from forearm skin of woman aged 20. Osmium fixation, lead staining. × 35,700.

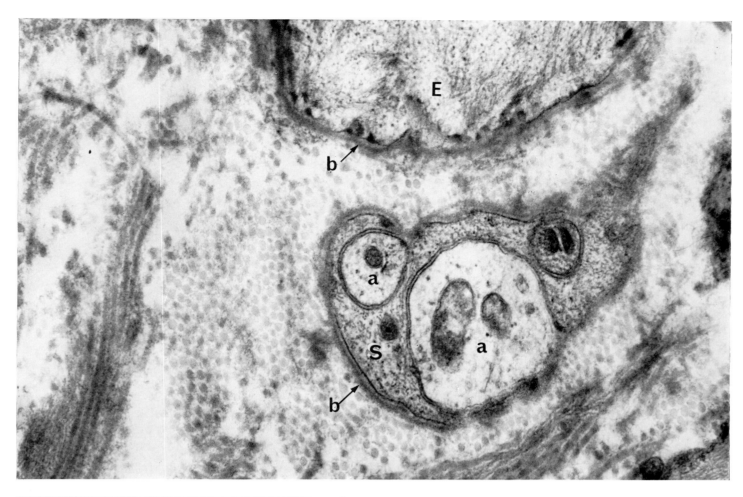

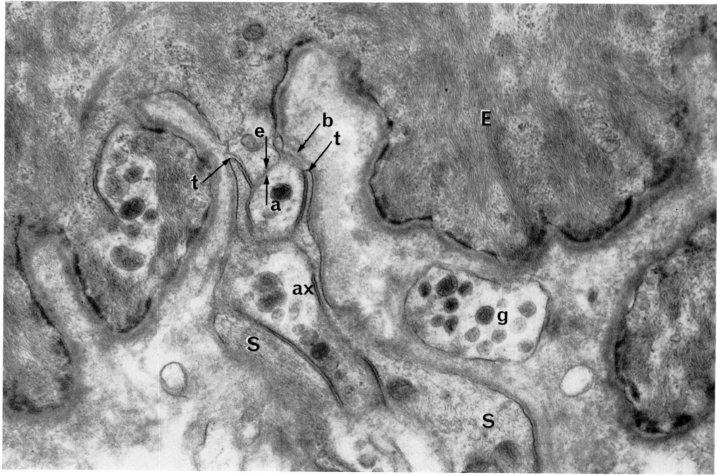

FIGURE 155

The Meissner corpuscle is a specialized touch receptor present in the hairless skin of the extremities. It is located in the dermal papillae close to the epidermis, and consists of expanded nerve terminals (T) surrounded by laminar cells (L) and their flattened processes (pr). The nerves supplying the corpuscle are branches of thick myelinated axons, but as they approach it, the myelin sheath is lost, so that in the immediate neighbourhood of the organ only Schwann cell processes (S) with unmyelinated axons are seen. These axons then enter the corpuscle, lose their Schwann cell sheaths, and become invested by the laminar cells.

FIGURE 156

This shows an axonal terminal (T) shortly after it has entered a Meissner corpuscle. It is ensheathed by a cellular process (pr) but whether this represents the termination of its Schwann cell sheath, or the commencement of the laminar sheath, is impossible to say. The laminar cells (L) have a typical basal lamina (b), which in places is difficult to distinguish from the fine fibrillar material (f) which occupies the intercellular intervals, and which is continuous with a capsule of similar structure surrounding the entire corpuscle. Note faint evidence of coarse periodicity (p) within the fibrillar intercellular material.

Fig. 155. Meissner corpuscle from digital skin of girl aged 8. Osmium fixation, lead staining. ×6,800.

Fig. 156. Peripheral area of Meissner corpuscle. Osmium fixation, lead staining. ×29,600.

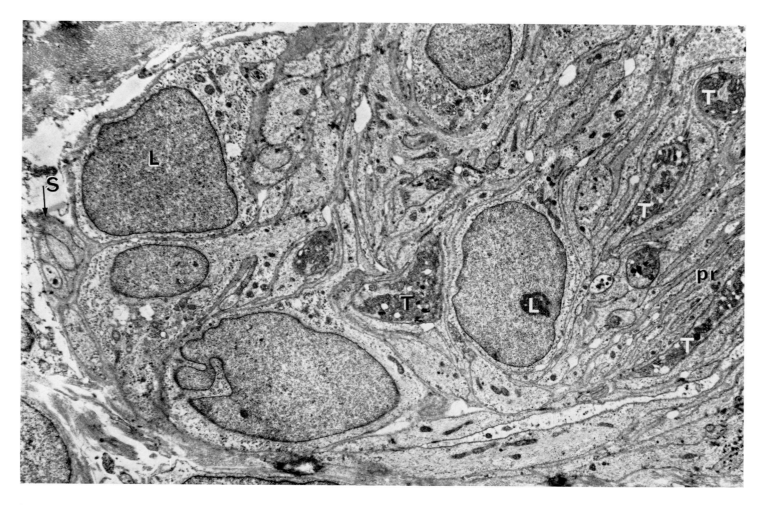

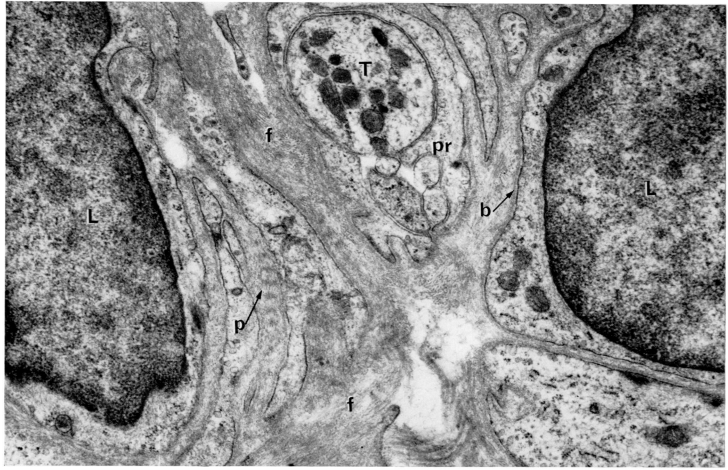

FIGURE 157

In this field from a central region of a Meissner corpuscle, two axonal terminals (T) are seen interposed between flattened processes of the laminar cells (L). There is close apposition between the limiting membranes of the two elements, though no evidence of membrane specialization which might suggest a synaptic relation. Specialized contacts (c) are, however, present along apposed membranes of laminar processes, which exhibit considerable evidence of pinocytotic activity (p). Fibrillar material (f) is present between some laminar processes.

The presence of a basal lamina, and the close relationship which exists between them and the axonal terminals, suggests that the laminar cells are of Schwann cell lineage. Some authors regard them as more akin to perineurial cells, but this seems unlikely since such cells never establish direct contact with neuraxons.

Nerve terminals associated with hair, Merkel cell, and arrector pili muscle are illustrated in Figs. 82, 63 and 64 and 253 respectively.

Fig. 157. Nerve terminals and laminar cells from central area of Meissner corpuscle. Osmium fixation, lead staining. × 44,400.

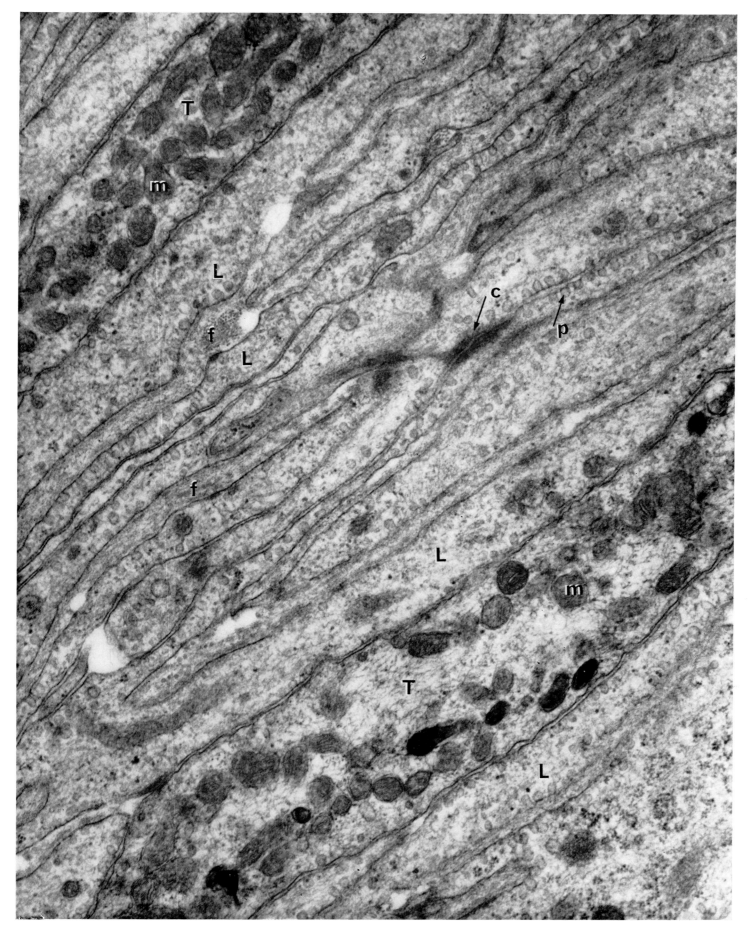

211

REFERENCES

SCHWANN CELL, MYELINATED AND UNMYELINATED FIBRES

Causey, G. "The Cell of Schwann". Edinburgh, E. & S. Livingstone, 1960.

Robertson, J. D. The ultrastructure of adult vertebrate peripheral myelinated nerve fibres in relation to myelinogenesis. *J. Biophys. Biochem. Cytol.*, **1**:271, 1955.

FIBROUS SHEATHS OF PERIPHERAL NERVE

Gamble, H. and Eames, R. An electron microscope study of the connective tissues of human peripheral nerve. *J. Anat.*, **98**:655, 1964.

Thomas, P. K. The deposition of collagen in relation to Schwann cell basement membrane during peripheral nerve regeneration. *J. Cell Biol.*, **23**:375, 1964.

CUTANEOUS INNERVATION IN GENERAL

Bourland, A. "L'innervation cutanée". Paris, Masson et Cie, 1968.

Kenshalo, D. R. (ed.). "The Skin Senses". Springfield, C. C. Thomas, 1968.

9 Elements of the Microvasculature

Endothelium — vascular smooth muscle — pericyte

FIGURE 158

Positive identification of the various segments of the microcirculatory bed in isolated sections is extremely difficult, because all of its elements—arterioles, capillaries and venules—exhibit the same basic structure, and the transition between one segment and another is gradual, being marked in the main, only by differences in calibre and in numbers of cellular layers surrounding the lining endothelium. Recognition of individual segments requires that extensive lengths of the vessels be available for longitudinal sectioning, a situation rarely encountered in human skin where the plane in which they are sectioned is usually haphazard. Accordingly, in the account which follows, attention is concentrated primarily upon structural features of the common cellular components of the microvasculature, and only marginally upon regional variations in their disposition which might allow one to classify individual vessels according to criteria which are at best arbitrary.

In this section of a small vessel, each of the basic cellular components of the microvasculature is represented. Enclosing the lumen—which is completely occupied by a white blood cell (W)—are two endothelial cells (E), one of which is sectioned through the nuclear region. An incomplete layer of smooth muscle cells (M) invests the endothelium, and on a more remote plane is another cell of a type commonly associated with vessels of this calibre, and classed as a pericyte (P).

FIGURE 159

This illustrates a segment of the wall of another vessel at higher magnification. Two endothelial cells (E) bounding the lumen (L) are seen to establish lateral contact at c. The closely apposed parallel plasma membranes are separated by a narrow uniform interval except near the lumen, where a tight junction (j) is present. This particular contact is relatively short and simple, but more extensive ones with complex interlocking of apposed membranes are frequently seen. Paralleling the abluminal plasma membrane of the endothelial cell is a basal lamina (b), which in this micrograph appears to merge with a similar lamina surrounding the smooth muscle cell (M), and this in turn merges with a basal lamina associated with the pericyte (P). More frequently, a distinct interval is observed between these apposed basal laminae, but which appearance more truly represents the actual condition, is difficult to say.

Vessels with more than one smooth muscle layer and ranging in diameter between 100 μm and 50 μm, are classed as arterioles, and those with a single muscle layer and a diameter less than 50 μm are terminal arterioles. A metarteriole is a smaller vessel with an incomplete smooth muscle layer composed of cells spaced at irregular intervals, and a capillary is an endothelial tube devoid of any external coat apart from an incomplete cuff of pericytes. The venous side of the microcirculatory bed has been described as consisting of post-capillary venules, collecting venules, and muscular venules, but these segments are even more difficult to specify than their counterparts on the arterial side.

Fig. 158. Vessel (metarteriole) from forearm dermis of girl aged 20. Osmium fixation, lead and uranyl acetate staining. × 13,000.

Fig. 159. Segment of vessel wall from forearm dermis of man aged 45. Osmium fixation, lead staining. × 39,600.

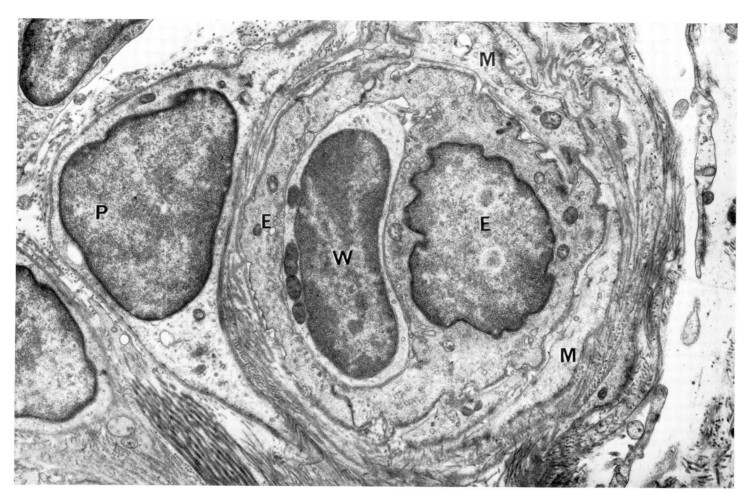

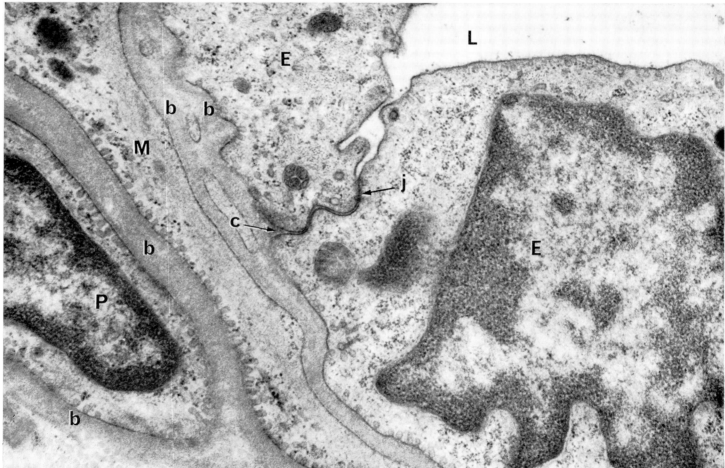

FIGURES 160 and 161

Endothelial cells from different segments of the micro-circulatory bed differ in some respects. In larger calibre vessels such as that shown in Fig. 160 they (E) tend to be flattened, with few processes projecting from the generally smooth luminal plasma membrane, and the lateral contacts (c) are simple with little interlocking of the apposed plasma membranes. With vessels of smaller calibre, as in Fig. 161, the cells (E) appear taller, and the luminal plasma membrane is more folded so that the sectional outline of the lumen (L) may be very irregular; lateral contacts are more complicated (see also Fig. 168).

The upper of these two vessels has up to three layers of smooth muscle cells (M) and therefore could be classed either as an arteriole or a muscular venule. Arterioles of this calibre and with more than one layer of smooth muscle cells usually have an internal elastic lamina associated with the abluminal plasma membranes of the endothelial cells (see Fig. 164). With this vessel, only a basal lamina (b) is present in this situation, so it is probably a venule. The smaller vessel in Fig. 161 has only isolated processes of smooth muscle cells (M) associated with the endothelium (E), and can be classed as a metarteriole. Were there no muscle present, it could be regarded as a capillary. Attention may be drawn to the replication of the basal lamina (b) in situations where the endothelial cells are not covered by muscle. This feature might be, and in fact has been, considered an abnormality, but it is commonly seen in biopsy specimens of clinically normal skin obtained from individuals of all ages. In many instances it probably does not represent a true replication of the basal lamina of the endothelial cell, but rather a prolongation of basal laminar material associated with smooth muscle cells beyond the (distal) level at which these latter peter out.

Fig. 160. Vessel (probable venule) from forearm dermis of woman aged 40. Osmium fixation, lead staining. × 13,600.

Fig. 161. Vessel (metarteriole) from forearm dermis of girl aged 20. Osmium fixation, lead staining. × 12,050.

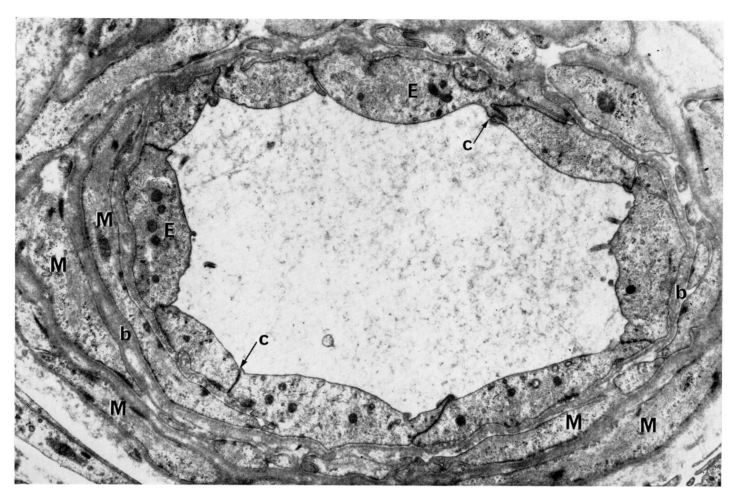

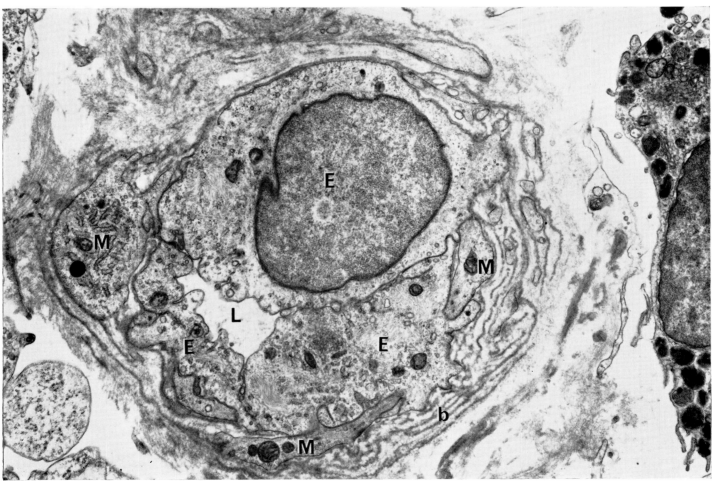

FIGURES 162 and 163

General cytoplasmic features of endothelial cells are illustrated by these two micrographs. The cells contain the common organelles, i.e. mitochondria (m), Golgi apparatus (go), rough endoplasmic reticulum etc., as well as lysosomes (ly) and the dense rod-shaped structures (r) already described as occurring in fetal endothelial cells (Fig. 85). Pinocytotic vesicles (p) are numerous, particularly in the region deep to the plasma membrane, and cytofilaments (f) tend to be concentrated in the juxta-nuclear region. Pedunculated processes (pr) of varying size and shape stem from the luminal plasma membrane.

Blood-tissue exchange must take place across the endothelial lining of the vessels, and considerable interest, therefore, has centred around possible transport mechanisms involving fluid and insoluble particles of different sizes. In some situations, such as the kidney, the endothelial cells have pores which permit passage of quite large molecules, but, to date, endothelial pores have not been demonstrated in vessels of human skin. There are, however, rumours that they have been observed by some workers, whose results will be awaited with interest. There is abundant evidence available that pinocytotic vesicles are involved in transport of materials across the endothelial cell, but whether this mechanism, together with direct diffusion of water and gases, is sufficient to account for passage of the large volumes often involved is uncertain. Passage of materials between the cells would appear to be prevented by the tight junctions, but it has been suggested that these may not be as impermeable as commonly thought.

Fig. 162. Endothelium of metarteriole from axillary dermis of man aged 21. Osmium fixation, lead staining. ×37,800. *Inset:* cytoplasmic filaments. ×74,100.

Fig. 163. Endothelium of metarteriole from axillary dermis of man aged 21. Osmium fixation, lead staining. ×31,000.

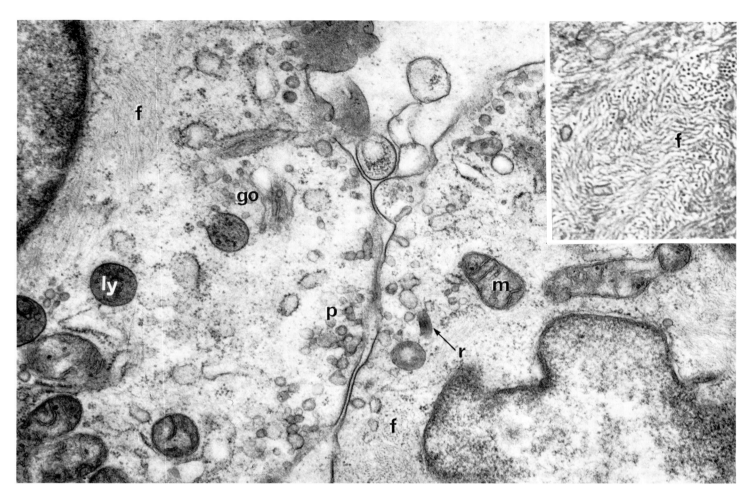

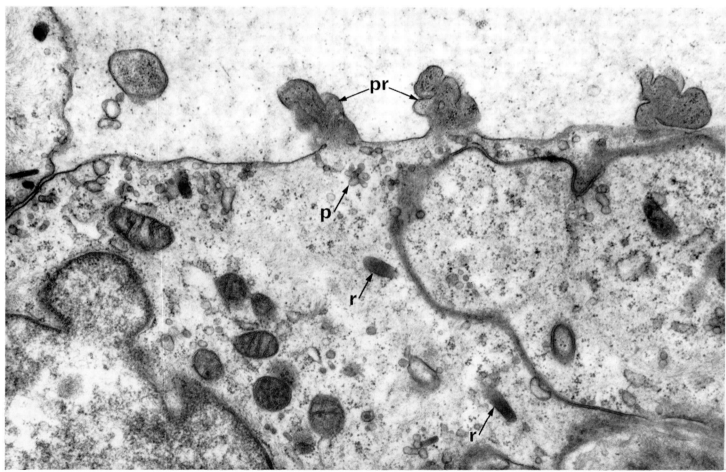

FIGURE 164

As indicated already, vessels can be classified according to the number of layers of smooth muscle cells (M) lying outside the endothelium (E). The cells are arranged generally in a circular or spiral fashion within the vessel wall, and since they overlap to some extent, it may be difficult at times, particularly with oblique longitudinal sections such as the one illustrated here, to decide how many layers are actually present. There are probably three layers involved here, and this, together with the presence of an internal elastic lamina (L) and the smooth character of the luminal plasma membrane of the endothelial cell, allows one to classify this vessel as an arteriole. The smooth muscle cells are surrounded by basal laminae (b) and separated in places by collagen fibres (c), but they also make direct membraneous contacts (m).

FIGURE 165

The basal laminae (b), intervening collagen fibres (c), and direct membraneous contacts (m), are more clearly seen in this micrograph of a tangential section of smooth muscle cells. The cytoplasm contains fine myofilaments (f) of low electron density, and more dense zones (d), frequently associated with the plasma membrane, along which there may be evidence of pinocytotic activity (p). Mitochondria, ribosomes, and a few profiles of rough endoplasmic reticulum can also be seen in the cytoplasm.

These micrographs of vascular smooth muscle may be compared with those of the arrector pili muscle (Figs. 251 and 252), and of the myoepithelial cells of the sweat glands (Figs. 187 and 188).

Fig. 164. Vascular smooth muscle and endothelium of arteriole from axillary dermis of man aged 21. Osmium fixation, lead and uranyl acetate staining. × 12,400.

Fig. 165. Vascular smooth muscle of arteriole from axillary dermis of man aged 21. Osmium fixation, lead and uranyl acetate staining. × 25,200.

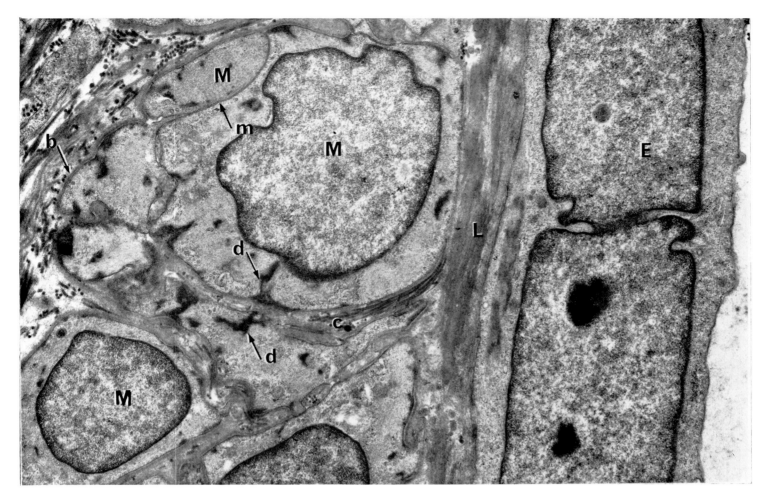

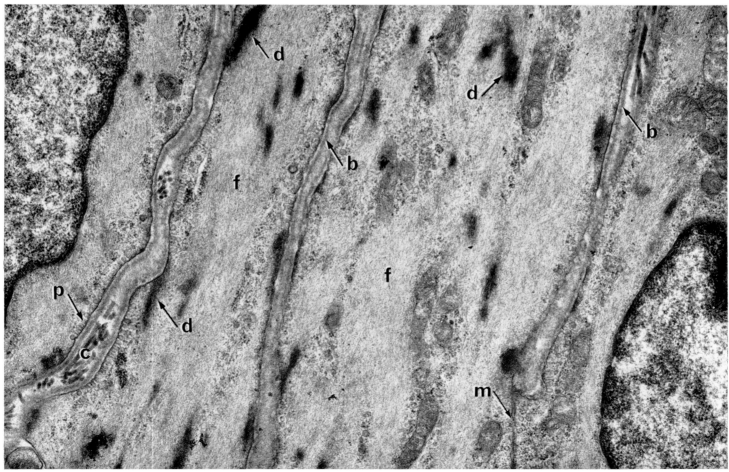

FIGURES 166 and 167

Pericytes (P) are periendothelial or perimuscular cells closely associated with capillaries, arterioles and venules, and present with sufficient constancy to be regarded as permanent and essential elements of the vascular wall. They are thought to be developed from perivascular mesenchymal cells, as are fibroblasts, but they can usually be distinguished from the latter by virtue of their close proximity to the vessel wall (E) which they partially envelop, and by the presence of a basal lamina (b). This last feature, however, renders them liable to be confused with smooth muscle cells, and indeed, with many sections of metarterioles and capillaries where only an incomplete layer of periendothelial cells is present, it may be impossible to say if these are muscle cells or pericytes. The general cytoplasm of the pericyte exhibits no particular distinguishing features. The common organelles are present, but the rough endoplasmic reticulum is poorly developed; fine filaments are widely scattered throughout the cytoplasm. Pinocytotic vesicles (p) are frequently associated with the plasma membrane, as also are very small densities (d) reminiscent of hemi-desmosomes. Similar densities are sometimes present along the plasma membrane of the terminal smooth muscle cell, and this adds further to the difficulty of distinguishing between the two.

A variety of functions have been attributed to the pericyte, i.e. mechanical support of the vessel wall, collagen synthesis, and detection of connective-tissue released substances which may affect the endothelium. In this last connection it has been suggested that the degree of sensitivity of particular segments of the microcirculatory bed may be dependent upon the number of associated pericytes. Pericytes are also thought to have the capacity to serve as precursors to other cells, particularly smooth muscle cells. If this be so, it is not surprising that it should be difficult to distinguish between the two at times.

Fig. 166. Pericyte and endothelium of metarteriole from forearm dermis of girl aged 20. Osmium fixation, lead and uranyl acetate staining. × 19,500.

Fig. 167. Cytoplasm of pericyte associated with metarteriole from forearm dermis of girl aged 20. Osmium fixation, lead and uranyl acetate staining. × 41,600.

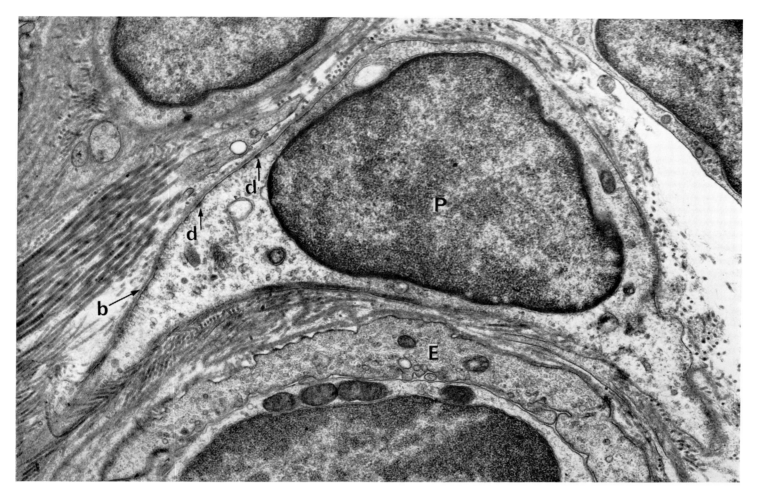

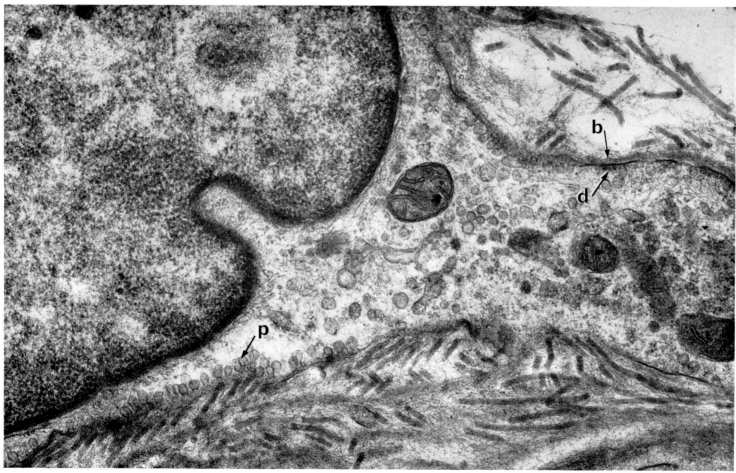

FIGURE 168

This vessel can be classed as a metarteriole because the endothelium (E) is surrounded by an incomplete layer of smooth muscle cells (M), containing myofilaments (f) and dense bodies (d). Basal laminar material (b) usually intervenes between the two, but in places the plasma membranes establish direct contact (c). These myoendothelial contacts are a constant feature of vessels of this calibre, and they also occur in small collecting venules. They may have a purely mechanical function of stabilizing the endothelium, but they could also provide a pathway for exchange of metabolites. Rhodin has advanced the interesting suggestion that they may serve as conduction devices for humoral transmitter substances which diffuse from the blood-stream across the endothelial cells to the smooth muscle cells. If this be so, control of the smooth muscle of these microvessels could be established not only through transmitters acting at myoneural junctions, but also through transmitters circulating in the blood-stream and reaching the muscle via myoendothelial contacts. Another interesting feature is shown in this micrograph, i.e. the process (pr) of the endothelial cell which is seen penetrating layers of basal laminae (b) to come into direct contact with the surrounding collagenous milieu. It will be recalled that similar, but longer processes characterize the early fetal endothelial cell (Fig. 83).

The cell labelled P may be classed as a pericyte, mainly because it lies in a plane beyond that of the smooth muscle cells. Since the muscle coat of the vessel is incomplete, it is unlikely to consist of two layers of cells, therefore the outer one is probably a pericyte. This may often be the sole basis for identification of pericytes in individual micrographs.

Fig. 168. Metarteriole from forearm dermis of girl aged 20. Osmium fixation, lead staining. × 22,800.

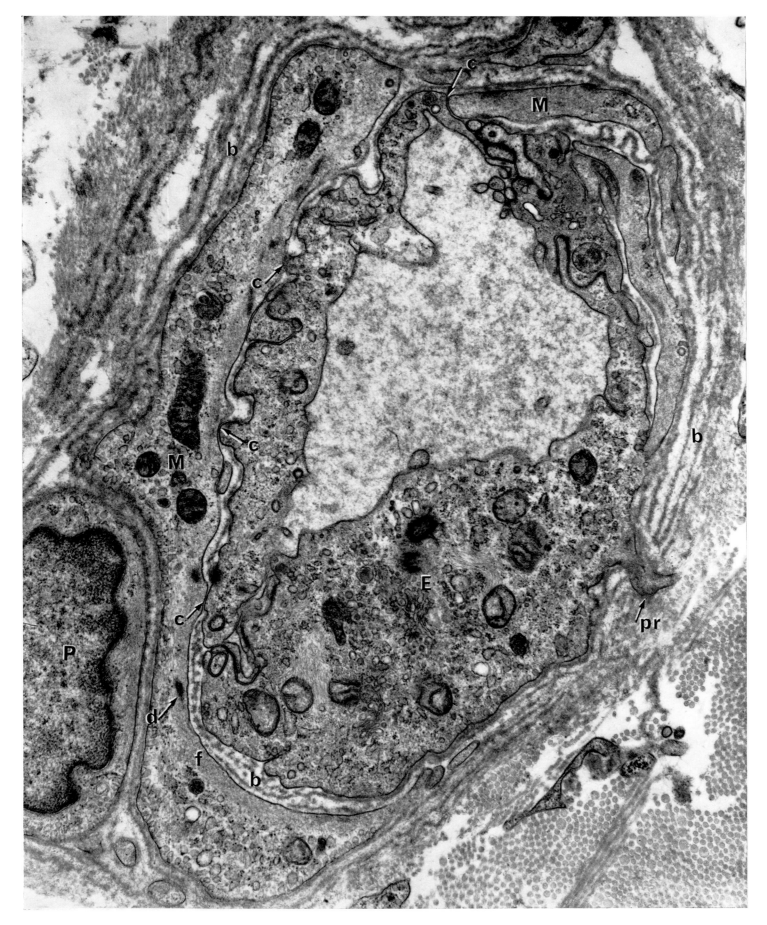

REFERENCES

Florey, Lord. The endothelial cell. *Brit. med. J.*, **2**:487, 1966.

Majno, G. Ultrastructure of the vascular membrane. In: "Handbook of Physiology", Section 2, Vol. 3, p. 2293. Washington, D.C. American Physiological Society, 1965.

Rhodin, J. A. G. The ultrastructure of mammalian arterioles and precapillary sphincters. *J. Ultrastruct. Res.*, **18**:181, 1967.

Rhodin, J. A. G. Ultrastructure of mammalian venous capillaries, venules, and small collecting veins. *J. Ultrastruct. Res.*, **25**:452, 1968.

White, J. G. and Clausen, C. C. Blood cells and blood vessels. In: "Ultrastructure of Normal and Abnormal Skin", ed. A. S. Zelickson. London, Henry Kimpton, 1967.

10 The Eccrine Sweat Gland

Germinative bud — intraepidermal sweat duct — intradermal sweat duct — secretory coil: mucous cells: serous cells: myo-epithelial cells.

FIGURE 169

Anlagen of sweat glands appear first in the palm and sole of the foot at the beginning of the fourth month, and progressively later in other regions. They commence as buds extending into the dermis from the basal layer (B) of the epidermis, and from an early stage consist of peripheral (P) and central (C) cells. The latter may contain large deposits of glycogen, and are continuous with the cells of the stratum intermedium (I). Sweat-buds contain fewer cells than hair-germs of comparable size (cf. Fig. 189), and are, on the whole, narrower.

As development proceeds the germinative bud migrates deeper into the dermis, and the bulbous expanded end ultimately develops into the secretory coil. This is connected to the basal layer of the epidermis by a solid cord of cells (Fig. 175), which, on acquiring a lumen, becomes the intradermal portion of the sweat duct. The intraepidermal portion of the duct is fore-shadowed by a concentric arrangement of cells in the stratum intermedium (Fig. 170), and its lumen is developed in association with the innermost cells of this complex.

Fig. 169. Germinative bud of sweat gland from palm skin of 140 mm C.R. (16 weeks) human fetus. Osmium fixation, uranyl acetate and lead staining. × 5,000 approx.

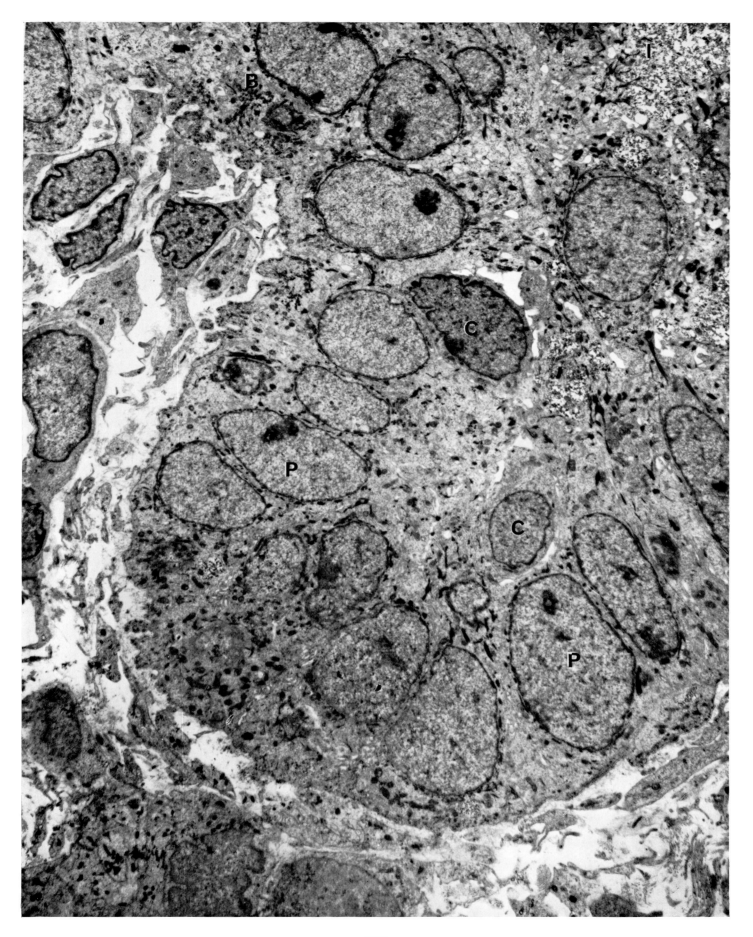

229

FIGURE 170

The intraepidermal sweat duct consists of a column of cells extending upwards in a coiled fashion through the intermediate layers of the epidermis. The column is composed of concentrically arranged outer (O) and inner (I) cells, which at first do not differ significantly from the surrounding cells. Soon, however, lysosomal structures (ly) appear in the cytoplasm of the inner cells, and according to Hashimoto, these give rise through autolysis, to vacuoles, which by fusion form the lumen. The lumen, therefore, is initiated intracellularly.

FIGURE 171

This tangential section of developing intraepidermal sweat duct shows an early stage in the formation of the lumen (L) through fusion of intracytoplasmic vacuoles (v). Note the presence already of luminal microvilli (m) which are a characteristic feature of the fully developed duct.

   These micrographs may be compared with the micrograph of the intraepidermal portion of the hair-tract (Fig. 205)

Fig. 170. Intraepidermal sweat duct from forearm skin of 215 mm C.R. (24 weeks) human fetus. Osmium fixation, lead staining. × 5,950.

Fig. 171. Lumen formation in intraepidermal sweat duct from forearm skin of 215 mm C.R. (24 weeks) human fetus. Osmium fixation, lead staining. × 7,600.

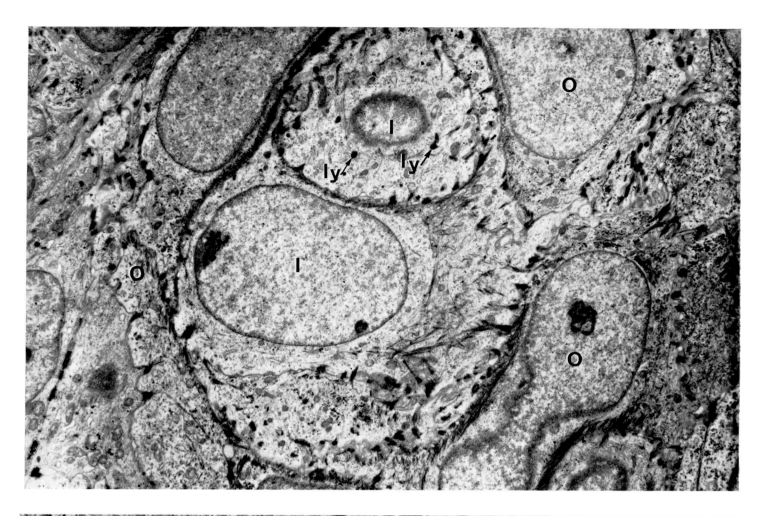

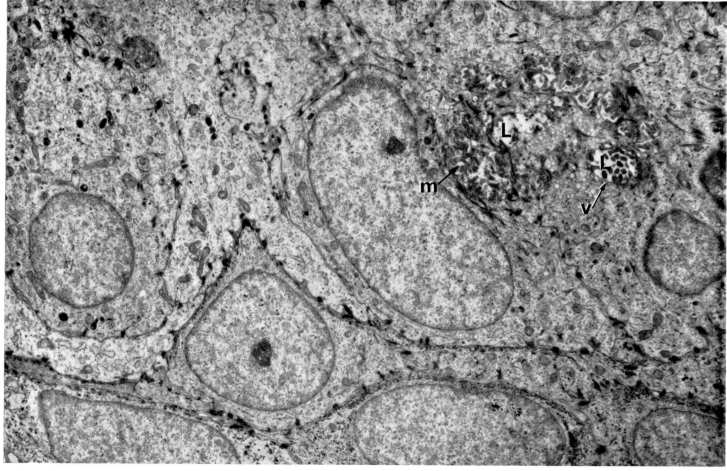

FIGURE 172

This micrograph illustrates the basal portion of the duct of a new-born infant. The dermis (D) lies just within the lower right-hand corner of the field. The lumen (L), full of exudate, is bounded by three inner cells (I), beyond which are encircling layers of outer cells (O). The cytoplasm of the inner cells in the neighbourhood of the lumen has a high concentration of tonofilaments and tonofibrils (f), and this region is known as the cuticular border. Some small vesicles are present among the filaments in this situation, but the majority of the organelles, including some lysosomes (ly), are located more peripherally. The outer cells do not differ significantly from surrounding general epidermal cells at this level.

Fig. 172. Intraepidermal sweat duct from forearm skin of infant aged 3 weeks. Osmium fixation, lead staining. × 7,400.

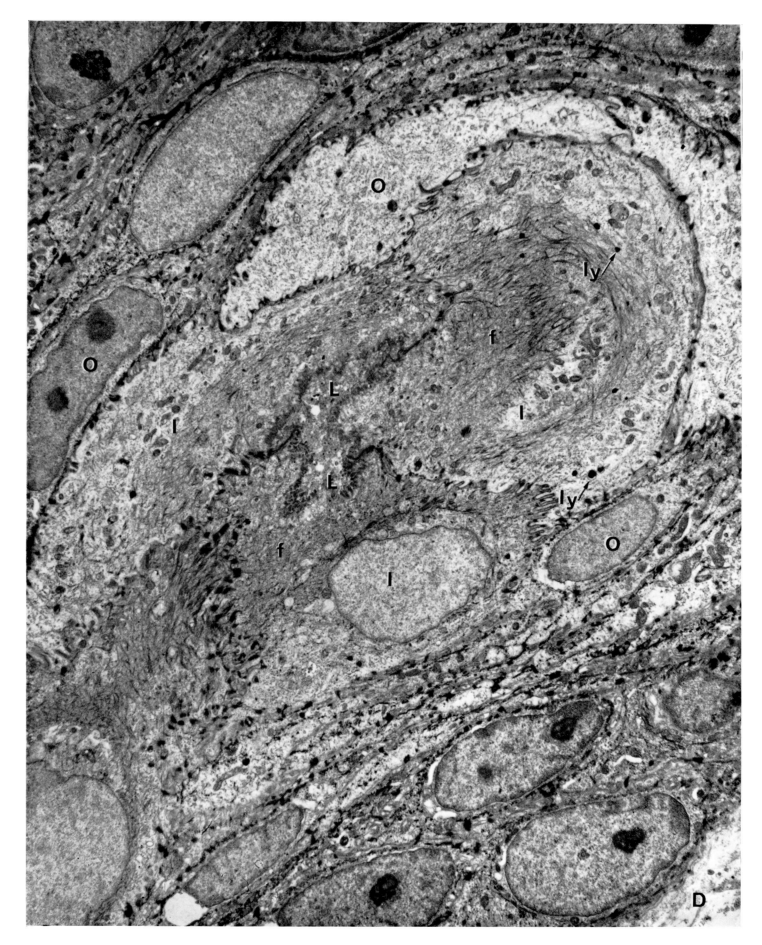

FIGURE 173

This illustrates some characteristic features of the inner cells lining the lumen at a mid-spinous level. The cytoplasm close to the luminal border is packed with clear vesicles (v), and a high concentration of similar vesicles is present within the lumen (L). It is generally held that the epidermal sweat duct has no function in relation to the excretion or reabsorption of sweat, but appearances such as those seen here could suggest the contrary. A few keratohyalin granules (k) are present, as well as bundles of tonofilaments, but a distinct filamentous cuticular border is not evident.

Closely spaced desmosomes (d) are present along the apposed lateral plasma membranes of the cells, and the luminal plasma membrane exhibits short, stumpy, microvilli (m). Finger-like processes (pr) formed by slender cytoplasmic extensions of apposed cells project into the lumen in places.

Fig. 173. Luminal cell and lumen of intraepidermal sweat duct from forearm skin of man aged 70. Osmium fixation, lead staining. × 37,000.

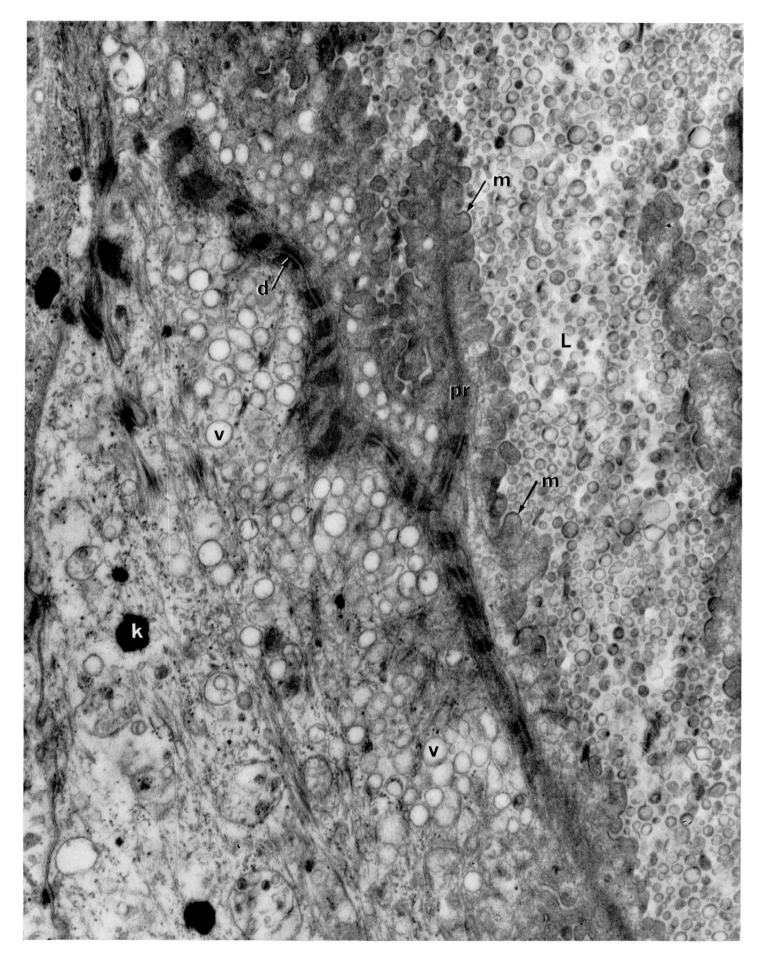

235

FIGURE 174

The lumen (L) is sectioned almost transversely in this micrograph and is seen once again to contain vesicles of similar type to those present (v) just within the luminal plasma membrane of the inner cell. The lines of desmosomes connecting the lateral plasma membranes of the cells lead to finger-like processes (pr) projecting into the lumen. Lysosomes (ly) and multivesicular bodies of various types, characteristically concentrated in the juxta-nuclear region, are often seen within the inner cells of the duct at the level of the upper stratum spinosum. At this level, the outer cells contain numerous keratohyalin granules (k) as well as membrane-coating granules (g) and in these respects closely resemble the surrounding general epidermal cells. They ultimately undergo a similar form of keratinization so that at the level of the stratum corneum, the two are indistinguishable. The inner cells with fewer keratohyalin granules, and no membrane-coating granules undergo an incomplete type of keratinization similar to that observed at a certain stage in fetal skin (Fig. 57), and are largely shed into the lumen at the level of the stratum corneum.

Some authors have described the intraepidermal sweat duct as a morphologic and biologic entity distinct from the general epidermis which it traverses. Certainly its cells differ in certain respects from the surrounding keratinocytes, and are known to react differently to disease processes. Whether or not this justifies the concept of an "epidermal sweat duct unit" is debatable. An interesting comparison which might be made in this general connection is one between the luminal cell with its vesicles and microvilli, and the periderm cell during its period of functional activity (see Section 2).

Fig. 174. Intraepidermal sweat duct in spinous layer of forearm epidermis of man aged 70. Osmium fixation, lead staining. × 15,000.

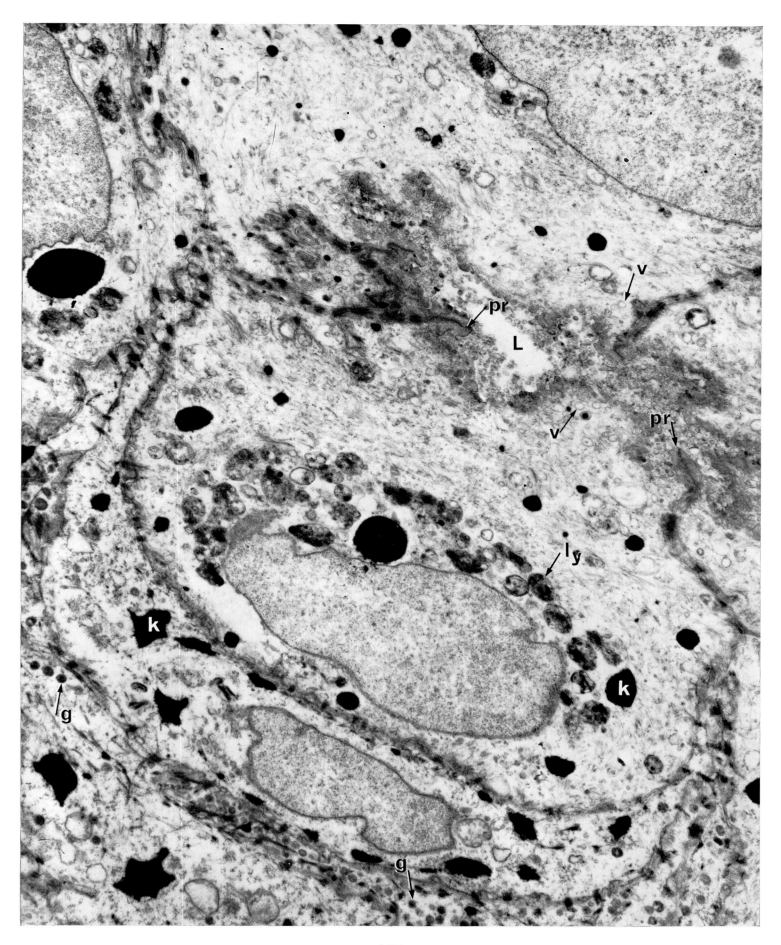

237

FIGURE 175

Before the lumen is developed, the intradermal sweat duct is a solid cord of cells extending deep into the dermis. On transverse section it appears as a knot of cells of obvious epidermal lineage lying free in the dermis. As such, it might be confused with a hair follicle at an early stage of development, and indeed structurally, the cells are very similar. However, the sweat duct is usually composed of fewer cells, and with experience it is not difficult to make the distinction.

FIGURE 176

This shows a stage in the formation of the lumen (L) of the intradermal sweat duct. It is by no means easy to interpret. It would appear that running across the centre of the field is the line of contact of two central ductal cells as indicated by desmosomes (d), and lengths of parallel plasma membrane (p). Between these latter, is an area occupied by interlocking folded membranes (f). Presumably this arrangement has arisen through localized growth of previously relatively straight lengths of apposed membranes and such, apparently, is the exuberance of membrane growth that in places it is invaginated into the cells to form clefts (c). Separation of the interlocked membranes, and opening out of the clefts could lead to the establishment of a lumen (L) and this apparently is what occurs at a later stage of development. The lumen of the intradermal duct therefore arises intercellularly, and not intracellularly as in the case of the intraepidermal duct.

Fig. 175. Intradermal sweat duct cord from forearm skin of 215 mm C.R. (24 weeks) human fetus. Osmium fixation, lead staining. × 4,800.

Fig. 176. Lumen formation in intradermal sweat duct from forearm skin of 215 mm C.R. (24 weeks) human fetus. Osmium fixation, lead staining. × 43,200.

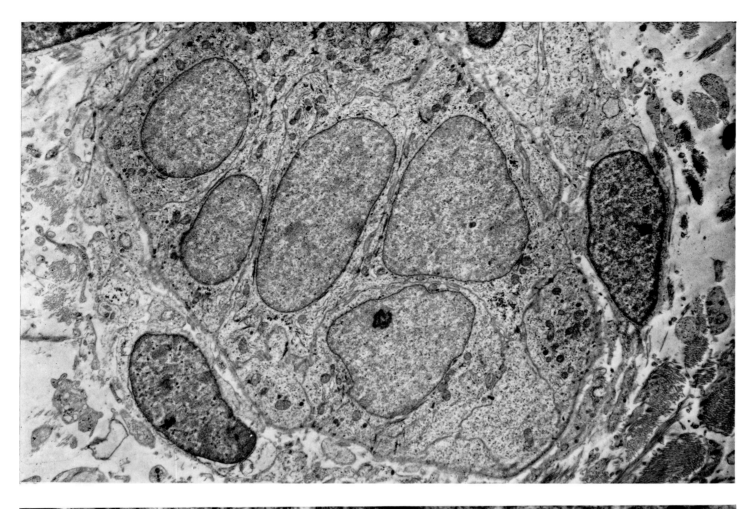

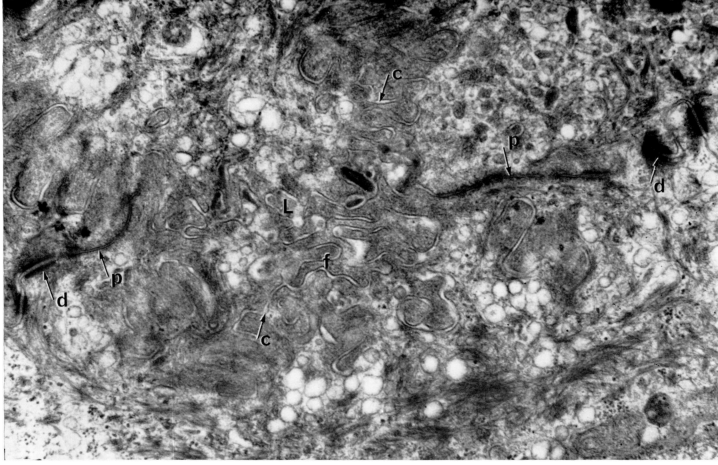

FIGURE 177

The intradermal sweat duct is formed of two layers of cells, an outer basal layer (B), and an inner layer of luminal cells (L) bounding the lumen (Lu). On section, the lumen presents an irregular outline, and is lined by microvilli. Two distinct zones can be discerned in the cytoplasm of the luminal cells. The supra-nuclear zone is largely filamentous (f), and at low powers of magnification the boundaries between the cells are clearly defined in this situation, due to close-packing of desmosomes. This circumluminal filamentous zone corresponds to the "cuticular border" of light microscopy. The majority of the organelles occupy the para- and infra-nuclear cytoplasm, which, due to a relative paucity of filaments, appears more translucent. The basal cells (B) exhibit no particular distinctive features at this magnification, apart from a somewhat indented nucleus.

FIGURE 178

The lateral plasma membranes (p) of the luminal cells (L) interlock to present a wavy outline, and as the lumen is approached, desmosomes become more numerous; tight junctions are present at the interface just short of the lumen, which is lined by short, stumpy microvilli (m). The filamentous zone (f) contains few organelles, but clear vesicles similar to those present in the luminal cells of the intraepidermal duct (Fig. 173) are often seen here. Conflicting views have been advanced concerning the functional significance of the filamentous zone. It is most prominent in the upper part of the duct, and but poorly developed in the region of the coiled duct close to the secretory coil of the gland. Its main function is probably supportive in maintaining the shape and patency of the lumen.

The basal cells (B) rest upon a basal lamina (b) and their apposed plasma membranes, with few associated desmosomes, do not interlock to any great extent. At the lower end of the duct the membranes are much more folded to form villous processes which project into spaces or channels between the cells. This lower part of the duct is concerned with reabsorption of sodium from the fluid produced by the secretory coil, and it is thought that the basal cells are the active elements involved in this process. Glycogen (gl) may be a prominent feature of the cytoplasm of the basal cells.

Fig. 177. Intradermal sweat duct from palmar skin of girl aged 7. Glutaraldehyde-osmium fixation, lead staining. × 4,560.

Fig. 178. Intradermal sweat duct from forearm skin of woman aged 40. Osmium fixation, lead staining. × 10,650.

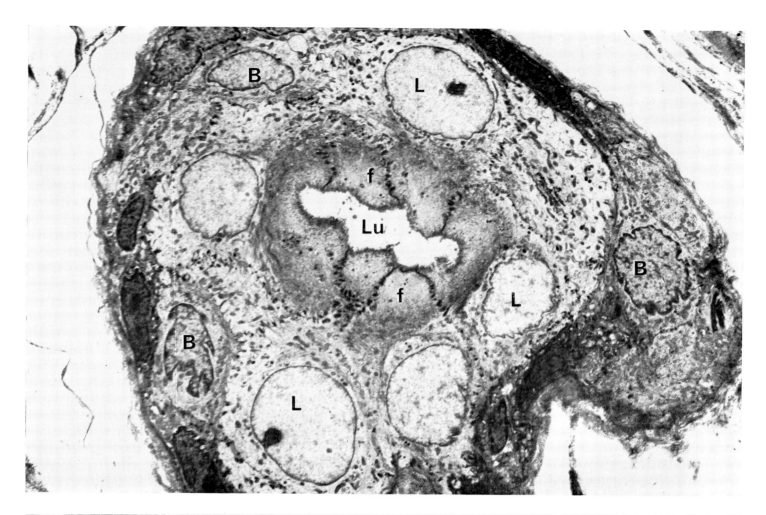

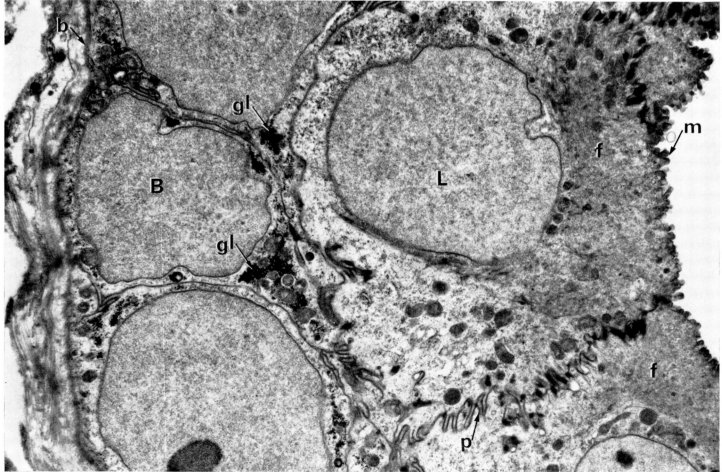

FIGURES 179 and 180

The secretory coil of the sweat gland lies deep in the dermis and contains three different types of cells, mucous cells (M), serous cells (S) and myo-epithelial cells (My). The mucous cells are the "dark cells" of light microscopy, and the serous ones the "light cells", but it may be confusing to carry these terms over to electron microscopy because the appearance of the cells varies with different fixatives. Thus, when glutaraldehyde is used, the mucous cells appear "dark", and the serous cells "light", whereas with osmium tetroxide fixation, as here, the picture is reversed. Whatever the fixative, the myo-epithelial cells (My, Fig. 180) are clearly distinguishable from the other two types because they contain typical myo-filaments, and are located basally, being separated from the surrounding collagen (C) by a basal lamina (l).

Owing to the coiled nature of the secretory portion of the gland, the lumen (Lu) may appear in several situations on a section. It is lined by microvilli, and bordered by both mucous and serous cells. Intercellular canaliculi (IC) which communicate with the lumen are present between the serous cells. Even at this low magnification (Fig. 179), clear-cut differences between serous and mucous cells are apparent. The mucous cells contain numerous vacuoles, and the mitochondria stand out clearly within the relatively translucent general cytoplasm. The cytoplasm of the serous cells appears much more dense, and the organelles are less evident. Scattered intensely staining deposits of glycogen are also seen within the serous cells.

Fig. 179. Secretory coil of sweat gland from palmar skin of girl aged 7. Osmium fixation, lead staining. × 5,100.

Fig. 180. Myo-epithelial cell of secretory coil of sweat gland from palmar skin of girl aged 7. Osmium fixation, lead staining. × 26,000.

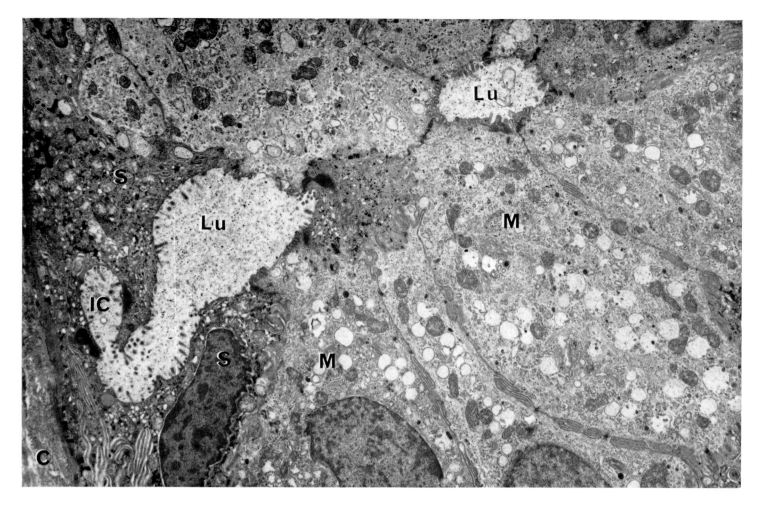

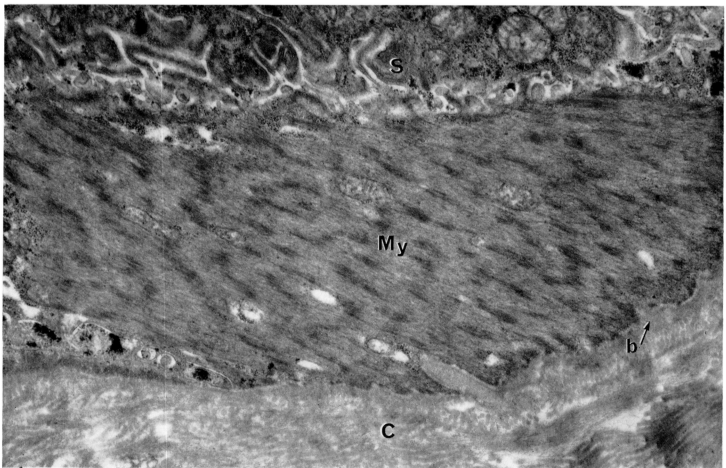

FIGURE 181

In this micrograph, the lumen (Lu) is seen to be bordered by mucous (M) and serous (S) cells, both of which exhibit microvilli (m) along the luminal plasma membrane. The lateral plasma membranes are joined by desmosomes (d), and tight junctions (j) are present just short of the lumen. The intercellular space, therefore, is closed off from the lumen.

FIGURE 182

Portions of two serous cells (S) bordering an intercellular canaliculus (IC), and of three mucous cells (M) are seen in this field. The plasma membranes of apposed mucous cells are studded with short desmosomes (d), and exhibit little folding, though closely interlocked villous folds do occur along their length (see Fig. 183). By contrast, long villous folds (f) are characteristic of the plasma membrane of the serous cell, and this feature is particularly evident in Figs. 185 and 186. Within the cytoplasm of the mucous cells are numerous free ribosomes, mito-chondria, a few profiles of rough endoplasmic reticulum, and fine filaments. This relatively simple appearance is not characteristic of all regions of the cell nor of all stages of the secretory cycle which it undergoes, and at times the cytoplasm is loaded with vacuoles and secretory granules. The cytoplasm of the serous cells contains clusters of glycogen granules and small vesicles (v) in the region bordering upon the intercellular canaliculus.

Fig. 181. Luminal region of secretory coil of sweat gland from palmar region of girl aged 7. Osmium fixation, lead staining. × 17,500.

Fig. 182. Mucous and serous cells of secretory coil of sweat gland from palmar region of girl aged 7. Osmium fixation, lead staining. × 41,800.

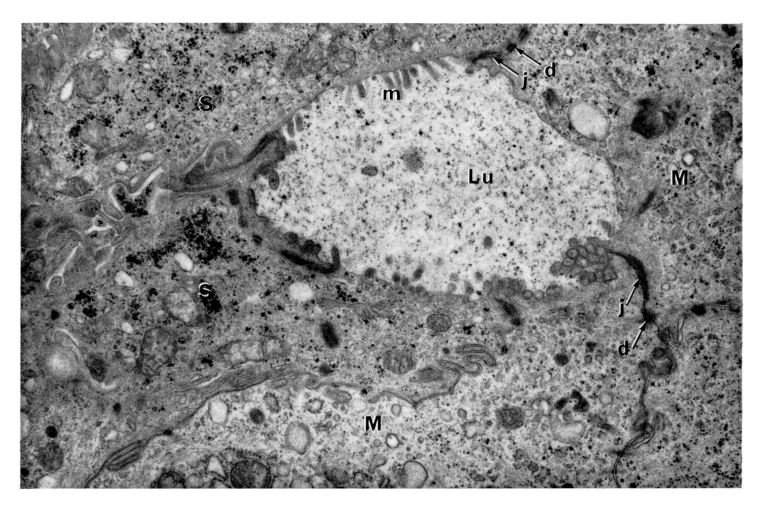

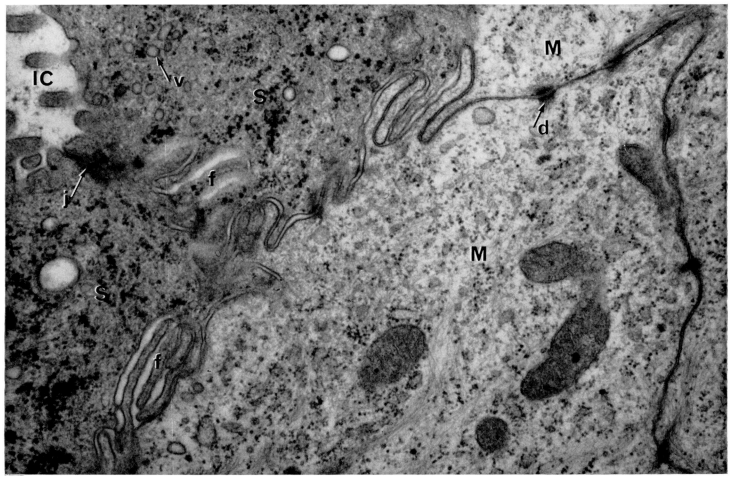

FIGURE 183

The closely-interlocked villous folds (f) of the plasma membranes of apposed mucous cells are well seen here. Numerous membrane-limited vacuoles (v) are present in the cytoplasm of all three cells illustrated. With osmium fixation, little more than a fine reticulum can be seen within these vacuoles, but in material fixed with glutaraldehyde, the contents appear densely flocculent. Presumably, the vacuoles contain the mucus secreted by the cells. Their concentration, as already mentioned, varies with a secretory cycle, and they tend to be located predominantly in the supra-nuclear region of the cytoplasm, i.e. between the nucleus and the lumen. Other cytoplasmic features of the mucous cells are a well-developed Golgi apparatus, large, densely-staining mitochondria (m), a high concentration of free ribosomes, and dense granules (g) of variable size. Lipid droplets are occasionally seen.

FIGURE 184

The Golgi apparatus (go) of the mucous cell is well developed, and consists of typical membranes and vesicles. The small dense granules (g) frequently located in its immediate neighbourhood are probably derived from it, and may represent formative stages in the development of the larger vacuoles, though details of this process remain to be worked out. Exactly how the contents of the vacuoles are liberated into the lumen is likewise not clear. It has been assumed that they become attached to the luminal plasma membrane and then rupture, but this appearance is rarely if ever, seen. However the mucin may be liberated, its probable function is to provide a protective coating for the cells lining the coil and duct, and possibly, for the skin surface as well. It is remotely possible that these cells contribute some constituents other than mucin to the sweat.

Fig. 183. Mucous cells of secretory coil of sweat gland from palmar skin of girl aged 7. Osmium fixation, lead staining. × 20,000.

Fig. 184. Cytoplasm of mucous cells of secretory coil of sweat gland from palmar region of girl aged 7. Osmium fixation, lead staining. × 29,700.

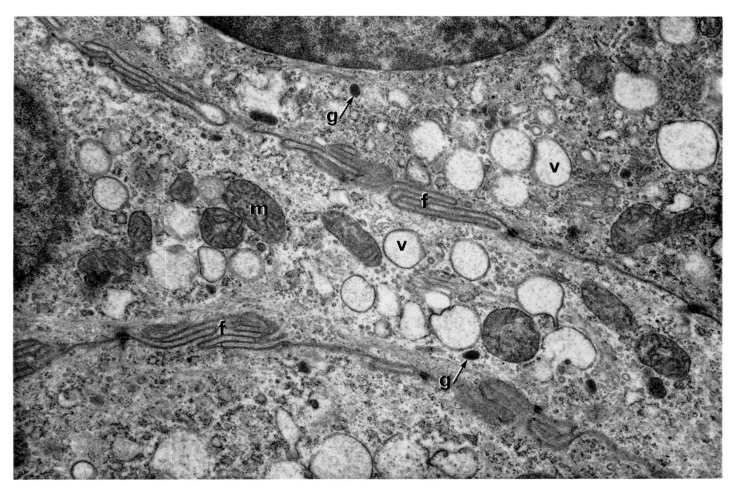

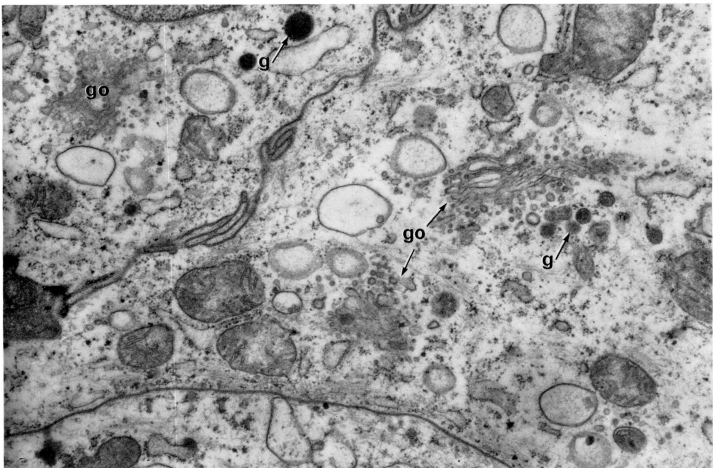

FIGURES 185 and 186

A most characteristic feature of the serous cell is the extensive plication of the plasma membrane to form long villous folds. These interdigitate in a complicated fashion with similar folds of adjacent serous cells, but the folds are not very closely apposed, so the intercellular space is fairly extensive. Short desmosomes (d) are infrequently seen. Where the folds abut against the basement membrane (b) they are reminiscent of "foot-plates". Where the plasma membrane is apposed to that of a myo-epithelial cell (My, see also Fig. 188), it is much less folded, and microvilli are present along the surface bordering intercellular canaliculi (IC).

The cytoplasm of the serous cell contains the common organelles, but displays no features that could be considered highly specific. Glycogen granules are fairly uniformly distributed throughout, but localized aggregations are also commonly seen. The serous cells produce a watery solution which is practically isotonic with blood. Its sodium content is significantly higher than that of the sweat which emerges on the surface of the skin, and this difference is thought to be due to active reabsorption of sodium by the basal cells of the lower part of the intradermal duct.

Fig. 185. Serous cells of secretory coil of sweat gland from palmar region of girl aged 7. Osmium fixation, lead staining. × 41,800.

Fig. 186. Serous cells of secretory coil of sweat gland from palmar region of girl aged 7. Osmium fixation, lead staining. × 44,950.

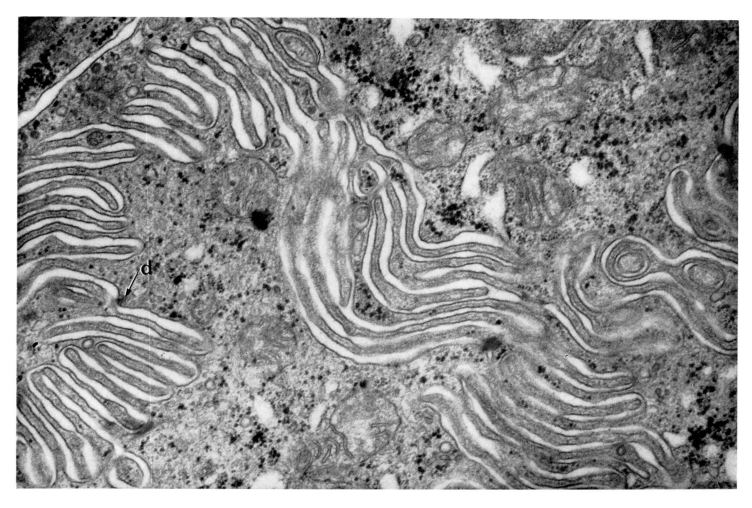

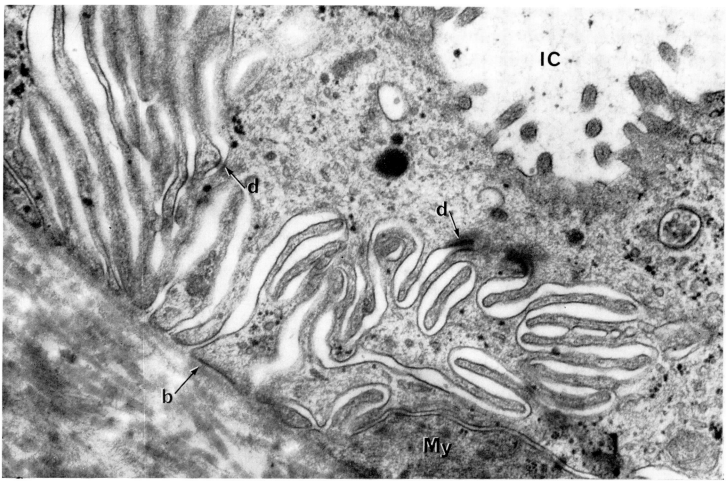

FIGURES 187 and 188

The myo-epithelial cells (My) occupy the basal region of the secretory coil, and rest upon a typical basal lamina (b) which separates them from the surrounding collagen (c). They do not form a complete layer, so that processes of serous cells reach the basal lamina between them (Fig. 186). Regular densities are present along the basal plasma membrane, and some of these (h) closely resemble hemi-desmosomes in appearance. Short desmosomes (de) connect the apposed lateral plasma membranes of myo-epithelial and serous (S) cells.

The infra-nuclear region of the cytoplasm is almost entirely occupied by myo-filaments (f), associated with which are the denser areas (d) already seen in vascular smooth muscle cells (Fig. 165) and also present in smooth muscle cells of the arrector pili (Fig. 252). The bulk of the cytoplasmic organelles are confined to the region lateral and superior to the nucleus, and are not remarkable in any way. Glycogen granules, disposed either singly or in small rosettes, are scattered throughout the cytoplasm, but their concentration is much less than in the serous cells, as a comparison of the two cells in the lower micrograph will show.

The function of the myo-epithelial cells is not clear, though it must be associated with the fact that they are contractile elements. The simplest explanation, that they are concerned with "squeezing" the sweat from the secretory coil into the duct, has received little support. Another suggestion that they serve to contain the gland against over-distension when large amounts of fluid are being secreted has more appeal. Ellis has advanced the opposing view that by contracting, the cells become more widely separated, thereby exposing a greater area of basal plasma membrane of interposed serous cells to the basal lamina, and indirectly through this, to the extra-cellular fluid. If this be so, the myo-epithelial cell could have a role in regulating the rate or amount of sweat production.

Fig. 187. Myo-epithelial cell of secretory coil of sweat gland from palmar region of girl aged 7. Osmium fixation, lead staining. × 50,400.

Fig. 188. Myo-epithelial and serous cells of secretory coil of sweat gland from palmar region of girl aged 7. Osmium fixation, lead staining. × 44,400.

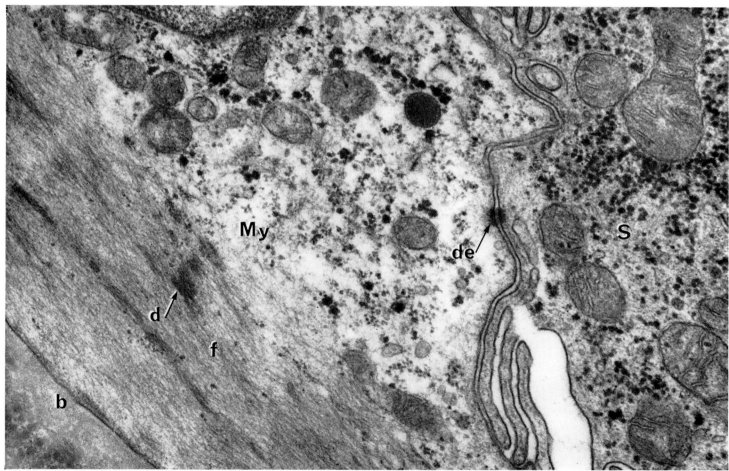

REFERENCES

Ellis, R. E. Eccrine sweat glands: electron microscopy, cytochemistry, and anatomy. In: "Handbuch der Haut und Geschlechtskrankheiten", Vol. I, O. Gans and G. K. Steigleder, eds. Berlin, Springer. 1968.

Hashimoto, K., Gross, B. G. and Lever, W. F. The ultrastructure of the skin of human embryos. The intraepidermal eccrine sweat duct. *J. invest. Derm.*, **45**:139, 1965.

Hashimoto, K., Gross, B. G. and Lever, W. F. Electron microscopic study of the human adult eccrine gland. The duct. *J. invest. Derm.*, **46**:172, 1966.

Hashimoto, K., Gross, B. G. and Lever, W. F. The ultrastructure of human embryo skin. The formation of the intradermal portion of the eccrine sweat duct and of the secretory segment during the first half of embryonic life. *J. invest. Derm.*, **46**:513, 1966.

11 Early Development of Hair Follicle

Hair germ — hair peg — bulbous peg — hair cone — hair tract — bulb and papilla — trichohyalin — differentiation and transformation of inner root sheath — hair tract.

FIGURE 189

The earliest signs of hair development appear on the eyebrows, lips and face, at about the beginning of the 3rd month, and at progressively later stages, proceeding caudad. Accordingly, in any individual fetus from the 3rd month onwards, hairs at different stages of development, depending upon site, may be seen. A crowding of cells in the basal layer of the epidermis is the first indication of the developing hair follicle, and is referred to as the pre-germ stage. Epidermal cells at this stage are similar in appearance to those illustrated in Fig. 45. Further accumulation of cells leads to the formation of a hair germ (HG) which protrudes into the mesoderm, and with which becomes associated an aggregation of mesenchymal cells to form a primitive dermal papilla (DP). Throughout subsequent development, these two fundamental components of the follicle remain closely associated.

The cells of the hair germ are closely-packed, and stand out clearly from overlying intermediate (I) and adjacent interfollicular basal cells by virtue of their significantly lower glycogen (gl) content and smaller size. In general, they appear to contain more mitochondria, ribosomes, and cytoplasmic filaments than cells in the other two situations. Cilia are occasionally seen stemming from the plasma membrane. The dermal papilla cells at this stage are loosely arranged and do not differ significantly from general mesodermal cells. Occasionally, Schwann cells with associated neuraxons are seen among the papilla cells, and small capillary vessels may be adjacent.

Little information is available concerning the factors which determine the actual site of individual hair formation, though it is probable that the primary organizational capacity resides in the mesoderm. Notwithstanding this, it is generally held that epidermal alterations, i.e. crowding of basal layer cells, precedes any accumulation of underlying mesodermal cells.

This micrograph may be compared with Fig. 169, illustrating the germinative bud of the sweat gland.

Fig. 189. Hair germ from back skin of 81 mm C.R. (14 weeks) human fetus. Osmium fixation, lead staining. × 4,950.

254

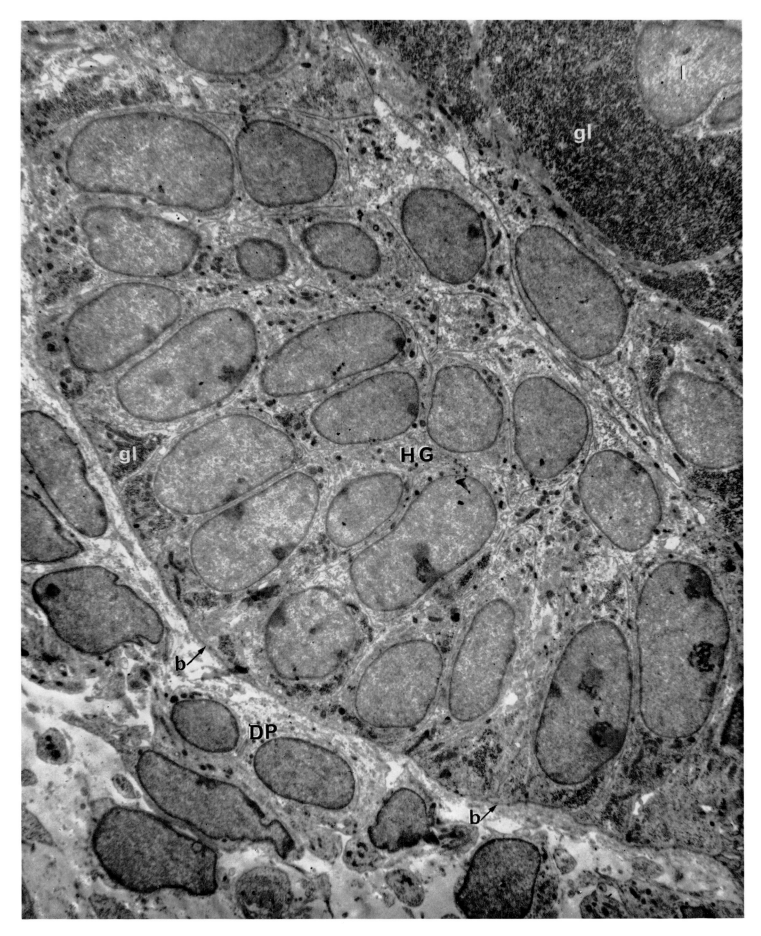

255

FIGURES 190 and 191

As the cells of the hair germ increase in number, it grows obliquely downwards into the meso-derm to form a club-shaped column of cells, the hair peg. The advancing basal end (B) of the hair peg is flattened, and abuts against the now more densely-packed cells of the dermal papilla (P). These latter are in continuity with two or three layers of mesenchymal cells which envelop the entire peg to form a sheath (S).

The outer cells (O) of the hair peg are arranged radially to the long axis, and the basal cells (B) are conspicuously tall and narrow, presenting a palisade arrangement. The central cells (C) are more rounded and less tightly packed, and intercellular spaces of varying size occur among them. Glycogen deposits are common within the central cells, particularly proximally. The proximal end of the hair peg joins the epidermis obliquely, and here, in the neck region of the follicle, the distinction between outer and central cells is less evident. Together, they form a group of elongated cells extending obliquely backwards into the epidermis to form the anlage of the hair tract (Fig. 195), along which the hair eventually emerges onto the surface.

Further growth of the hair peg leads to its elongation, and the advancing end becomes bulbous and gradually envelops the dermal papilla. This is known as the "bulbous peg" stage of the follicle (*see* Figs. 192, 193 and 194), and it is at this stage that two or three cellular accumulations appear along its posterior aspect. These are, from above downwards, the apo-crine (Fig. 269), sebaceous (Fig. 254) and bulge (Fig. 193) swellings.

Figs. 190 and *191*. Central longitudinal sections through lower part of hair peg from scalp of 109 mm C.R. ($15\frac{1}{2}$ weeks) human fetus. The lower part of the field covered in Fig. 190 is also represented in Fig. 191. Osmium fixation, lead staining. ×4,000 approx.

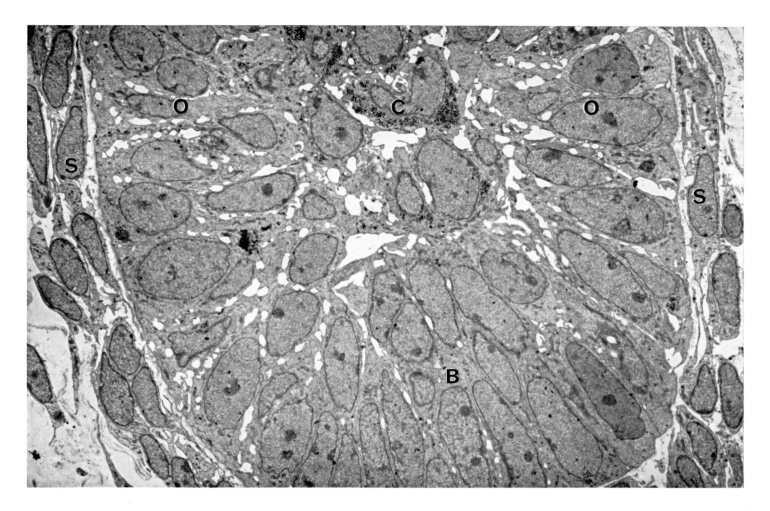

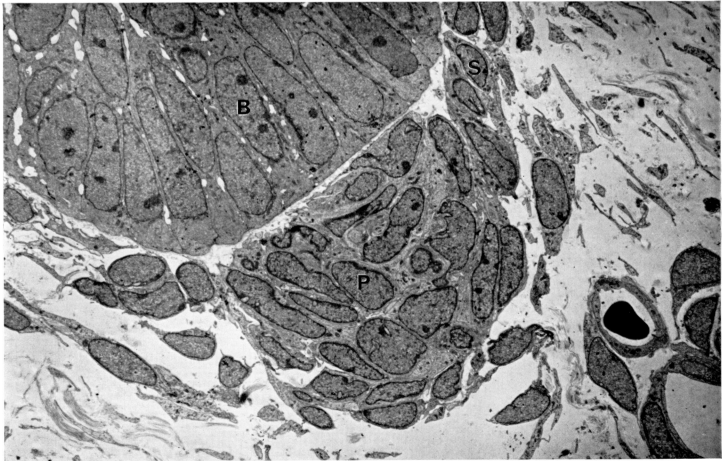

FIGURE 192

This is a longitudinal section of the lower end of a follicle at the early bulbous-peg stage of development. The dermal papilla (P) is now partially enveloped by cells of the epidermal component of the follicle, and those (M) situated below the level of the apex of the papilla (a) are in a position occupied by the matrix cells of the fully-developed hair bulb. Above the level of the papilla apex, the more centrally lying cells form a compact mass which constitutes the base of a conical arrangement of cells—the hair cone—which at a higher level (*see* Fig. 194) extends upwards parallel to the long axis of the follicle. These cells therefore can be designated presumptive hair-cone cells (PHC). More laterally situated cells are continuous at a higher level with the outer cells of the bulbous peg which give rise to the outer root sheath of the mature follicle, and can in turn be labelled as presumptive outer root sheath cells (ORS). At this stage of development the cytoplasmic features of cells in the two situations are practically identical, but at a slightly later stage, associated with further envelopment of the dermal papilla, deposits of trichohyalin appear within the cells of the hair cone (*see* Fig. 198), and this renders them readily distinguishable from prospective outer root sheath cells.

The succeeding Figs. 193–195 illustrate sections at progressively higher levels of follicles at a comparable stage of development.

Fig. 192. Longitudinal section through one half of bulbar region of bulbous peg from upper lip of 115 mm C.R. (15½ weeks) human fetus. Glutaraldehyde-osmium fixation, lead staining. ×6,800.

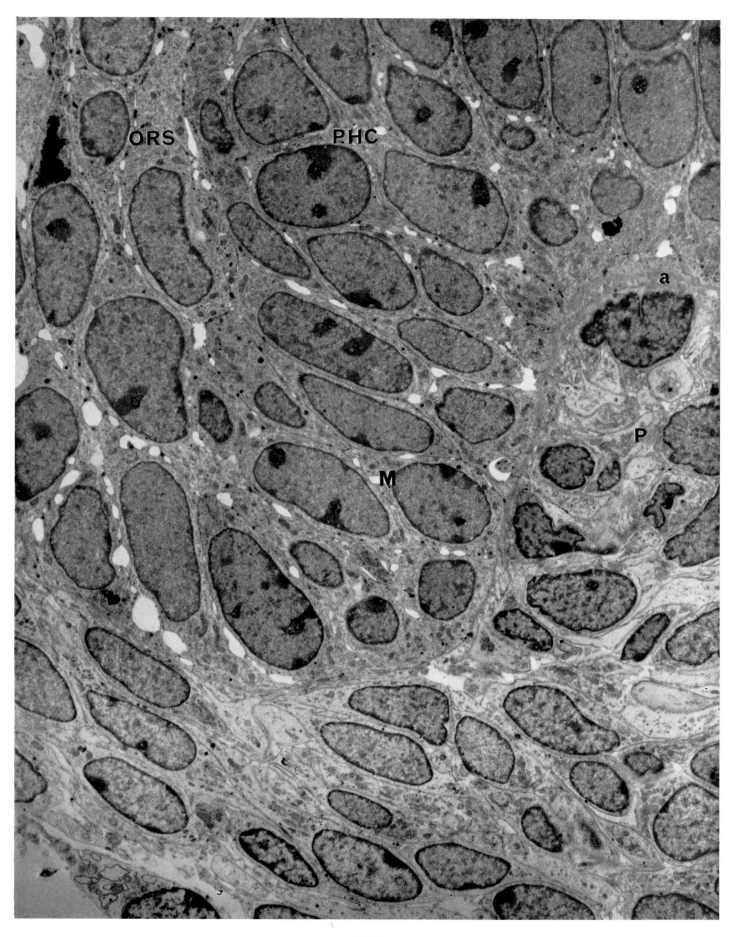

FIGURES 193 and 194

The lower of these two micrographs (Fig. 194) presents a longitudinal section through the supra-bulbar region of a bulbous-peg follicle at a stage of development comparable to that shown in Fig. 192, and the upper one presents a section of the same follicle at a slightly higher level. In the lower figure (194) a compact conical unit of cells, the hair cone (HC), is seen extending proximally from a base (B) of presumptive hair-cone cells. On either side of the hair cone are cells destined to form the outer root sheath of the follicle (ORS) and these are orientated almost at right angles to those of the cone. Comparison of this micrograph with Figs. 190 and 191 illustrating the earlier hair-peg stage, shows that the hair cone is extending proximally into the region previously occupied by loosely-packed central cells. The hair cone is the anlage of the hair itself and of its inner root sheath, and as development proceeds, many distinctive layers of cells are differentiated within it. These cannot be said even to be fore-shadowed at the stage illustrated here, and the only distinctive feature of the main mass of the cells is their orientation, and the presence of small trichohyalin deposits in the more outlying ones (see Fig. 198). A few elements (d) of the hair cone, however, have a highly characteristic appearance, being markedly electron-dense and of irregular shape. At higher powers of magnification these have been shown to be degenerating and dying cells involved in the process of morphogenetic cell death which is a regular feature of developing and differentiating organs, particularly in association with changes in shape and size, such as occur in the fetal hair follicle.

The upper micrograph (193) illustrates the "bulge" (Bu) which is such a characteristic feature of the fetal follicle. It is a swelling produced by an accumulation of prospective outer root sheath cells (ORS) along the posterior aspect of the follicle below the apocrine and sebaceous swellings, and the upper margin projects at a sharper angle than the lower. Its inner limit is clearly demarcated from the underlying hair cone (HC). The functional significance of "the bulge" is obscure, but it is the future site of attachment of the arrector pili muscle.

Fig. 193. Longitudinal section along bulge of bulbous peg from scalp of 109 mm C.R. (15½ weeks) human fetus. Osmium fixation, lead staining. ×4,000 approx.

Fig. 194. Longitudinal section through region of hair cone of same bulbous peg as in Fig. 193 above. Osmium fixation, lead staining. ×3,500 approx.

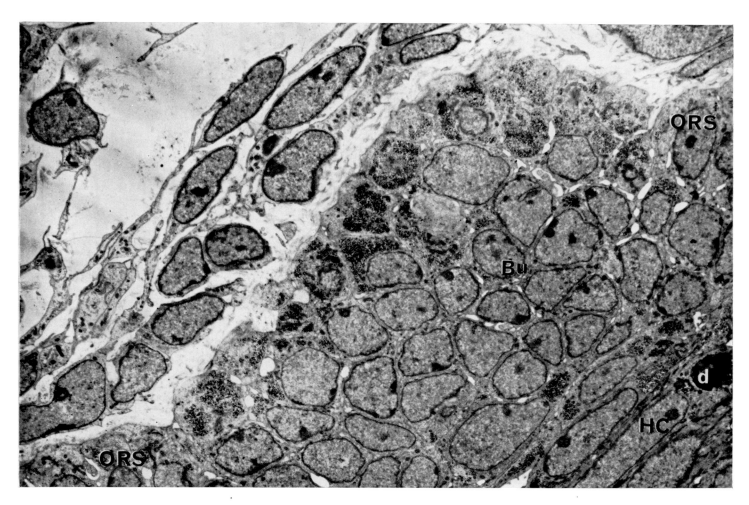

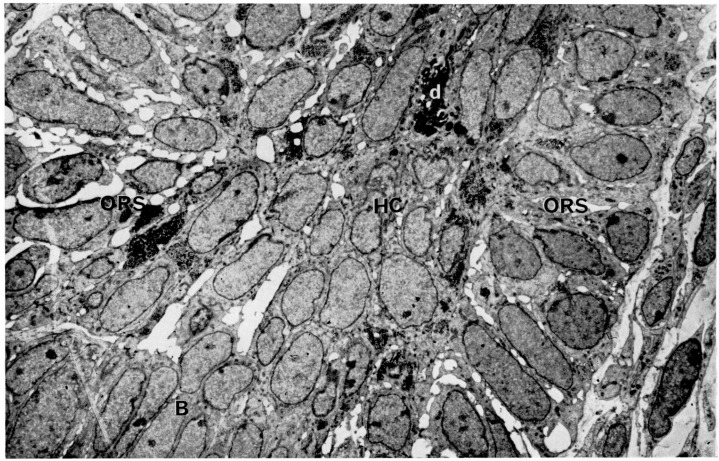

261

FIGURE 195

During the hair-peg and early bulbous-peg stages of development, a solid cord of elongated cells stems from the neck region of the follicle, and grows upwards and backwards into the epidermis. This is the hair tract along which the hair eventually emerges. It consists of epidermal (hair-canal, HTC) and sub-epidermal (infundibulum, HTI) parts, though the cells in the two situations are indistinguishable. They occupy the posterior half or so of the neck region of the follicle and stand out clearly from cells of the anterior half (A), and the overlying intermediate epidermal cells (I), by virtue of their orientation and more elongated form. A characteristic feature of the cells of the hair tract is the presence of coarse filamentous bundles (f) which may traverse the entire length of the cell, and membrane coating granules are present from an early stage in cells of the epidermal portion. Morphogenetic cell death is frequently seen within the hair tract, and the central cells rapidly undergo keratinization (*see* Figs. 203 and 205), being the first cells to do so within the epidermis. A lumen appears in the centre of the keratinized tissue, but its exact manner of formation remains to be established, and shortly after its appearance it is traversed by the tip of the emerging hair.

The upper end of a swelling (S) formed by the outer cells along the posterior aspect of the follicle lies just within the lower limit of the field. This is the anlage of the sebaceous gland.

Fig. 195. Longitudinal section through neck region of bulbous peg from scalp of 109 mm (15½ weeks) human fetus. Osmium fixation, lead staining. × 5,000 approx.

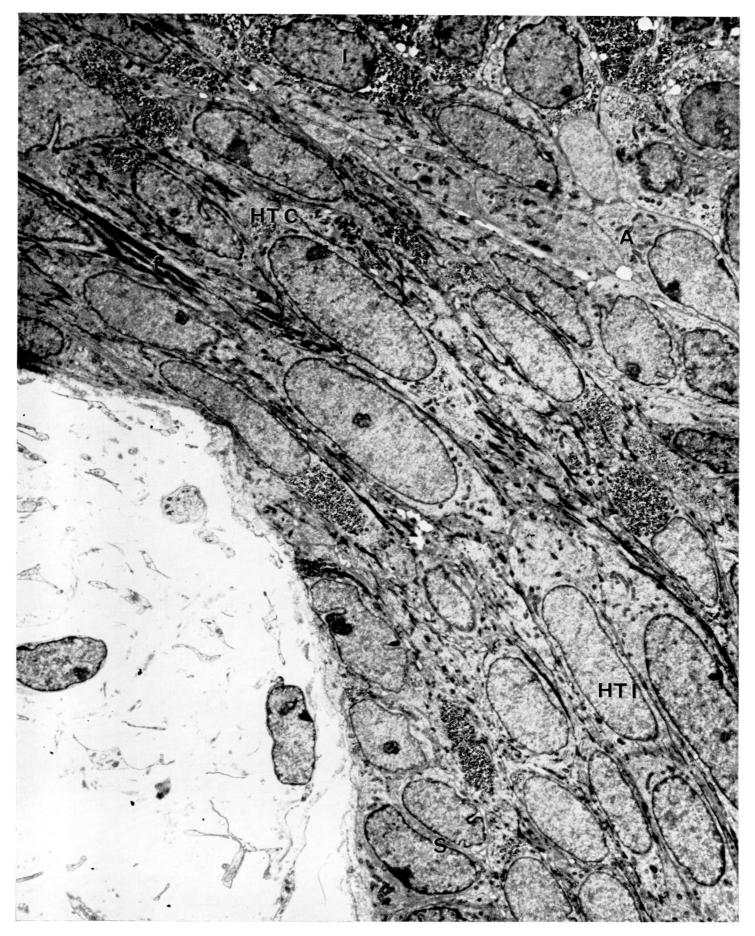

FIGURE 196

This micrograph shows the basal part and associated dermal papilla of a hair peg at a stage of development comparable to that illustrated in Figs. 190 and 191. The palisade arrangement of the basal cells (B) is clearly seen, and they rest upon a basal lamina (b). Short filamentous bundles (f) are present in the cytoplasm of the basal cells, but otherwise they exhibit no distinctive features, and differ little if at all, from cells of the earlier hair germ (Fig. 189). The cells of the dermal papilla (P) are closely packed, and specialized contacts (c) are occasionally seen associated with the apposed plasma membranes; single cilia may also be seen. The cytoplasm of the papilla cells at this stage presents a generally inactive appearance, but later, the number of mitochondria increases, and the rough endoplasmic reticulum becomes more prominent. Apart from these features the papilla cells undergo little further differentiation throughout fetal or post-natal life.

In Section 1, mention was made of epithelial-mesenchymal interactions and inductive processes operating at the epidermal-dermal junction. These involve exchange of substances at the molecular level with little or no morphologic manifestation. Similar interactions take place between the epithelial and mesodermal (papilla) elements of the hair follicle, and here, at the slightly later bulbous-peg stage (*see inset*), single or pedunculated processes (pr) may be seen extending from the plasma membranes of the basal cells (B) to establish direct contact with papilla cells (P). This feature might be regarded as indicative of particularly active transfer of substances in either direction between the two.

Fig. 196. Basal cells of hair peg and dermal papilla from scalp of 142 mm C.R. (16 weeks) human fetus. Millonig fixation, lead staining. × 7,200. *Inset:* Processes extending from basal cell of hair peg. Osmium fixation, lead staining. × 37,000.

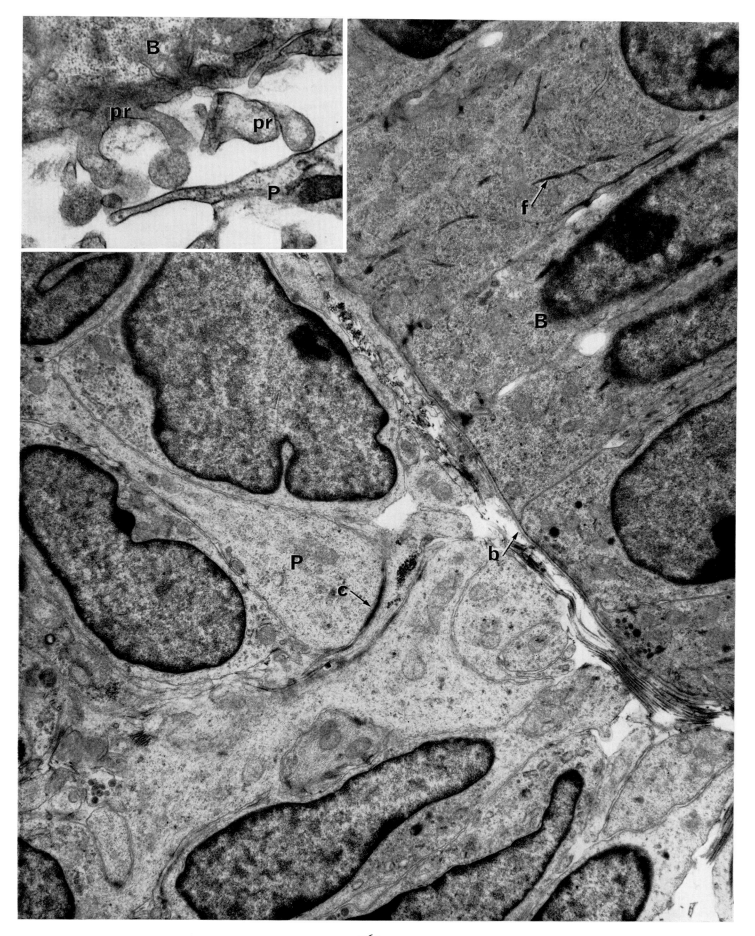

FIGURE 197

This presents presumptive hair cone (PHC) and presumptive outer root sheath (ORS) cells at the level of the apex of the dermal papilla of a follicle at a stage of development comparable to that shown in Fig. 192. The presumptive hair-cone cells are narrower and more elongated in the direction of the long axis of the follicle (f), but otherwise, cells in the two different situations do not differ in any significant respect. At a slightly higher level, however, as seen in the lower micrograph (Fig. 198), trichohyalin granules are present in the cells of the hair cone.

FIGURE 198

At the stage of initial differentiation of the hair cone, the cells are similar in appearance to those of the presumptive hair-cone cells illustrated above. Soon, however, trichohyalin granules (t) appear in the cytoplasm. These are invariably associated from first appearance with filaments (f) which appear to run into the granules (*see inset*). At one stage it was thought that the trichohyalin granules gave rise to the filaments, but this view is no longer tenable since filaments antedate trichohyalin in ontogeny, and in the process of differentiation of post-natal hair. Purely morphological observations on fetal and fully-developed hair have, so far, failed to provide any information concerning the origin of trichohyalin, and its chemical constitution is largely unknown. It has been suggested that the increase in density whereby the granules become manifest is due to the deposition of an added amorphous component along or between the filaments, but there is really little evidence to support this view.

Once it has appeared, trichohyalin builds up rapidly to form large irregular deposits in the peripheral cells of the hair cone, and associated with this is a marked increase in filaments. Soon, two layers of cells loaded with granules are seen encircling (on transverse section) more central less differentiated cells. These former are the Henle and Huxley layers of the inner root sheath which are the first elements to be differentiated within the hair cone, and which reach an advanced stage of maturation before presumptive cuticular or cortical components can be recognized.

Fig. 197. Presumptive hair-cone and outer root sheath cells from bulbous peg in scalp of 115 mm C.R. (15½ weeks) human fetus. Glutaraldehyde-osmium fixation, lead staining. × 17,700. In this and succeeding micrographs, broad arrow in right lower corner indicates direction of hair growth.

Fig. 198. Trichohyalin granules in hair-cone cell of bulbous peg from upper lip of 115 mm C.R. (15½ weeks) human fetus. Glutaraldehyde-osmium fixation, lead staining. × 77,300. *Inset:* Trichohyalin granules and filaments × 52,400. Arrow indicates direction of hair growth.

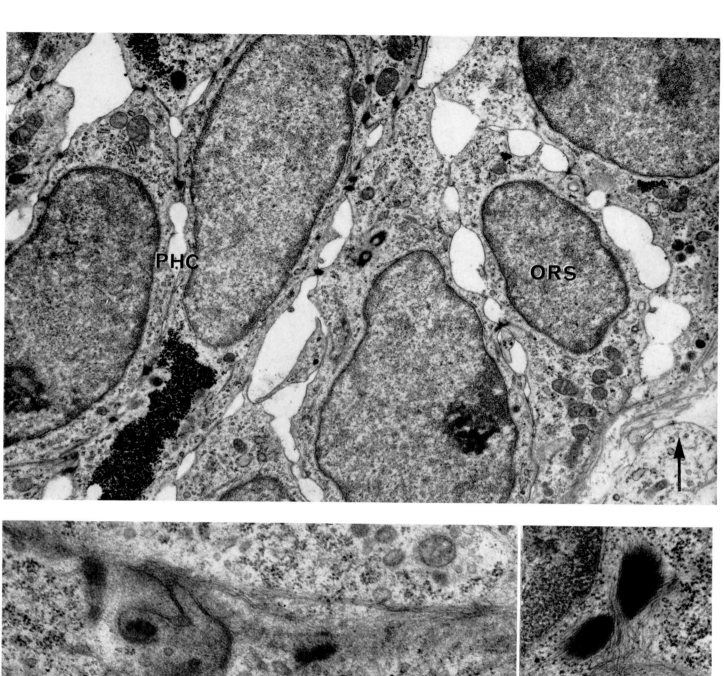

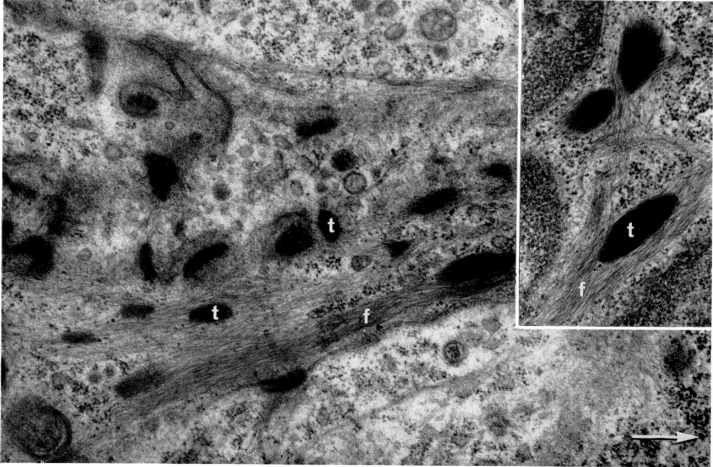

267

FIGURE 199

As development proceeds, and as the cells ascend from the bulbar region, the build-up of tri-chohyalin granules (t) and filaments within the inner root sheath cells (IRS) continues. The cells of the outer root sheath (ORS) do not contain trichohyalin, but gradually accumulate deposits of glycogen (g). At high powers of magnification (*see inset*) trichohyalin granules exhibit a speckled pattern which does not seem to represent unaltered filaments set in an amorphous matrix, but possibly some fundamental reorganization of filamentous protein.

FIGURE 200

The next change which occurs within the growing hair cone is the abrupt transformation of apical inner root sheath cells such as those illustrated above, into elements with largely filamentous cytoplasm devoid of trichohyalin granules, and with nuclei (n) showing various degrees of degeneration. In longitudinal sections through the hair cone, these transformed inner root sheath cells (IRST) are seen to form a cap over untransformed cells (IRSU) lying more distally, and they provide the hardened tip which traverses the developing lumen of the hair tract at a higher level (*see* Figs. 204 and 207).

The inner root sheath consists of two layers of cells, an outer Henle's layer, and an inner Huxley's layer, both of which become transformed as described, the former at a lower level than the latter. In the present general description of the inner root sheath, it is not necessary to deal separately with these two layers. A more detailed account is presented in the following section.

Fig. 199. Inner and outer root sheath cells from hair cone of bulbous peg from upper lip of 115 mm C.R. (15½ weeks) human fetus. Glutaraldehyde-osmium fixation, lead staining. × 10,400. *Inset:* Trichohyalin × 280,000.

Fig. 200. Longitudinal section along apical region of hair cone of bulbous peg from scalp of 116 mm C.R. (15½ weeks) human fetus. Osmium fixation, lead staining. × 5,000 approx.

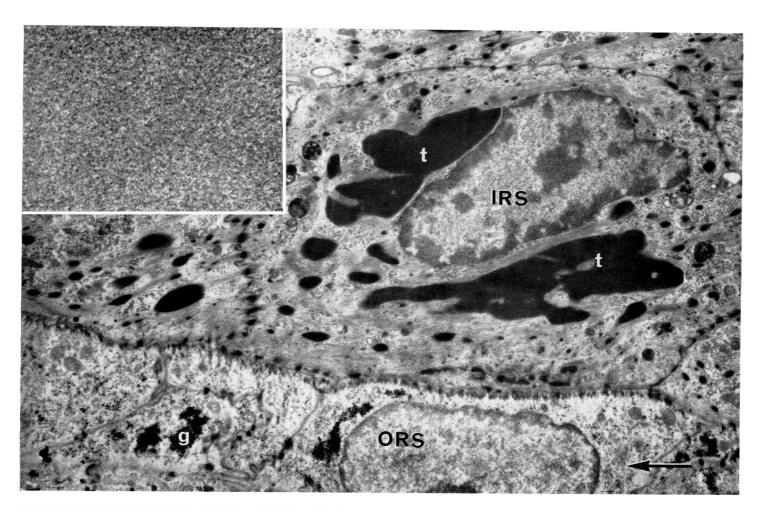

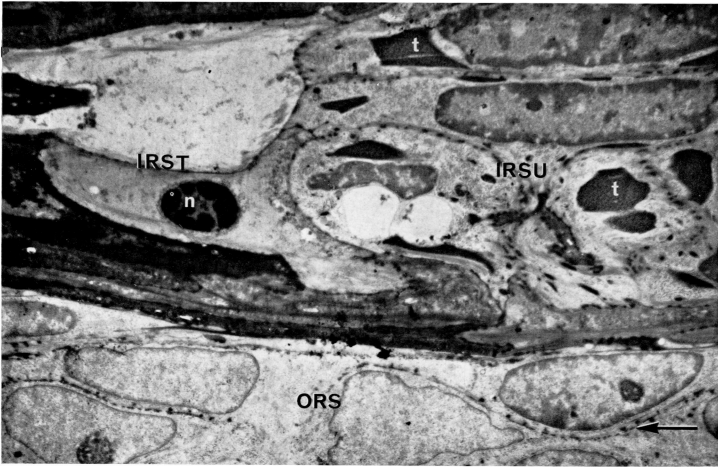

FIGURE 201

This micrograph illustrates portions of adjacent untransformed (U) and transforming (T) cells of the Henle layer of the inner root sheath. The untransformed cell is one of the type illustrated in Fig. 199, and one can note the presence of trichohyalin (t) and filamentous bundles (f) in the cytoplasm. The transforming cell presents an entirely different appearance. The filamentous bundles are less compactly arranged, and interposed between them are islands of ribosomes (r). Trichohyalin granules are completely absent from cells of this type, and the plasma membrane (m) is characteristically thickened.

FIGURE 202

This transformed inner root sheath cell is from a slightly higher level of the advancing tip of the hair cone. The cytoplasm is packed with filaments (f) among which are occasional islets of ribosomes (r) but no trace of trichohyalin granules. Ribosomes are also present close to the nucleus (n), which lacks a membrane and which exhibits clumping of the chromatin to form granular patches of different densities. Observations at later fetal stages reveal that apart from some increase in electron density of the filamentous cytoplasm, and disappearance of the nucleus, inner root sheath cells do not differentiate significantly beyond the condition illustrated here.

Analysis of the process of transformation illustrated here, presents a number of problems, such as the fate of the trichohyalin granules, and the source of the apparently higher concentration of filaments in the transformed cell. In the fetal hair cone, transformation of inner root sheath cells is somewhat less abrupt than in the mature post-natal hair follicle, and the cell in Fig. 201 represents an earlier stage of the process than that in Fig. 202. It might be thought that examination of a large number of hair cones at slightly different stages of maturation would throw further light on the mechanism of transformation. This approach, however, has not proved very fruitful so far, and it is doubtful if further purely morphological observations will advance understanding to any extent. The difficulty is akin to that involved in analysis of the keratinization of interfollicular epidermis.

Fig. 201. Transforming inner root sheath cell in hair cone of bulbous peg from scalp of 120 mm C.R. (16 weeks) human fetus. Glutaraldehyde-osmium fixation, lead staining. ×64,450. Arrow indicates direction of hair growth.

Fig. 202. Transformed inner root sheath cell in hair cone of bulbous peg from upper lip of 115 mm C.R. (15½ weeks) human fetus. Glutaraldehyde-osmium fixation, lead staining. ×60,600.

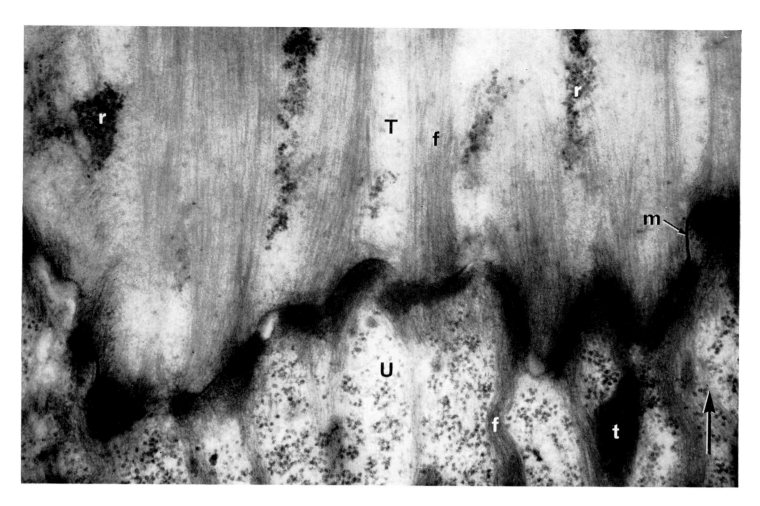

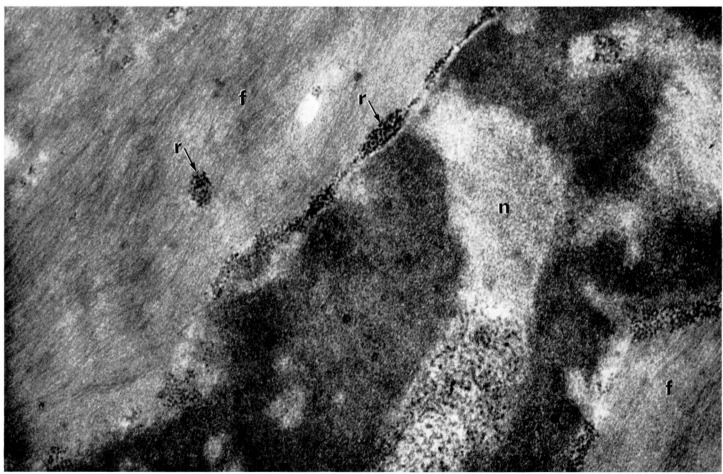

FIGURE 203

The hair tract at the early bulbous-peg stage has already been figured (Fig. 195), and attention was drawn to the particularly high concentration of filaments within the cells. As the follicle lengthens, and the hair cone is differentiating, the central cells of the hair tract acquire deposits of keratohyalin (k), and soon, as in this transverse section of the infundibular (sub-epidermal) segment, a central keratinized patch (c) becomes apparent, in which a number of cells may be involved. Disintegration of this keratinized tissue leads to the formation of a lumen which is soon traversed by the advancing tip of the hair anlage, which, as already mentioned, is formed by transformed cells of the inner root sheath. Note glycogen (g) deposits in cells of outer root sheath.

FIGURE 204

This is from a longitudinal section along the infundibular portion of the hair tract of a more advanced follicle than that figured in the micrograph above. The advancing, transformed, inner root sheath of the hair (IRS) is present in the lumen, and separated by a gap from the keratinized (Ke) luminal border. Keratohyalin granules (k) and cytoplasmic organelles, including membrane coating granules (g), are present within the non-keratinized cells. At the interface between keratinized and non-keratinized portions of the wall of the tract, appearances are seen which are reminiscent of discharge of membrane-coating-granules into the space between stratum granulosum and stratum corneum of interfollicular epidermis (Fig. 100).

The region figured here corresponds to the pilary canal of post-natal skin (Fig. 250).

Fig. 203. Transverse section of intradermal hair tract of follicle from scalp of 113 mm (15 weeks) human fetus. Osmium fixation, lead staining. × 4,600.

Fig. 204. Longitudinal section along intradermal hair tract of follicle from scalp of 112 mm C.R. (15 weeks) human fetus. Osmium fixation, lead staining. × 29,000. Arrow indicates direction of hair growth.

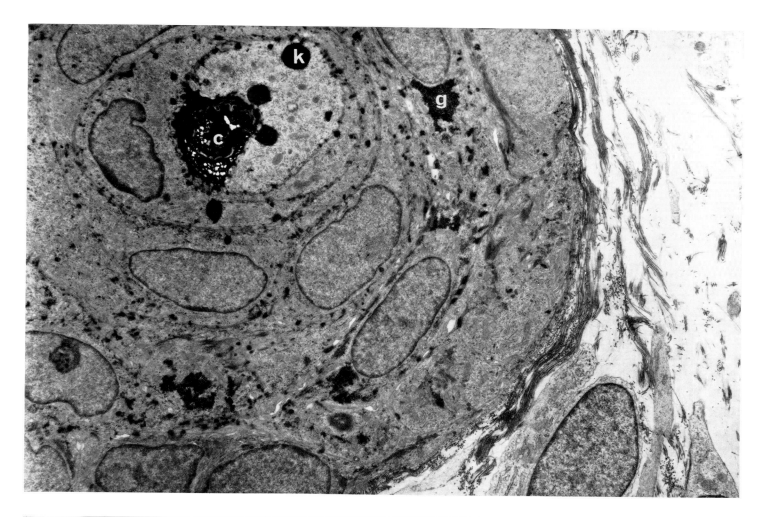

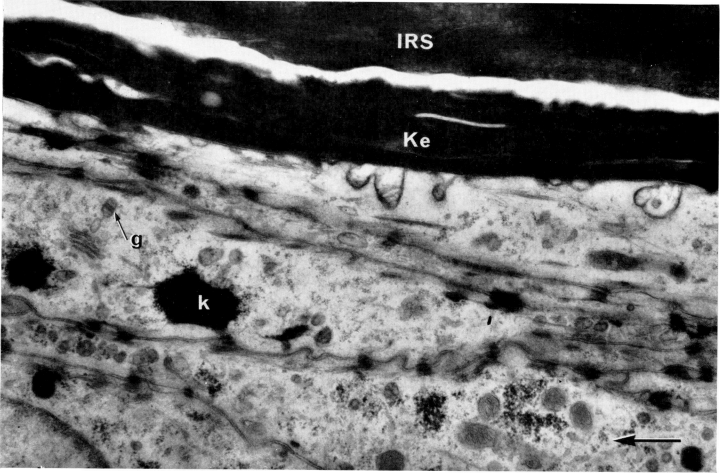

FIGURE 205

Lumen formation within the intraepidermal portion of the hair tract appears to follow the same course as in the infundibular portion, and one can note again the central keratinized patch (c), surrounded by cells containing keratohyalin granules (k). This micrograph may be compared with Figs. 170 and 171 illustrating the intraepidermal portion of the sweat duct.

FIGURE 206

The passage of the hair tract through the epidermis is very oblique, and its terminal part is disposed almost horizontally parallel with the surface. This can lead to some difficulty in interpretation of micrographs, especially where restricted fields at moderate or high magnification are concerned. For example, this micrograph might be interpreted as illustrating precocious keratinization (Ke) of interfollicular epidermis to judge from the condition of the overlying periderm (P) which has not undergone transformation, and which still exhibits globular elevations. It is in fact representative of a tangential section of the wall of the hair tract, which, as already mentioned, is the site of earliest appearance of keratinization within the epidermis. The adjacent interfollicular epidermis showed no evidence of keratinization. That this is the hair tract is also indicated by a particular feature of the nucleus of the cell underlying the keratinized layers. This exhibits discrete, round, dense inclusions (d) which are not seen in nuclei of granular layer cells of interfollicular epidermis. These nuclear densities appear to be characteristic of cells of the hair tract at a stage when keratinization is well advanced, but their significance is obscure.

Fig. 205. Intraepidermal hair tract from scalp of 113 mm C.R. (15 weeks) human fetus. Osmium fixation, lead staining. × 11,700.

Fig. 206. Terminal region of intraepidermal hair tract from scalp of 120 mm C.R. (16 weeks) human fetus. Glutaraldehyde-osmium fixation, lead staining. × 8,250.

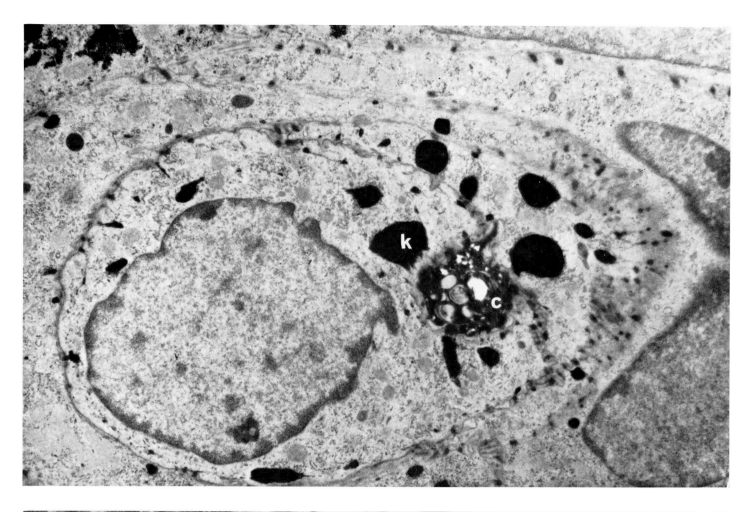

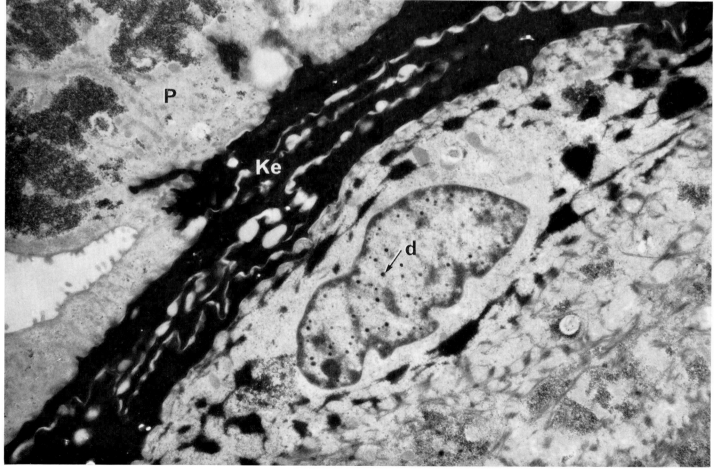

FIGURE 207

This micrograph features part of the wall of the basal portion of the intraepidermal hair tract at a stage when the inner root sheath (IRS) of the emerging hair has already entered the lumen (L). One may note again the keratinized layer (Ke), keratohyalin granules (k), and nuclear densities (d). A moderate amount of glycogen is present within the more outlying cells.

FIGURE 208

Here is illustrated a segment of the wall of the hair tract close to the surface at a stage when the hair has emerged. The cells deep to the keratinized layer (Ke) resemble granulosa layer cells of interfollicular epidermis (*see* Figs. 57 and 100) as regards general cytoplasmic features and presence of keratohyalin granules (k). The plasma membrane, however, shows the characteristic thickening one associates with fully keratinized cells, or with "transitional cells" (Fig. 101). Preliminary observations indicate that many of these cells do not progress further towards keratinization, and that near the terminal part of the tract, they undergo disintegration, and are shed into the lumen, carrying with them the overlying keratinized layers.

Though it is difficult to say in precisely what respect, morphological observations suggest that the process of keratinization of the hair tract is different to that occurring in the neighbouring interfollicular epidermis. Whether or not this is so, must await further work, and in particular, biochemical studies.

Fig. 207. Section along basal part of intraepidermal portion of hair tract from scalp of 120 mm C.R. (16 weeks) human fetus. Glutaraldehyde-osmium fixation, lead staining. × 12,600.

Fig. 208. From wall of terminal part of intraepidermal hair tract from arm of 169 mm C.R. (21 weeks) human fetus. Osmium fixation, lead staining. × 20,800.

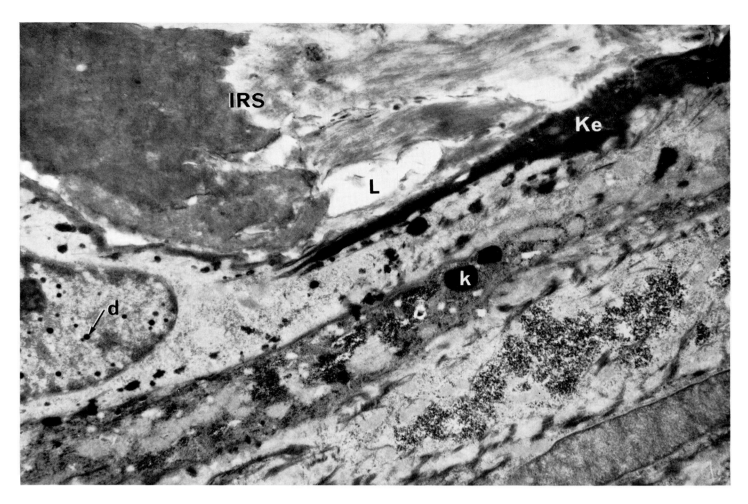

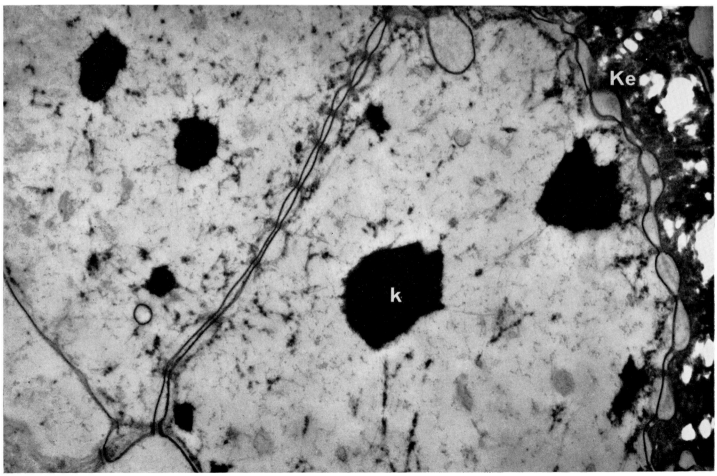

277

REFERENCES

Breathnach, A. S. and Smith, Jacqueline. Fine structure of the early hair germ and dermal papilla in the human fetus. *J. Anat.* **102**:511, 1968.

Robins, E. J. and Breathnach, A. S. Fine structure of the human fetal hair follicle at hair-peg and early bulbous-peg stages of development. *J. Anat.* **104**:553, 1968.

Robins, E. J. and Breathnach, A. S. Fine structure of bulbar end of human fetal hair follicle at stage of differentiation of inner root sheath. *J. Anat.* (in the press).

Pinkus, H. Embryology of hair. In: "The Biology of Hair Growth", W. Montagna and R. A. Ellis, eds. New York, Academic Press, 1958.

Saunders, J. W. Jr. and Fallon, J. F. Cell death in morphogenesis. In: "Major problems in developmental biology", M. Locke, ed. New York, Academic Press, 1966.

12 Further Differentiation of Fetal Hair Follicle

In the previous Section, 11, development and differentiation of the hair follicle was followed to the stage when the dermal papilla is enveloped by the distal, bulbar, end of the bulbous peg, and definitive inner root sheath elements can be identified within the hair cone. As development proceeds, the papilla becomes further enveloped, and cuticular and cortical elements are differentiated. This Section presents an account of the fully differentiated fetal hair follicle which, apart from the absence of a medullary component, does not differ significantly in structure from the post-natal follicle. In the following Section, 13, particular features of the post-natal follicle are considered, and the two Sections taken together provide an overall picture of the ultrastructure of the hair and its sheaths.

279

FIGURE 209

A line drawn across the widest diameter of the hair bulb or "critical level" (CL) divides it into the lower matrix region (Ma) of undifferentiated cells, and the upper bulb (Bu), formed of cells streaming upwards from the matrix, and which at an immediately higher level (Fig. 210) differentiate into the various layers of the hair and its sheaths. The matrix cells have no particular distinguishing features, and differ very little in appearance from corresponding cells of the earlier hair-germ (Fig. 189), hair-peg (Fig. 191), and bulbous-peg (Fig. 192) stages of development. Above this critical level, the cells closest to the dermal papilla (DP) may be labelled presumptive cortical (PCo), and beyond these lie presumptive cuticular (PCu) and presumptive inner root sheath (PIR) cells. The latter exhibit impending signs of differentiation—in the form of trichohyalin granules (t)—at a lower level of the bulb than any other element. The outermost cells of the bulb (outside the field) constitute presumptive outer root sheath cells.

FIGURE 210

This is a longitudinal section through one-half of the upper bulb of a follicle in which all layers of the hair and its sheaths were differentiated. From without inwards, just above the level of the apex of the dermal papilla (P), one can distinguish an outer root sheath (ORS), Henle (He) and Huxley (Hu) layers of the inner root sheath, cells of the cuticle of the inner root sheath (CI), and of the cuticle of the hair (CH), and, most centrally, cells forming the cortex (Co) of the hair. All of these different layers are derived from undifferentiated matrix cells (Fig. 209) which stream up from the lower part of the bulb, and while they will receive detailed individual attention in the following pages, mention may be made of the main distinguishing features of each at this level of the follicle.

Glycogen deposits (g) are a feature of outer root sheath cells, and trichohyalin granules (t) are prominent in the cytoplasm of the Henle layer cells. Trichohyalin (t) is also present in Huxley layer cells, but in lesser amount, and it is practically absent from those in the lower part of the field at a level where large amounts are already present in Henle cells. Little cytoplasmic detail, apart from a suggestion of fine filamentous bundles, can be seen in the cuticular cells at this magnification, and they are identified by position more than anything else. The cortical cells which occupy the central region of the hair root are characterized by compact, filamentous bundles (f) and numerous melanosomes (m). These latter are derived from the hair-bulb melanocytes (M) which lie among the basal cells just above the tip of the dermal papilla.

Fig. 209. Longitudinal section of hair bulb and dermal papilla of follicle from scalp of 113 mm C.R. (16 week) human fetus. Osmium fixation, lead staining. Arrow at bottom right in this and succeeding micrographs indicates direction of hair growth. × 10,800.

Fig. 210. Central longitudinal section through upper bulb of follicle from scalp of 120 mm C.R. (16½ week) human fetus. Glutaraldehyde-osmium fixation, lead staining. × 5,000 approx.

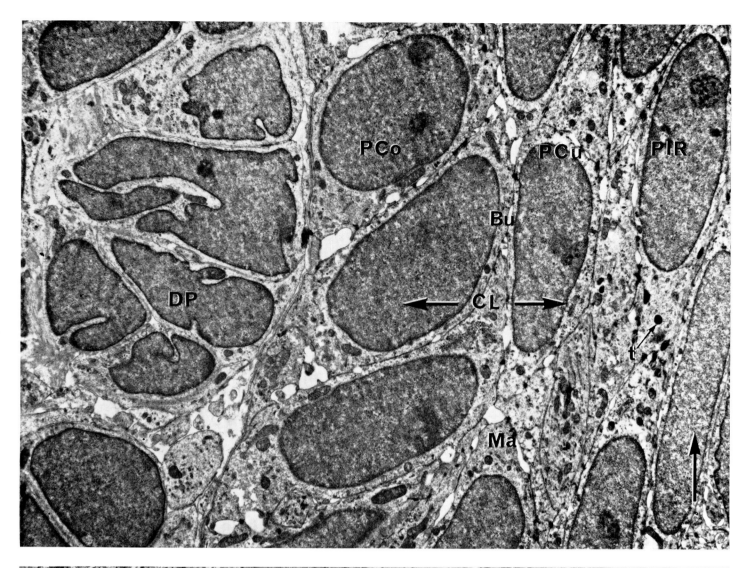

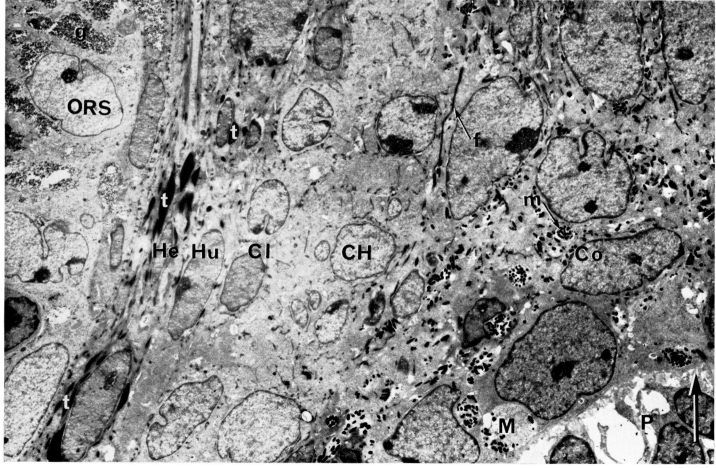

FIGURE 211

Melanocytes may be randomly distributed throughout the follicle at the hair-peg stage, but in the fully differentiated bulbous peg they are mainly confined to upper levels of the outer root sheath, and to the hair bulb above the critical level. In this latter situation they lie among the basal bulbar cells surrounding the apex of the dermal papilla. This micrograph presents a bulbar melanocyte (M) from a bulbous peg at a comparatively early stage of differentiation. It is readily distinguishable from the adjacent basal bulbar cell (B) by virtue of cytoplasmic vesicles (v), premelanosomes (p) and melanosomes (m) exhibiting varying degrees of melaniz-ation. Note also Golgi apparatus (go) and numerous mitochondria (mi). The basal plasma membrane of the cell and the associated basal lamina (b) have both been sectioned tangen-tially, and therefore are not clearly distinguishable. Apical cells of the dermal papilla (DP) are also present within the field.

FIGURE 212

In this micrograph of the cytoplasm of a bulbar melanocyte from a more advanced hair, numerous melanosomes sectioned in various planes may be seen. Partially melanized melano-somes exhibit the characteristic internal structure already described in Section 6, and the general sequence of events involved in melanogenesis is the same in bulbar melanocytes as in those of interfollicular epidermis. The melanocytes are not involved in the general upward movement of cells of the other elements of the follicle, but remain adjacent to the dermal papilla, and feed melanosomes to the cortical cells as they stream past. Transfer of melano-somes appears to be effected by "phagocytosis" of portions of dendritic processes by the cortical cells.

Fig. 211. Bulbar melanocyte in follicle from forearm of 215 mm C.R. (24 week) human fetus. Osmium fixation, lead staining. × 30,600.

Fig. 212. Cytoplasm of bulbar melanocyte in follicle from arm skin of 215 mm C.R. (24 week) human fetus. Osmium fixation, lead staining. × 43,400.

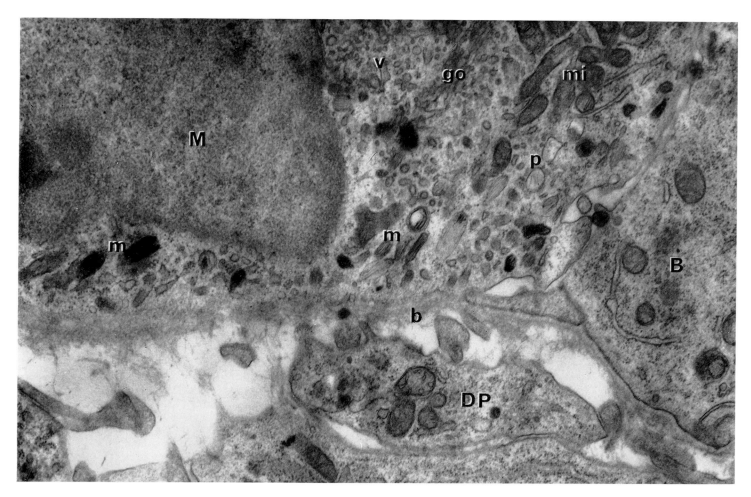

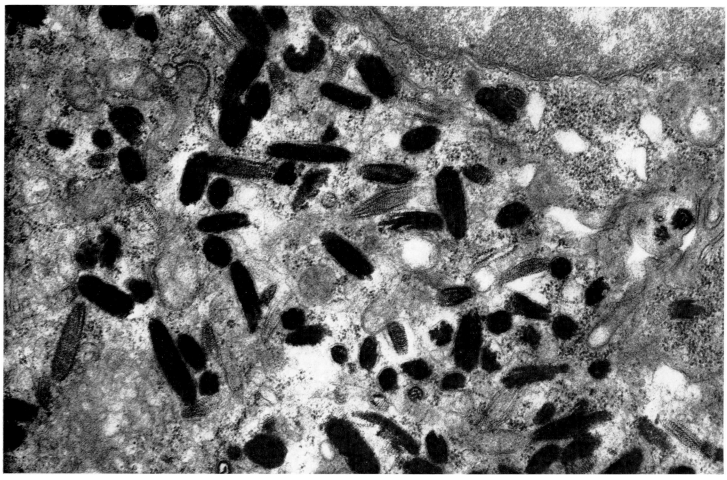

FIGURE 213

In this field taken from a transverse section of the bulb of a follicle just above the level of the apex of the dermal papilla, the concentric arrangement of the various cell layers can be seen. Peripherally (on the left) are glycogen-containing cells of the outer root sheath (ORS), within which are cells of the Henle layer (He) of the inner root sheath containing large irregular trichohyalin granules (t). Cells of the immediately more central Huxley layer (Hu) also contain trichohyalin granules (t), but these are neither as large nor as numerous as those of the Henle layer, and cells of the cuticle of the inner root sheath (CI) contain only isolated single granules (t) at this level. Trichohyalin is the characteristic differentiation product of the three layers of cells constituting the inner root sheath, and as pointed out in the previous Section, the granules are invariably associated with filaments (f). Differences in the concentration of these two products within cells of the three layers at a given level, as here, are indicative of relative degrees of maturity, or progress towards transformation into entirely filamentous elements at a higher level. Cells of the Henle layer undergo transformation at the level of the upper part of the bulb (Fig. 216), and those of Huxley's layer and the cuticle, about half-way up the follicle, the latter at a slightly lower level than the former (Fig. 221).

Cells of the cuticle of the hair (CH) present a relatively undifferentiated appearance at this level, and there is little or no indication of the dense granules which are such a prominent feature at higher levels (Fig. 218). Portion of a cortical cell (Co) falls just within the right hand edge of the field, and the electron-dense structures present in the cytoplasm are melanosomes, and cross-sections of longitudinally orientated bundles of filaments (see Figs. 219 and 226).

Fig. 213. Transverse section through upper bulb of follicle from arm skin of 215 mm C.R. (24 week) human fetus. Osmium fixation, lead staining. ×6,800.

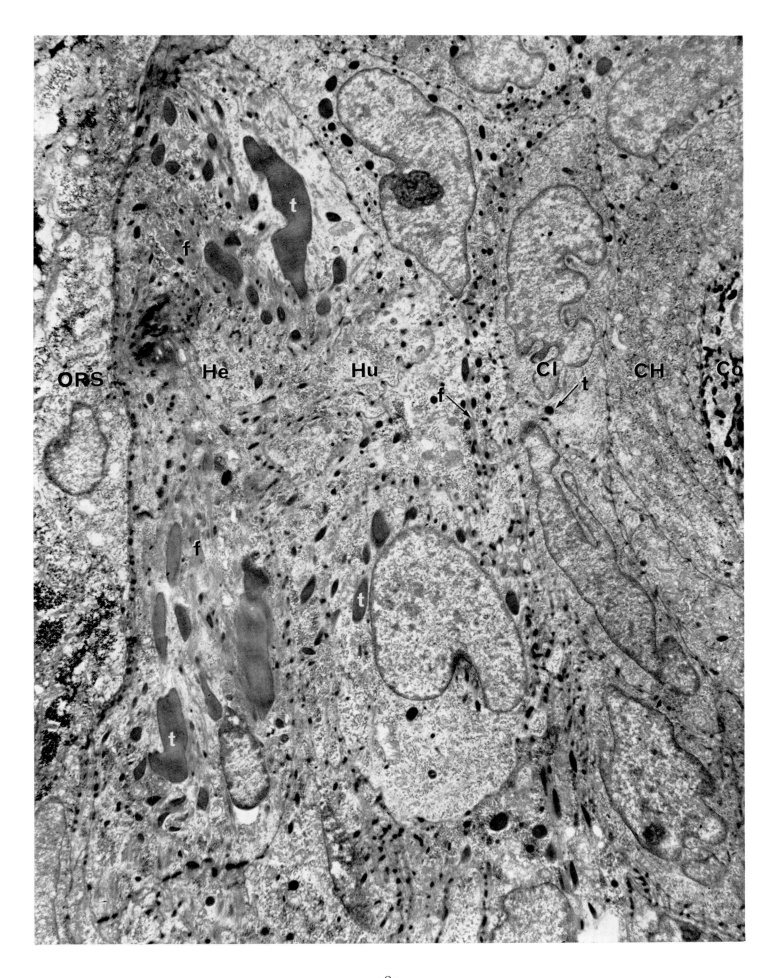

FIGURE 214

This is a longitudinal section passing tangentially from superficial (above) to deep (below) through the outer (ORS) and inner root sheaths in the upper bulbar region of a follicle just below the level at which the Henle layer undergoes transformation. Henle's layer (He) of the inner root sheath occupies the upper part of the field, and the underlying Huxley's layer (Hu) the lower part. The massive build-up of trichohyalin granules (t) and filaments (f) within the Henle layer cells is evident, as is also their orientation parallel with the long axis of the follicle.

FIGURE 215

This is a similar section through a follicle at a slightly higher level. The Henle layer cells (He) are transformed, and one may note the filamentous character of the cytoplasm, the absence of any trace of trichohyalin granules and the degenerative condition of the nuclei (n). Features of transforming and transformed Henle layer cells at higher magnification have already been illustrated in the previous Section (Figs. 201 and 202). In any relatively low-power field such as this, transformed Henle layer cells of different densities may be seen, and a particularly dense one (d) is present at the top left-hand corner here. In general, the cells increase in density as they ascend to higher levels, and nuclear remnants become fewer.

Fig. 214. Angled para-central longitudinal section along upper bulbar region of follicle from scalp of 120 mm C.R. (16½ week) human fetus. Glutaraldehyde-osmium fixation, lead staining. × 4,000 approx.

Fig. 215. Angled para-central longitudinal section along follicle from scalp of 120 mm C.R. (16½ week) human fetus, just above level of transformation of Henle's layer. Glutaraldehyde-osmium fixation, lead staining. × 5,400.

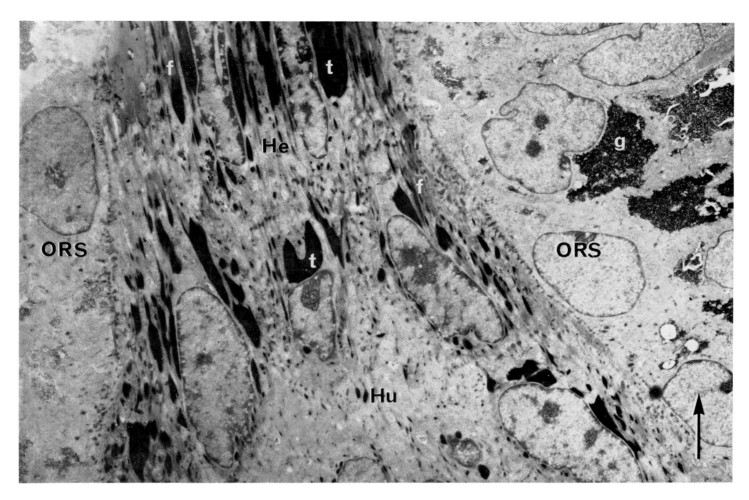

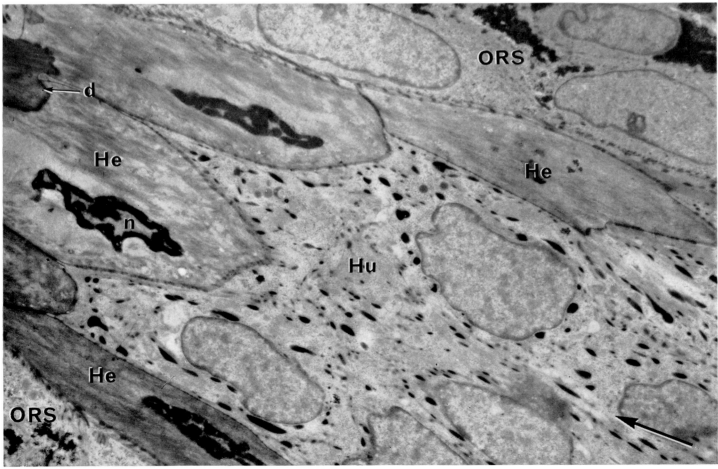

FIGURE 216

This field is taken from a central longitudinal section of a follicle at the level of transformation of the Henle layer (He) of the inner root sheath. The outer root sheath (ORS) consists of two layers, an outer layer, the cells of which are orientated at right angles to the long axis of the follicle, and an inner layer disposed parallel with the long axis. Extensive deposits of glycogen (g) are present in cells of both layers. At higher levels of the follicle, the outer root sheath consists of more than two layers of cells, and melanocytes, Langerhans cells, and Merkel cells may be present.

The abruptness of transformation of the Henle layer is well seen here, and attention may be drawn to the thickening of the plasma membrane (p) which is associated with this. Even over the short length figured here, it is evident that the trichohyalin granules (t) within cells of Huxley's layer are larger in those occupying the higher level.

Fig. 216. Central longitudinal section along follicle from scalp of 120 mm C.R. (16½ week) human fetus, at level of transformation of Henle's layer. Glutaraldehyde-osmium fixation, lead staining. × 7,800.

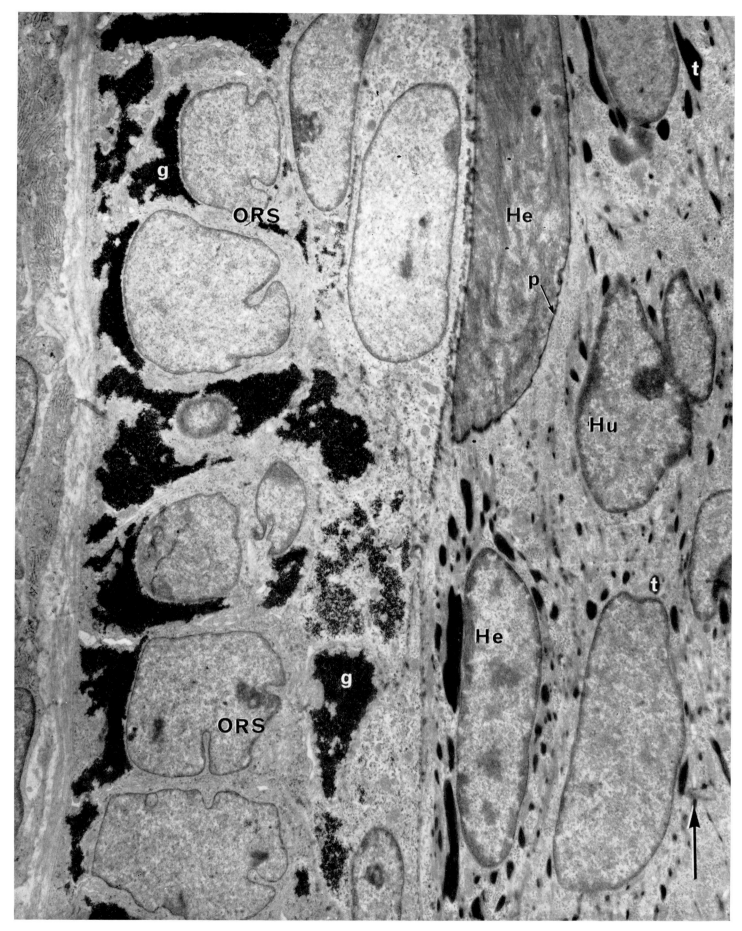

FIGURE 217

In an earlier micrograph (Fig. 213) attention was drawn to the presence of isolated small trichohyalin granules within cells of the cuticle of the inner root sheath at the level of the upper bulb; scattered fine filamentous bundles are also present at this level, but they are not very evident at the magnification shown. Higher up the follicle, both elements become more prominent, as may be seen in this micrograph illustrating a longitudinal section of portions of two cuticular cells, the boundary between which is indicated by a line of desmosomes (d). As in the case of the other two layers (Henle and Huxley) of the inner root sheath, there is an intimate association between the trichohyalin granules (t) and the filamentous bundles (f), but the granules of the cuticle, even at higher levels, remain on the whole smaller. Numerous ribosomes are present between the bundles of filaments.

FIGURE 218

The characteristic differentiation product of the cells of the cuticle of the hair is an amorphous electron-dense substance which appears as granules (g) concentrated mainly, though not exclusively, along the plasma membrane (p) facing the inner root sheath. These granules appear initially at or just above the level of transformation of Henle's layer, and their size is of the order of 30–40 nm (300–400 Å). In cells higher up the follicle, they are larger, and they ultimately coalesce to form a continuous electron-dense zone (Figs. 224 and 225). Filamentous bundles (f) are also present in the cytoplasm, but unlike the filaments of inner root sheath cells which are intimately associated with trichohyalin granules, they bear no specific relation to the granular deposits. The apposed plasma membranes (p) of the cells are prominent, not, as might appear, because they are thickened, but due to deposition of an amorphous substance between them. This is a prominent feature of the fully transformed cuticle (Fig. 238). The cortex (Co) falls just within the lower limit of the field.

Fig. 217. Cells of the cuticle of the inner root sheath from mid-level of a follicle from scalp of 120 mm C.R. (16½ week) human fetus. Glutaraldehyde-osmium fixation, lead staining. ×35,000.

Fig. 218. Cells of cuticle of hair from mid-level of a follicle from scalp of 120 mm C.R. (16½ week) human fetus. Glutaraldehyde-osmium fixation, lead staining. ×44,850.

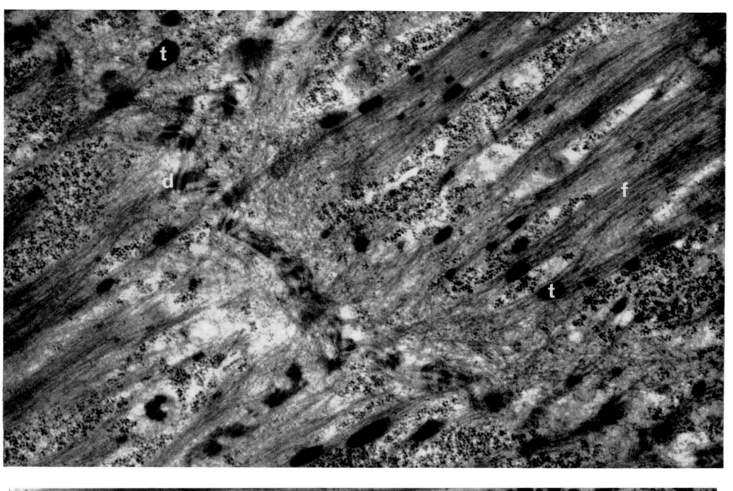

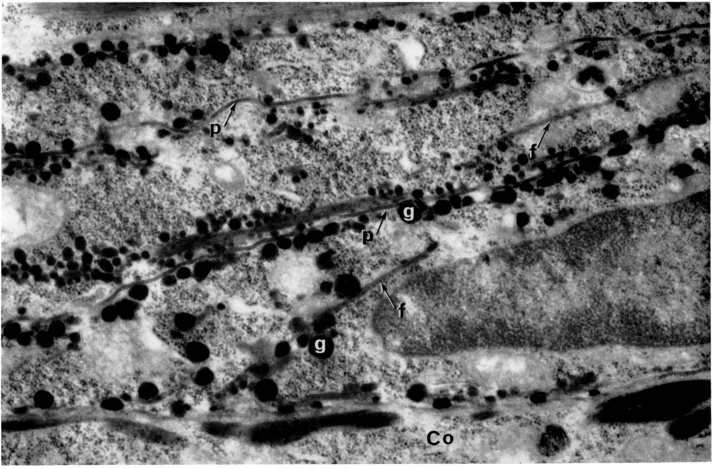

FIGURE 219

This field is taken from a central longitudinal section of a follicle at some distance above the level of transformation of Henle's layer, i.e. in the lower part of the keratogenous zone. It shows the various cell layers and their degree of differentiation at this level. Proceeding from without inwards there are the outer root sheath (ORS), the transformed Henle layer (He) and the Huxley layer (Hu) with trichohyalin granules (t) and filaments (f) orientated along the axis of the follicle. The cells of the cuticle of the inner root sheath (CI) and of the cuticle of the hair (CH) are also disposed longitudinally, and can be seen to be arranged in an overlapping manner. At this magnification the trichohyalin granules and filaments of the inner root sheath cuticular cells are not very evident, but the granules (g) within cells of the cuticle of the hair are clearly seen. The cells of the cortex (Co) contain coarse filamentous bundles (f) and melanosomes (m), and a high concentration of free ribosomes.

Fig. 219. Central longitudinal section along lower supra-bulbar region of follicle from scalp of 120 mm C.R. (16½ week) human fetus. Glutaraldehyde-osmium fixation, lead staining. × 7,000.

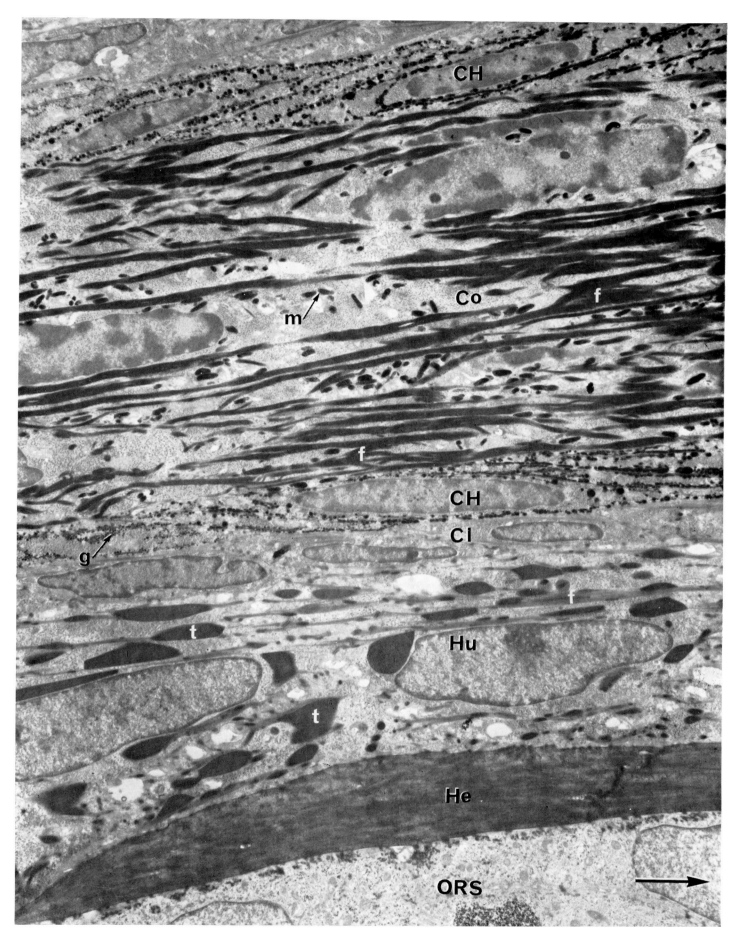

FIGURES 220 and 221

These two micrographs together illustrate a continuous field. The plane of section is longitudinal, but somewhat angled so as to traverse progressively deeper levels of the follicle from below upwards, i.e. from left to right in each case. In the lowest part of the field (left, Fig. 220) the section passes through the cuticle of the inner root sheath (CI), and at a higher level (right, Fig. 221) through the more deeply situated cuticle of the hair (CH). The coalescence of the granules (g) within the cells of this latter layer to form continuous bands (gb) at a higher level is well seen. Note the manner in which the cells overlap, and interlock (i) with the cells of the cuticle of the inner root sheath.

A particular feature of the Huxley layer is illustrated in the lower micrograph (Fig. 221). Whereas, in general, cells of Huxley's layer (Hu) are enclosed by a continuous sheath of transformed Henle cells (He), some at intervals along the follicle send lateral cytoplasmic processes (pf) across Henle's layer to establish direct contact with cells of the outer root sheath. Such cells are known as "Flügelzellen", and they are thought to provide bridges across which nutrients may pass from the outer root sheath to the still untransformed cells of Huxley's layer.

Fig. 220. Angled para-central longitudinal section along mid-level of a follicle from scalp of 120 mm C.R. (16½ week) human fetus. Glutaraldehyde-osmium fixation, lead staining. × 5,000 approx.

Fig. 221. Upward continuation of field shown in Fig. 220. × 5,500 approx.

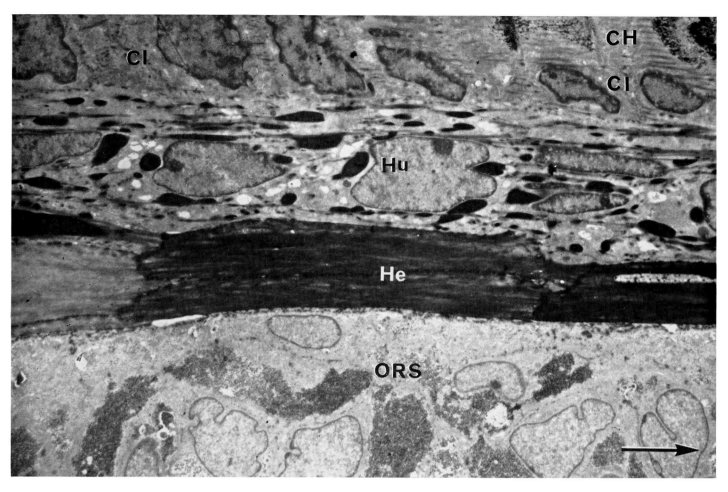

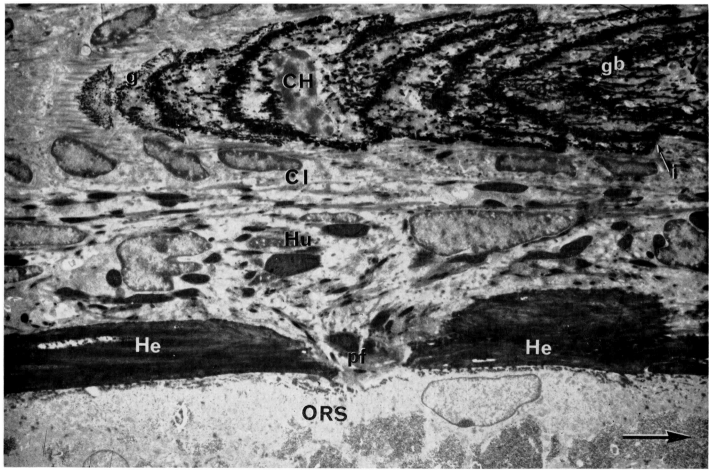

FIGURE 222

This low-power survey micrograph of a slightly angled longitudinal section along a follicle includes the region in which Huxley's layer (Hu), the cuticle of the inner root sheath (CI), the cuticle of the hair (CH), and the cortex (Co) become transformed, as indicated by the addition of the letter T to the appropriate label in each case. The cuticle of the inner root sheath becomes transformed at a lower level than Huxley's layer, and the cuticle of the hair at a slightly lower level than the cortex. Towards the right hand limit of the field, the final condition has been attained where all elements of the follicle, apart from the outer root sheath (ORS), have undergone transformation.

FIGURE 223

This features part of the field covered by Fig. 222 at higher magnification. The abrupt transformation of Huxley layer (Hu) cells with massive trichohyalin granules (t) into filamentous elements (HuT and inset) without any trace of trichohyalin is striking. The interlocking of the cells of the transformed cuticles (CIT and CHT) may also be noted. In the lower part of the field individual coarse bundles of filaments can still be distinguished in the cortex (Co) but these are no longer evident as such following transformation (CoT). The Huxley layer and cortex receive further attention in the following Section dealing with post-natal hair.

Fig. 222. Angled near-central longitudinal section along follicle from scalp of 120 mm C.R. ($16\frac{1}{2}$ week) human fetus, at level of transformation of cuticles and Huxley's layer. Glutaraldehyde-osmium fixation, lead staining. ×4,000 approx.

Fig. 223. Longitudinal section along follicle from scalp of 120 mm C.R. ($16\frac{1}{2}$ week) human fetus at level of transformation of Huxley's layer. Glutaraldehyde-osmium fixation, lead staining. ×6,400 approx. *Inset:* Filamentous cytoplasm of transformed Huxley cell. ×63,000.

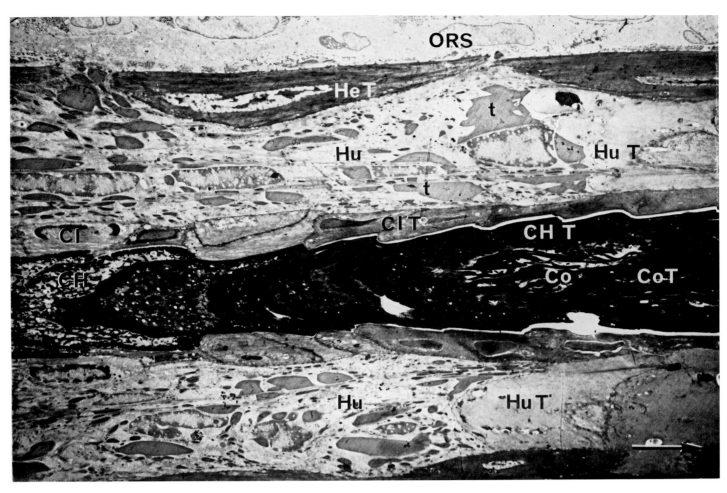

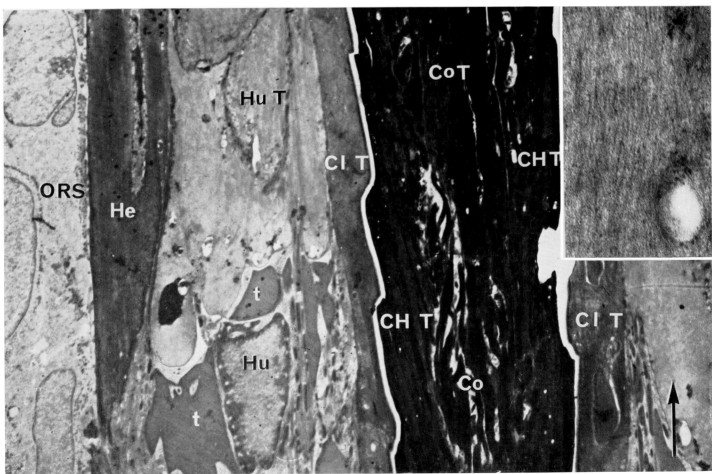

FIGURES 224 and 225

These two micrographs, in longitudinal sequence starting at the left of Fig. 223, and ending at the right of Fig. 225, cover the region of transformation of the cuticle of the inner root sheath, and the cuticle of the hair. Towards the left of the upper micrograph an untransformed cell of the cuticle of the inner root sheath (CI_1) is seen with trichohyalin granules (t) and filaments (f) in the cytoplasm. The plasma membrane of the cell, and the apposed plasma membrane of the adjacent Huxley layer cell (Hu), is not very apparent. The immediately higher situated cell (CI_2, in both micrographs) lacks trichohyalin granules, has a higher content of filaments (f), and the plasma membrane (p) is clearly defined because it is thicker; the nucleus (n) exhibits areas of different densities. These features are typical of transforming inner root sheath cells (cf. Figs. 201 and 202). The process of transformation is practically complete in the next cell (CIT), the cytoplasm of which presents a more homogenous appearance of filaments with islands of ribosomes.

In Fig. 224, the cells of the cuticle of the hair (CH) are in the untransformed condition, and one may note again the dense substance (g) concentrated mainly along the outer plasma membrane and formed by the coalescence of granules individually apparent in this situation at lower levels in the follicle (Fig. 218). The deeper part of the cell contains the nucleus (n) and a zone of cytoplasm with ribosomes and some dense granular substance. In the transformed cell (CHT, Fig. 225) the granular substance is seen to form a continuous dense band of amorphous material (d) along the outer plasma membrane, and the deeper part of the cell is also more electron dense, and undergoing transformation of a nature which is not very well understood. In completely transformed cuticular cells of post-natal hair, corresponding inner and outer zones can be detected (Figs. 238 and 244), and they will receive further consideration later.

Fig. 224. Longitudinal section along follicle from scalp of 120 mm C.R. ($16\frac{1}{2}$ week) human fetus at level of transformation of cuticles. Glutaraldehyde-osmium fixation, lead staining. × 28,350.

Fig. 225. Upward continuation of field shown in Fig. 224. × 28,350.

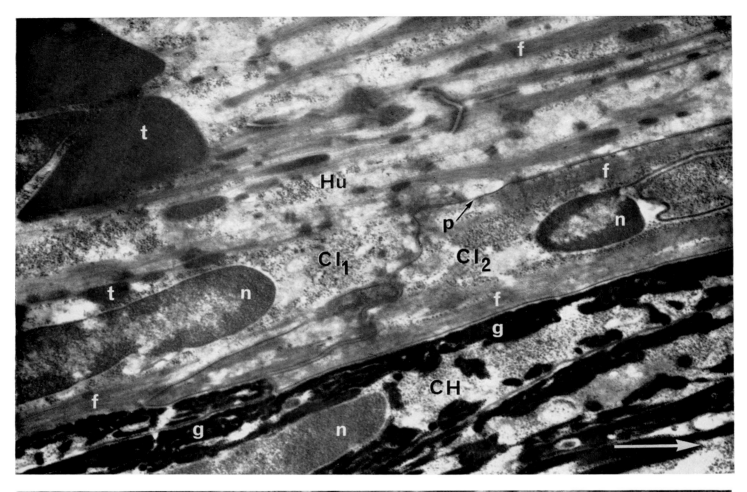

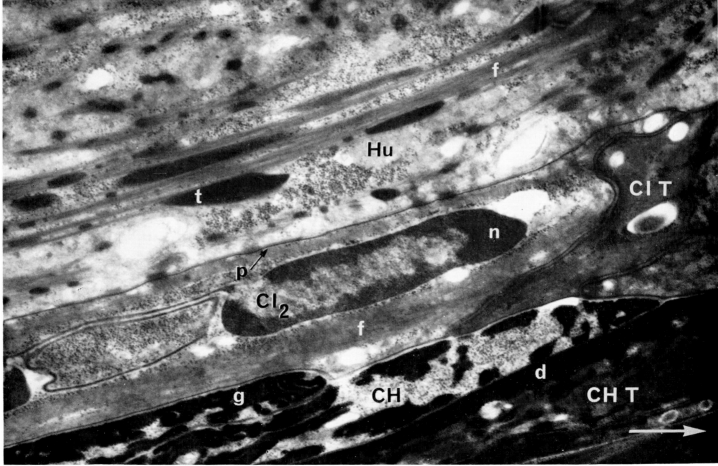

FIGURE 226

This micrograph features cortical cells from a transverse section of a follicle just above the level of the apex of the dermal papilla. Apart from the common organelles, the cytoplasm contains melanosomes (m) and closely knit filamentous bundles (f). Trichohyalin granules are not present in cortical cells. Higher up the follicle (Figs. 219 and 222) the longitudinally orientated filamentous bundles increase in diameter, the intervening areas of cytoplasm become smaller, and the cells undergo an abrupt transformation, the mechanism of which is poorly understood.

FIGURE 227

This presents a transverse section of a hair just above the level of entry of the duct of the sebaceous gland into the follicle. At this level, the inner root sheath (IRS) is undergoing disintegration, and the cuticle of the hair (CH) has become freed from it. The cortex (Co) is fully transformed at this level, and its original cellular constitution (see Fig. 226) is not very apparent, though plasma membranes (p) may be defined in places. Structurally, the transformed cortical cell consists of bundles of filaments (b) outlined by interspersed amorphous material (a) and melanosomes (m). The individual filaments which make up the bundles are not apparent at this magnification, but they are illustrated in micrographs of the following Section (Figs. 245 and 246).

Fig. 226. Cortical cells as seen on transverse section through upper bulbar region of a follicle from arm of 215 mm C.R. (24 week) human fetus. Osmium fixation, lead staining. × 12,600.

Fig. 227. Transverse section of hair from arm of 215 mm C.R. (24 week) human fetus. Osmium fixation, lead staining. × 27,300.

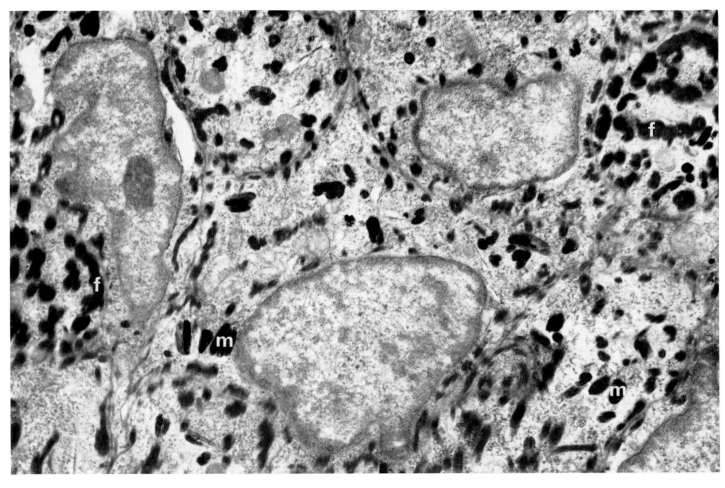

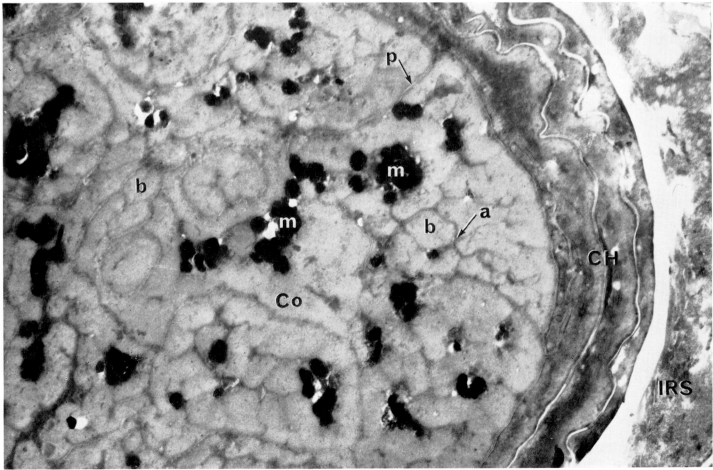

FIGURE 228

The outer root sheath is present in many of the preceding micrographs, from which it will be apparent that the cells present roughly the same appearance whatever their level in the follicle. Their most characteristic feature is the presence of glycogen deposits of varying size. This micrograph is taken from a transverse section of a follicle just below the level of entry of the sebaceous duct, and corresponds approximately in position to the section of the hair tract of a follicle at an earlier stage of differentiation illustrated in Fig. 203. The plasma membranes of the outer root sheath cells (ORS) exhibit desmosomes, and the cytoplasm contains glycogen (g) and filaments (f). A narrow keratinized strip (k) abuts against the transformed Henle layer (He) cells, and this is presumably a persistent remnant of the central keratinized zone which at an earlier stage (Fig. 203) is associated with canalization of the hair tract. Such a keratinized strip is not usually evident at this level of post-natal follicles.

Fig. 228. Transverse section through outer and inner root sheaths of follicle from arm of 215 mm C.R. (24 week) human fetus, just below level of entry of sebaceous duct. Osmium fixation, lead staining. × 17,500.

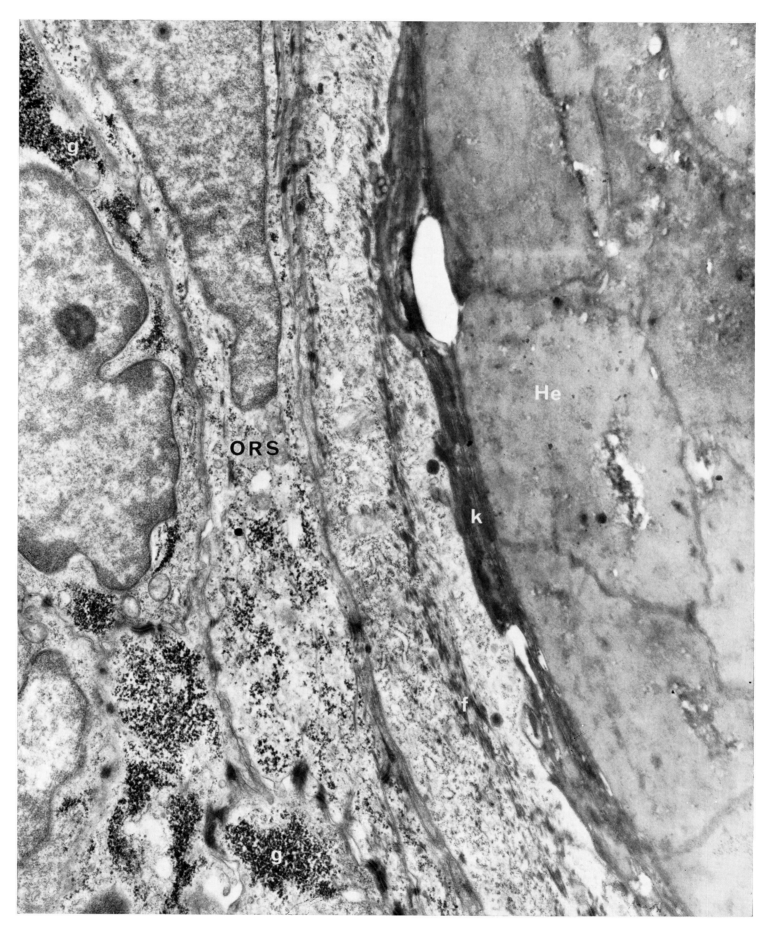

ORS

He

k

f

g

g

303

FIGURE 229

This transverse section of a follicle just below the level of entry of the sebaceous duct gives an over-all picture of the differentiated fetal hair and its sheaths. Peripherally is the connective tissue sheath (s) consisting of fibroblasts and layers of collagen. Within this is the outer root sheath (ORS) with its deep keratinized strip (k), and more centrally the transformed cells of Henle's (He) and Huxley's (Hu) layers. A few Flügelzell processes (pf) may be seen. The cuticles (Cu) lie within Huxley's layer, and the cortex (Co) occupying the centre of the follicle is slightly displaced. A distinct medulla is not present in fetal hair, but apart from this, the basic structure of the follicle is essentially similar to that seen in post-natal hair.

Fig. 229. Transverse section through hair and its sheaths just below level of entry of sebaceous duct. From arm of 215 mm C.R. (24 week) human fetus. Osmium fixation, lead staining. × 5,250.

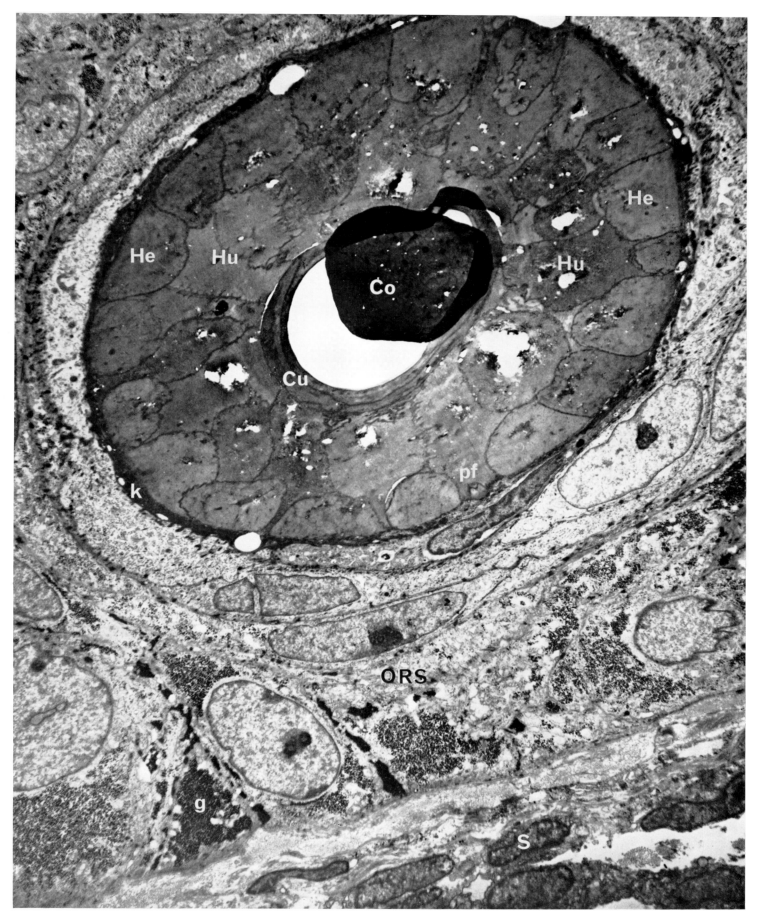

REFERENCES

Birbeck, M. S. C. and Mercer, E. H. The electron microscopy of the human hair follicle, Parts 1–3. *J. biophys. biochem. Cytol.*, **3**:203, 215, 223, 1957.

Charles, A. Electron microscope observations of hardening in the hair follicle. *Expl Cell Res.*, **18**:138, 1959.

Happey, F. and Johnson, A. G. Some electron microscope observations on hardening in the human hair follicle. *J. Ultrastruct. Res.*, **7**:316, 1962.

Kint, A. Le follicule pileux. Étude au microscope électronique. *Annls Derm. Syph.*, **94**:19, 1967.

Parakkal, P. F. and Matoltsy, A. G. A study of the differentiation products of the hair follicle cells with the electron microscope. *J. invest. Derm.*, **42**:23, 1964.

Puccinelli, V. A., Caputo, R. and Ceccarelli, B. The structure of the human hair follicle and hair shaft: an electron microscope study. *G. ital. Derm.*, **108**:1, 1967.

Roth, S. I. and Clarke, W. H. Jr. Ultrastructural evidence related to the mechanism of keratin synthesis. In, "The Epidermis", W. Montagna and W. C. Lobitz, eds. New York, Academic Press, 1964.

13 Features of Fully Developed Hair

*Inner root sheath: transformation of Huxley's layer: cuticle of inner root sheath —
cuticle of the hair — cortex — medulla — pilary canal — arrector pili muscle.*

FIGURE 230

The relatively undifferentiated bulbar and supra-bulbar regions of fully developed hair up to the level of transformation of Henle's layer do not differ significantly from fetal hair as already illustrated (Figs. 209 and 210), apart, of course, from the presence of a medulla (see Figs. 247 and 248). This micrograph is taken from a transverse section a short distance above the level of transformation of Henle's layer. The outer root sheath (ORS) has become rolled up, but that does not matter, as it is not under consideration here. Within Henle's layer (He) are two or three layers of Huxley cells (Hu), and at this low magnification all that can be distinguished inside them are the nuclei (n) and trichohyalin granules (t) of varying size and shape. Deep to Huxley's layer is the cuticle of the inner root sheath (CI), and deeper still the cuticle of the hair (CH) comprising 8–10 cellular layers. Deepest of all in this field can be seen the peripheral part of the cortex (Co), the cells of which contain numerous dense bundles of compacted filaments.

FIGURE 231

This micrograph is taken from a more central area of the section illustrated in Fig. 230, and shows medullary cells (M) surrounded by the cortex (Co). The cells of the medulla have nuclei (n) with prominent nucleoli, and the cytoplasm contains abundant glycogen (g), mitochondria (m), the occasional melanosome (me), and isolated short filamentous bundles (f). Dense spherical granules (d), known as medullary granules, and vesicles (v) of varying size are highly characteristic of medullary cell cytoplasm, which presents a totally different appearance to the cytoplasm of adjacent cortical (Co) cells.

Further details of medullary cells are illustrated in Figs. 247 and 248.

Fig. 230. Segment of transverse section of lower end of plucked eye-brow hair of woman aged 25. Osmium fixation, lead staining. × 4,000 approx.

Fig. 231. Transverse section of medulla and central cortex from lower end of plucked eye-brow hair of woman aged 25. Osmium fixation, lead staining. × 6,000.

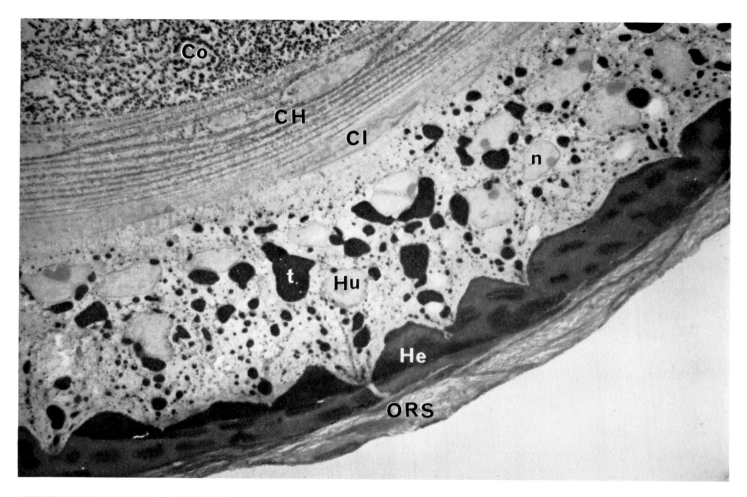

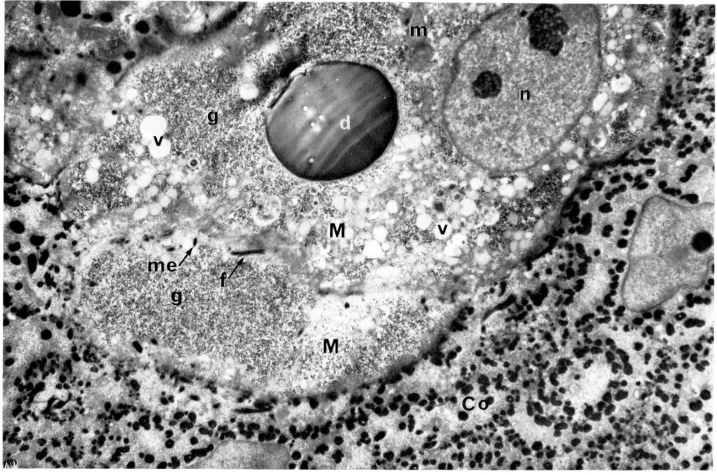

FIGURE 232

In the previous Section, 12, it was pointed out that, structurally, the cells of Henle's and Huxley's layers of the inner root sheath are identical, and micrographs illustrating transformation of Henle's layer were presented (Figs. 215 and 216). In this and the following two micrographs, cells of Huxley's layer of fully developed hair are featured for comparison. Portions of two cells are figured here, and it may be noted that in addition to desmosomes, tight junctions (j) are associated with the apposed plasma membranes. Portion of the nucleus (n) of one cell is present, and within the cytoplasm of both are the typical dense trichohyalin granules (t) with associated filaments (f), many of which appear to run into the granules. Bundles of filaments unassociated with trichohyalin granules are also present, and it is evident that the diameter of the individual filaments is approximately half that of ribosomes (r).

The trichohyalin granules present a uniformly dense appearance, and reveal no pattern such as can be discerned within similar granules of early fetal hair (see inset, Fig. 199). This applies to even the smallest granules visible here, and in so far as they represent early formative stages, it is evident that purely static ultrastructural appearances yield no information concerning their nature or mode of formation.

Fig. 232. Transverse section of cells of Huxley's layer from lower end of plucked eye-brow hair of woman aged 25. Osmium fixation, lead staining. × 74,100.

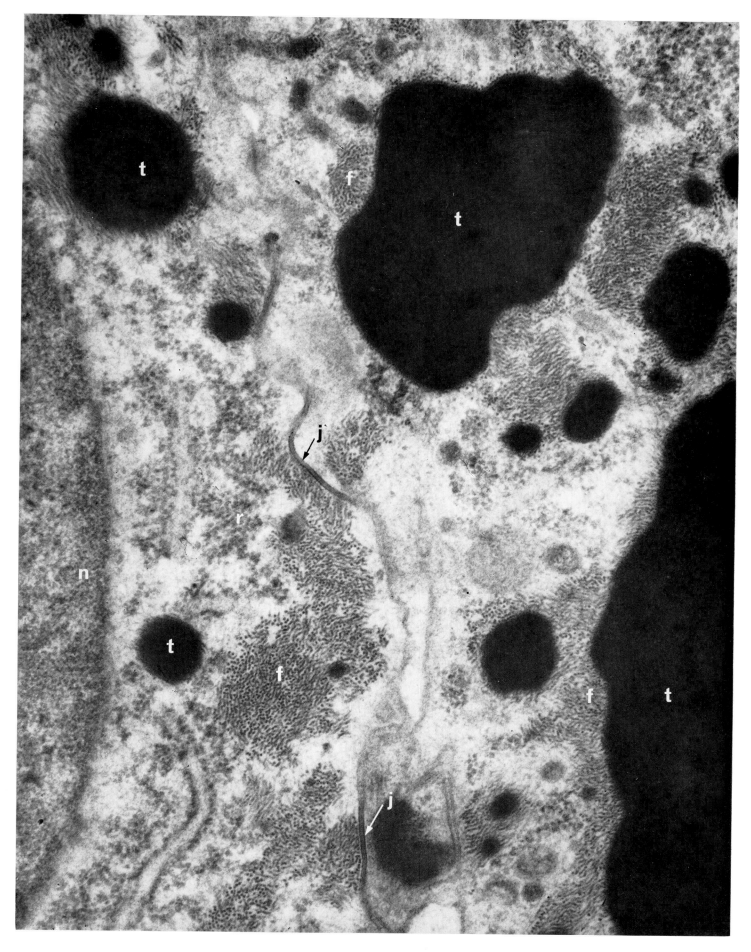

311

HUXLEY'S LAYER—TRICHOHYALIN, FILAMENTS, AND TRANSFORMATION

FIGURE 233

This micrograph illustrates a particular feature of the relation between trichohyalin granules and filaments, which may or may not be of significance. In previous micrographs attention has been drawn to the manner in which the filaments (f) appear to run into the granules (t) so that the latter frequently present a ragged outline; the granule in the right half of the field is a typical example of this. This appearance is consistent with the suggestion that filaments, whether altered or unaltered, constitute an essential component of the granule though not individually identifiable within it. The appearance of the granule (t) on the left, however, could lead one to question this concept. Over a considerable extent, the margin appears sharply defined and smooth, and the immediately adjacent filaments (f) are clearly separate from it and do not run into it. It may be that this is a truer picture of the relation obtaining between granule and filaments, and that the more frequently observed appearance of filaments running into the granules is a sectional artifact due to the irregular shape of the granules and the undulant character of the filaments. If this be so, it could be postulated that trichohyalin and filaments are entirely separate substances, and that the granules do not consist of filaments plus amorphous substance, but of this latter alone. However this may be, an even greater problem surrounds the abrupt transformation of cytoplasm of the type illustrated here and in the previous figure into that seen in Fig. 234.

FIGURE 234

The interior of the transformed Huxley layer cell (Hu) consists of filaments (f) which, when sectioned transversely (tr), are so loosely arranged that it seems necessary to postulate the presence of an interfilamentous matrix. Many authors believe in the existence of such a matrix, and that it is derived from the trichohyalin granules of the untransformed cell, the absence of which from the transformed cell could then be explained on the basis of a general dispersal of their substance.

Attention may be drawn to the somewhat different appearance of the adjacent Henle layer cell (He). Cells of Henle's layer become transformed at a much lower level of the follicle than those of Huxley's layer, and shortly after transformation they are similar in appearance to the Huxley cell figured here (see also Figs. 202 and 216). Higher up the follicle, however, they present the more compact almost amorphous appearance seen here, and it is difficult or impossible to identify individual filaments within them. A similar change occurs in Huxley's layer at higher levels, but whether this is due solely to a further compacting of filaments, or to some molecular re-arrangement, is difficult to say. It may be indicative of the impending dissolution of the cells which occurs at the level of the isthmus of the follicle (see Fig. 249).

Fig. 233. Trichohyalin granules and filaments in cell of Huxley's layer. Osmium fixation, lead staining. ×133,000.

Fig. 234. Cells of transformed Huxley's and Henle's layers of plucked eye-brow hair of woman aged 25. Osmium fixation, lead staining. ×44,800.

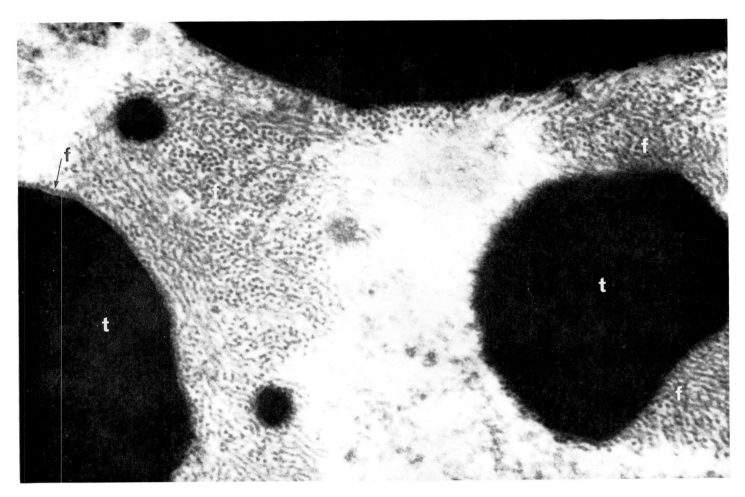

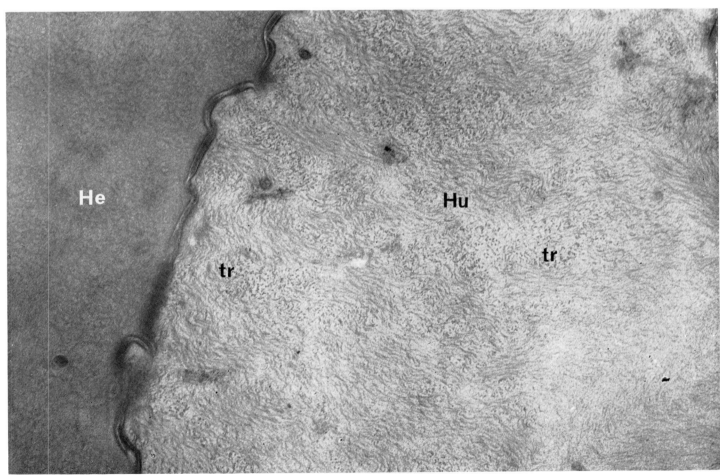

313

FIGURE 235

This micrograph features cells of the cuticle of the inner root sheath (CI) at a low suprabulbar level of the follicle. The cells are flattened, and desmosomes (d) and tight junctions (j) are associated with the plasma membranes. Small round trichohyalin granules (t) are present in the cytoplasm, as well as filamentous bundles (f). The majority of the small dense granules scattered among the filaments and other organelles are ribosomes, but some glycogen granules are also present. Peripheral cells of the cuticle of the hair (CH) are visible at the top of the field, and one may note a degree of imbrication between apposed cells of the two cuticles.

FIGURE 236

The cells of the cuticle of the inner root sheath have essentially the same structural components as those of Henle's and Huxley's layers, and immediately following transformation (Figs. 224 and 225) present a similar appearance. At higher levels of the follicle as illustrated here (CI), their contents likewise become more compacted, so that the basic filamentous substructure is no longer clearly evident. Nuclear remnants (n) may still be present within cells at this level.

One may sum up differentiation, or maturation, of the three elements of the inner root sheath—Henle's layer, Huxley's layer, and the cuticle—by stating that their characteristic differentiation products are trichohyalin granules and filaments, which, following transformation, become re-arranged to present a sub-structure of filaments embedded in an amorphous matrix without any clear-cut pattern such as is apparent in the cortex (Fig. 246). Little or nothing is known of the origin or nature of trichohyalin granules, or of the processes and alterations involved in transformation. As the transformed cells ascend to higher levels of the follicle their sub-structure appears to undergo some further change of a nature not clearly understood.

Fig. 235. Transverse section of cuticle of inner root sheath of plucked eye-brow hair of woman aged 25. Osmium fixation, lead staining. × 30,500.

Fig. 236. Transverse section of transformed cuticle of inner root sheath of hair follicle from axilla of man aged 25. Osmium fixation, lead staining. × 132,500.

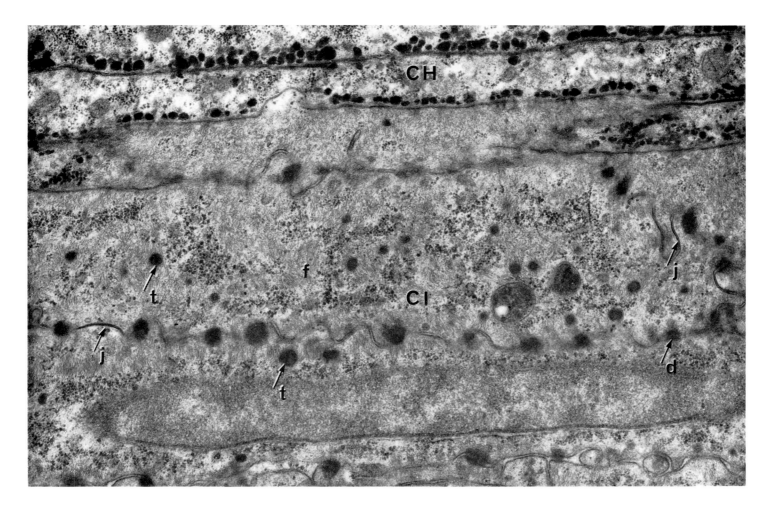

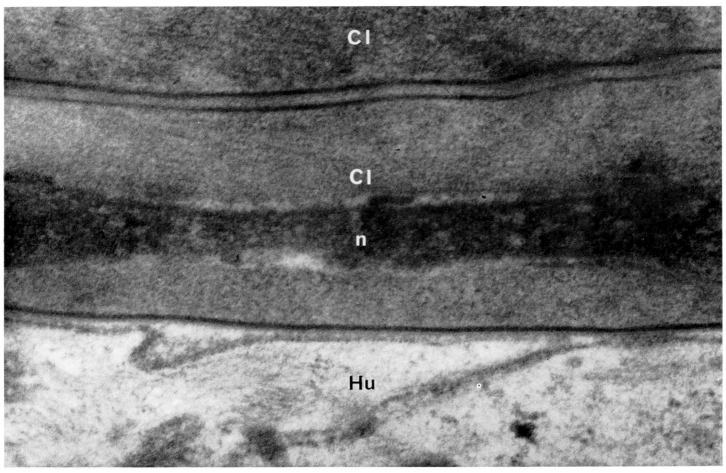

FIGURE 237

As already seen (Figs. 218 and 221) the characteristic feature of the cells of the cuticle of the hair is the presence of dense amorphous granular deposits (g) aligned predominantly along the outer plasma membrane towards the cuticle of the inner root sheath (CI); the cells also contain isolated short filamentous bundles (f), and the nucleus (n) occupies the deeper part of the cell. Five to ten layers of cuticular cells may be present, and in the hair illustrated, ten were seen. Higher up the follicle the amorphous granules coalesce to form a continuous band (Figs. 223 and 224), and the cells undergo transformation to the condition seen in Fig. 238.

FIGURE 238

The fully transformed cuticular cell exhibits outer (Ou) and inner (In) zones of different densities. The outer less dense zone, paradoxically, is the region which is occupied by the dense granules of the untransformed cell, and the inner dense zone corresponds to the region containing the nucleus and fewer granules (see Figs. 224 and 225). Membrane-limited structures (r) of round or elongated shape are frequently seen within the dense zone, and may represent remnants of the nucleus or cytoplasmic organelles. Treatment of the hair with thioglycollic acid reverses the appearance shown here, the outer zone appearing dense, and the inner one less dense. A band of dense intercellular substance (i) lies between the cells.

At high resolution both outer and inner zones present an amorphous finely granular appearance (see inset) which contrasts with the filament-matrix complex occupying the interior of transformed inner root sheath (Fig. 234) and cortical (Fig. 246) cells.

Fig. 237. Transverse section of cuticle of plucked eye-brow hair of woman aged 25. Osmium fixation, lead staining. × 12,900.

Fig. 238. Transverse section of transformed cuticle of plucked eye-brow hair of woman aged 25. Osmium fixation, uranyl acetate and lead staining. × 55,800. *Inset:* × 149,500.

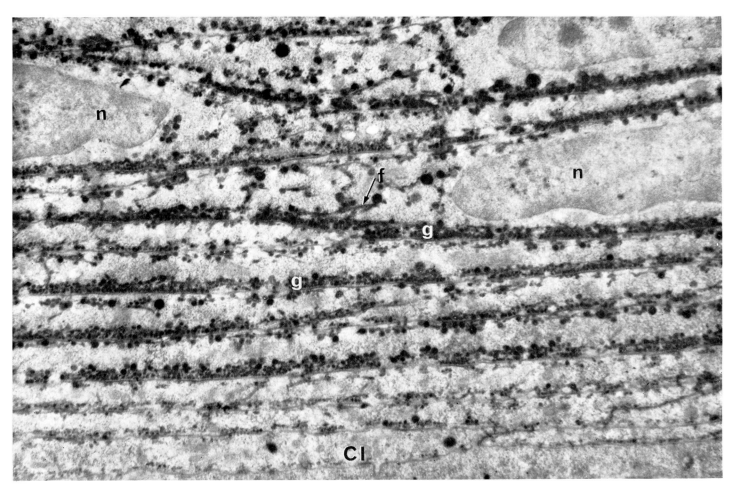

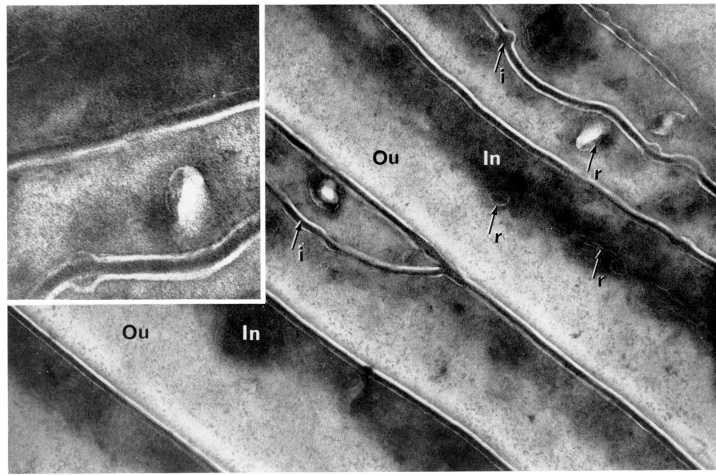

FIGURE 239

This is a typical low-power field taken from a transverse section of the cortex just above the level of transformation of Huxley's layer. The nucleus of the cortical cell has a prominent nucleolus (n), and the cytoplasm is packed with electron-dense bundles of compacted filaments arranged parallel with the long axis of the follicle. Melanosomes, also present in the cytoplasm, are difficult to distinguish from the smaller filamentous bundles at this magnification.

FIGURE 240

In this higher-power micrograph, the filamentous sub-structure of the very dense bundles (f) is still not apparent, and indeed they might be taken for trichohyalin granules. Less dense areas within some bundles towards the top of the field are small portions of cytoplasm "trapped" so to speak by close approximation or coalescence of adjacent bundles. The general cytoplasm has a high content of ribosomes (r), and a few ill-defined mitochondria are also present. At this magnification, melanosomes (m) are readily distinguishable from the filamentous bundles.

Fig. 239. Transverse section of cortex of plucked eye-brow hair of woman aged 25. Osmium fixation, lead staining. ×6,900.

Fig. 240. Transverse section of cortex of plucked eye-brow hair of woman aged 25. Osmium fixation, lead staining. ×40,000.

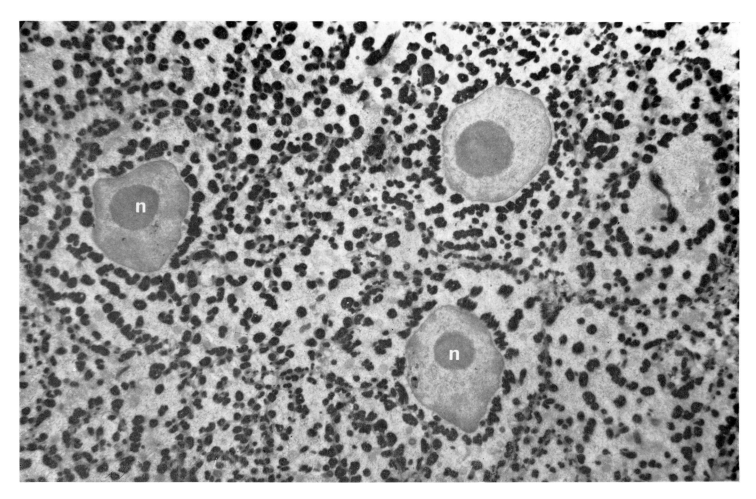

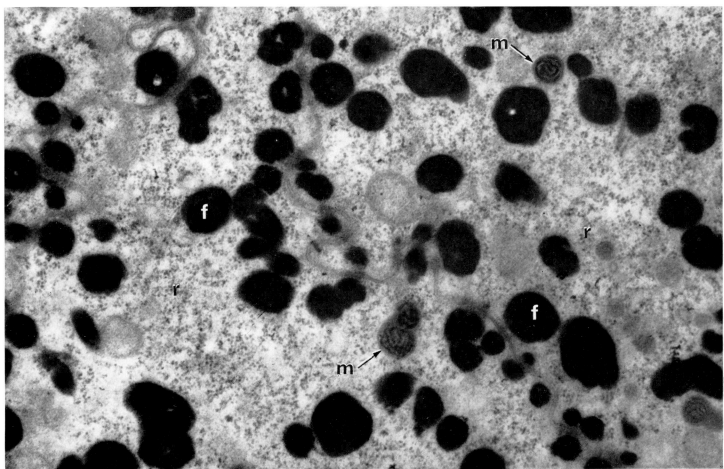

FIGURES 241 and 242

The tight packing and, in places, regular arrangement of the filaments constituting the bundles is well seen in these two micrographs. The individual filaments have a diameter of 7–8 nm (70–80 Å), and are apparently embedded in a less dense matrix. In the lower micrograph, some filaments (arrowed) exhibit a less dense central core, and each bundle has an area of cytoplasm (c) entrapped within it.

It is of some interest to compare these filaments with the less closely-packed filaments present within inner root sheath cells (Fig. 233).

Fig. 241. Transverse section of filamentous bundles in cortical cell of plucked eye-brow hair of woman aged 25. Osmium fixation, lead staining. ×200,000.

Fig. 242. Transverse section of filamentous bundles in cortical cell of plucked eye-brow hair of woman aged 25. Osmium fixation, lead staining. ×280,000.

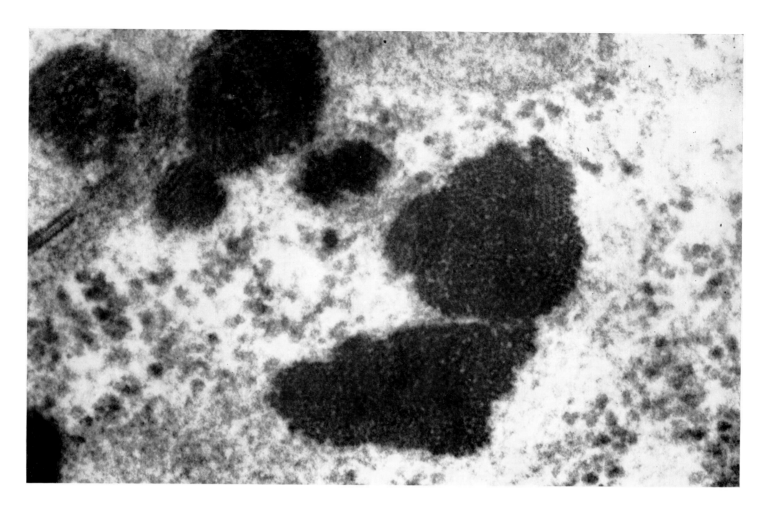

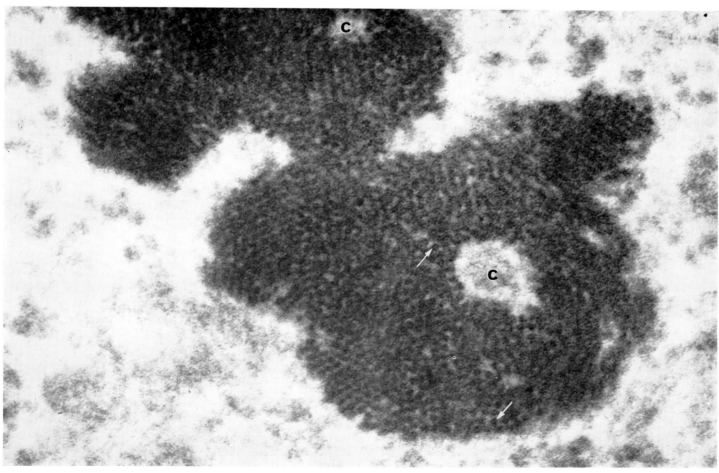

FIGURE 243

As the cortical cells ascend to higher levels of the follicle the existing filamentous bundles increase in size by accretion of more filaments, and new bundles are also formed. The bundles (fb) coalesce in irregular fashion so that just before final transformation, as here, the cortex presents an irregular jig-saw appearance of dense bundles with intervening less dense regions containing remnants (r) of nuclei and degenerating cytoplasmic organelles. The cuticle of the hair (CH) can be seen here at the periphery of the cortex.

FIGURE 244

This micrograph presents the peripheral part of the transformed cortex (Co) and the adjacent cuticle of the hair (CH). Plasma membranes (p) of cortical cells are evident with intervening dense intercellular material as in the case of the cuticle. Similar material is present at the interface between the innermost cuticular cell and the cortex. At this magnification, it is not apparent that the cortex has a filamentous sub-structure, and indeed, its appearance is very similar to that of the amorphous cuticle. There is little evidence either of individual bundles, and one might conclude that during the process of transformation they have coalesced almost completely, and undergone a marked change in density. This is, in fact, the case, but at higher magnifications (Figs. 245 and 246) it is evident that the filamentous sub-structure remains.

Fig. 243. Transverse section of transforming cortex of hair from axilla of man aged 25. Osmium fixation, lead staining. × 25,200.

Fig. 244. Transverse section of cuticle and transformed cortex of plucked eye-brow hair of woman aged 23. Osmium fixation, uranyl acetate and lead staining. × 41,600.

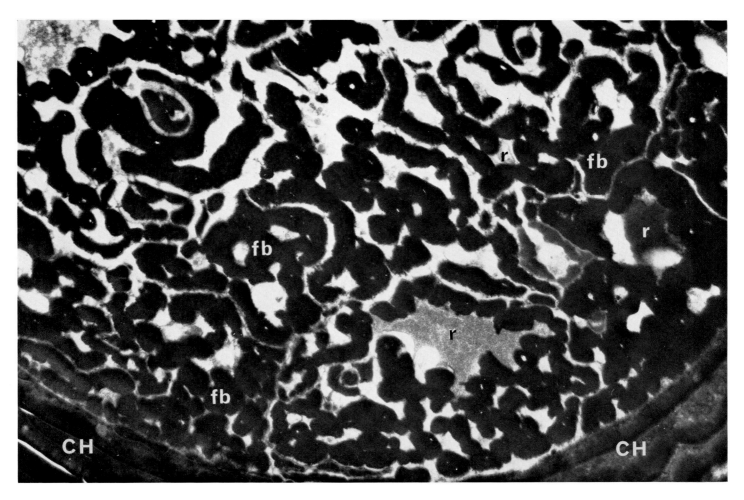

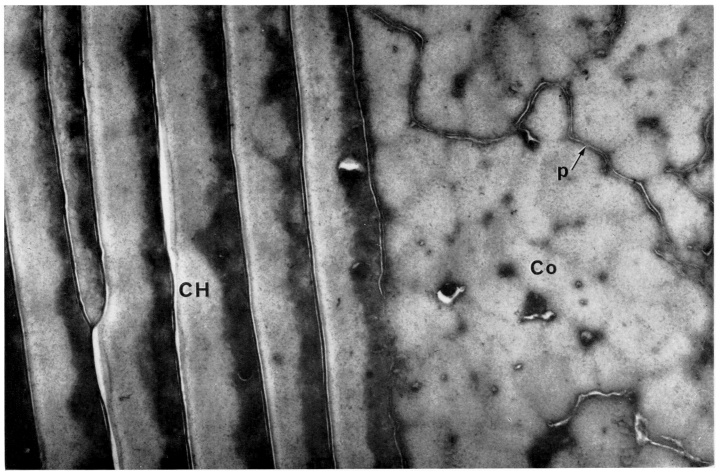

FIGURE 245

Portions of three or four transformed cortical cells are seen in this micrograph, and one may note again the presence of dense intercellular material (i). Within one cell is a nuclear remnant (n) and within another irregular masses of dense material (d) which by comparison with Fig. 243 would appear to be derived from cytoplasmic substance occupying the intervals between coalescing filamentous bundles at this stage. These nuclear and cytoplasmic remains serve partially to outline the transformed bundles (b) which, particularly in the central cell, present a characteristic "thumb-print" appearance.

FIGURE 246

High resolution micrographs of transformed cortical cells reveal a pattern which has been interpreted as being due to relatively translucent filaments (f inset) set in a more dense amorphous matrix. These differences in density are the reverse of those obtaining in un-transformed cortical cells (see Fig. 242). In transverse sections, such as here, groups of axially oriented filaments (a) may be seen surrounded by others (l) dispersed in the form of concentric lamellae, or whorls, and it is this arrangement which accounts for the "thumb-print" appearance. The lamellar or whorled arrangement has been interpreted as being due to twisting of filaments developed in the later stages of maturation before transformation, but this suggestion must be regarded as speculative. Some of the filaments seen in the inset exhibit a central dense dot, which may represent protofilaments more clearly seen in the cortex of wool fibres. These micrographs may be compared with Figs. 106 and 107 illustrating the stratum corneum of interfollicular epidermis.

Fig. 245. Transverse section of transformed cortex of plucked eye-brow hair of woman aged 25. Osmium fixation, uranyl acetate and lead staining. × 67,500.

Fig. 246. Transverse section of transformed cortex of plucked eye-brow hair of woman aged 25. Osmium fixation, uranyl acetate and lead staining. × 116,000. *Inset:* × 116,000.

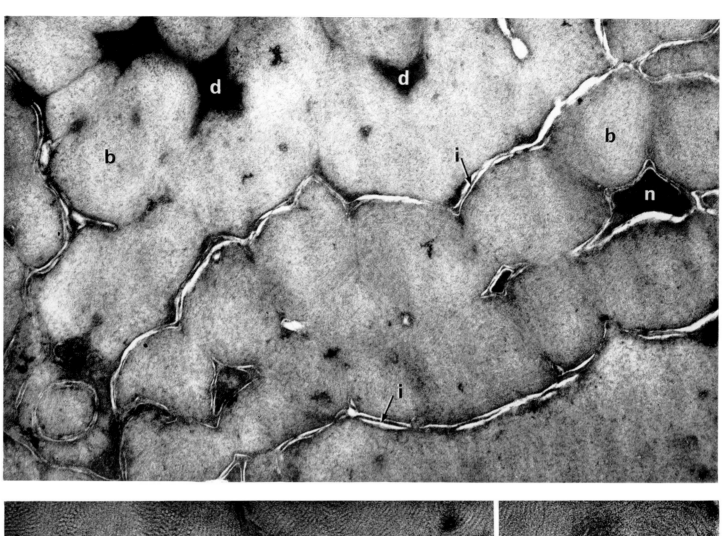

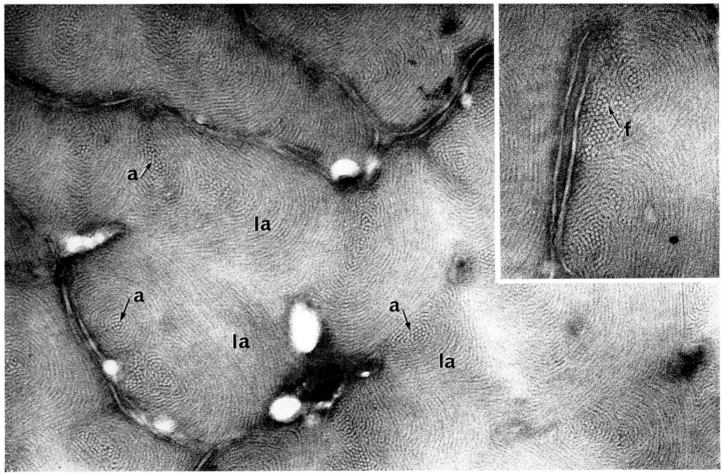

FIGURES 247 and 248

These two micrographs illustrate the main features of medullary cells a short distance above the level of transformation of Henle's layer. The dense medullary granules (d) have no limiting membrane, and no definite structure can be resolved within them. Some workers believe the granules to be trichohyalin, but there is considerable doubt about this. The few filamentous bundles randomly distributed within the cytoplasm are thought not to be specifically related to the medullary granules, but the filaments (f) seen in the lower micrograph appear to run into immediately adjacent granules. Glycogen (g) is abundant within medullary cells as are also membrane limited vesicles or vacuoles (v) the contents of which may be extremely variable as shown. Some of these, especially at higher levels, may represent degenerating mitochondria (m), but the exact nature of the others is unknown.

Higher up the follicle the medullary granules increase in size and number, become irregular in shape, and coalesce. At the same time the vacuoles increase in size, the mitochondria and nucleus show signs of degeneration, and the cell becomes transformed eventually into an irregular element containing apparently empty vacuoles surrounded by an amorphous electron-dense granular matrix.

Throughout this account of the structure and differentiation of hair in fetal and post-natal skin, the term "transformation" has been employed to refer to the final stages of maturation of cells of the different layers of the follicle. This has been done in order to avoid use of the terms "keratin" and "keratinization" in this context. They have been given many different meanings in the literature, and the fact that they cannot as yet be precisely defined in terms either of structure or chemical constitution has led to much confusion. Speaking somewhat generally, keratins may be regarded as fibrous proteins characterized by marked insolubility and stability, and the cells which contain them may be referred to as keratinized cells. On a purely morphological level, it is evident that the keratins produced by the different components of the hair follicle are not structurally identical, but until their chemical constitution is clarified, it is impossible to state in exactly what way they differ, or to understand the steps involved in their synthesis. These problems are discussed at length in references cited at the end of this Section.

Fig. 247. Transverse section of medullary cell of plucked eye-brow hair of woman aged 25. Osmium fixation, lead staining. × 14,800.

Fig. 248. Cytoplasm of medullary cell of plucked eye-brow hair of woman aged 25. Osmium fixation, lead staining. × 27,700.

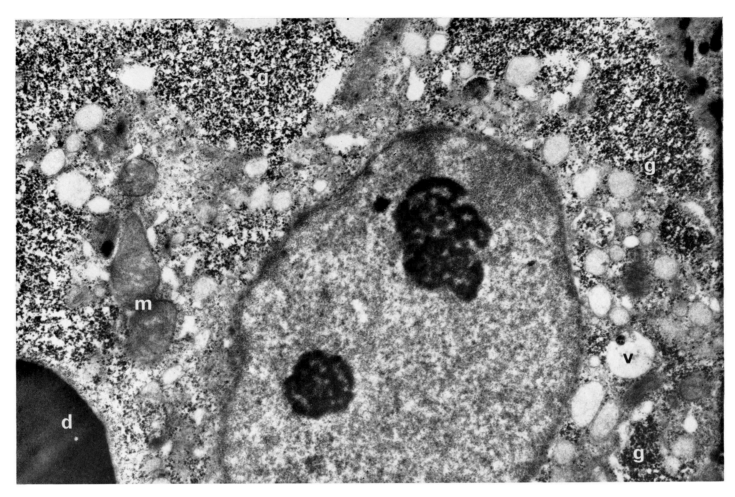

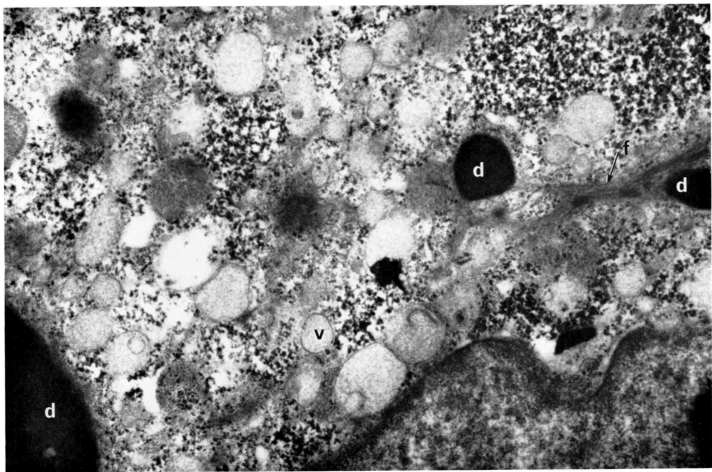

327

FIGURE 249

Just below the level of entry of the duct of the sebaceous gland into the follicle, the hair becomes separated from the inner root sheath and lies free in the pilary canal. The wall of the canal at and above this level is quite thick, and the lumen (Lu) is bounded by the inner root sheath (IRS) which is undergoing disintegration and fragmentation, and its individual layers are no longer clearly distinguishable. Outside the inner root sheath are central cells of the outer root sheath (ORS C), arranged in concentric flattened layers, and containing prominent filamentous bundles. The exact boundary between outer and inner root sheaths is difficult to define. The outer part of the wall of the canal is formed by peripheral outer root sheath cells (ORS P), which are less flattened, and contain fewer filaments.

FIGURE 250

Here, a segment of a hair exhibiting cortex (Co) and cuticle (CH) is seen occupying the lumen of the pilary canal above the level of entry of the sebaceous duct. It is difficult to say if anything of the inner root sheath remains at this level, or if the rather ragged zone of electron dense scales bordering the lumen should be regarded as representing entirely the keratinized inner edge of the outer root sheath (ORS). Dense granules (k) within cells deep to this latter zone are usually taken to be keratohyalin, but it is of interest to note that they are much more regularly rounded than keratohyalin granules of interfollicular epidermis (see Fig. 100). Lamellar granules in small numbers are also present in these cells.

Fig. 249. Transverse section of pilary canal of hair from scalp of man aged 32. Osmium fixation, uranyl acetate and lead staining. × 5,700.

Fig. 250. Transverse section of hair and pilary canal from scalp of man aged 32. Osmium fixation, PTA staining. × 5,900.

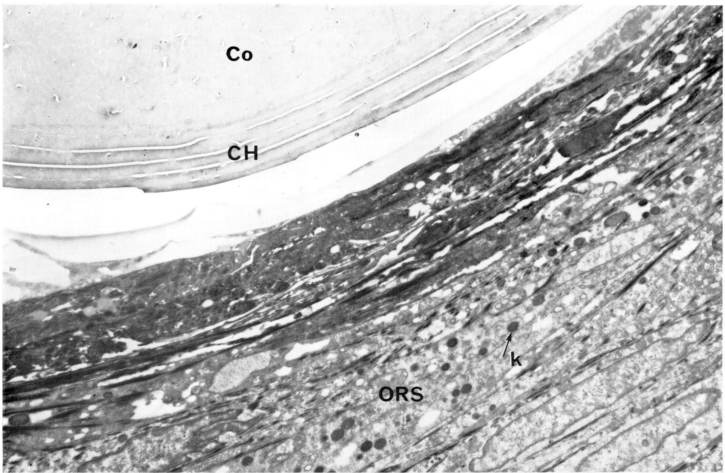

FIGURE 251

The arrector pili muscle arises in the superficial dermis and is inserted into the outer root sheath of the hair follicle in the region corresponding to the bulge of the fetal follicle (Fig. 193). It consists of typical smooth muscle cells (M) the majority of which are separated by narrow intervals containing collagen fibres (c), but direct membranous contacts (m) also occur. Interspersed among the muscle cells are Schwann cells and their processes (S) with associated unmyelinated axons (a).

The smooth muscle cell contains a nucleus (n) and surrounding this is a zone free of myofilaments containing common cellular organelles. Otherwise, the cytoplasm is filled with myofilaments (f) apart from the region just deep to the plasma membrane where pinocytotic vesicles (p), mitochondria, and glycogen particles are present (see Fig. 253). A basal lamina is associated with the plasma membrane.

This micrograph may be compared with those illustrating vascular smooth muscle (Figs. 164 and 165) and the myo-epithelial cell of the sweat gland (Figs. 187 and 188).

Fig. 251. Arrector pili muscle from scalp of man aged 32. Osmium fixation, PTA staining. × 10,800.

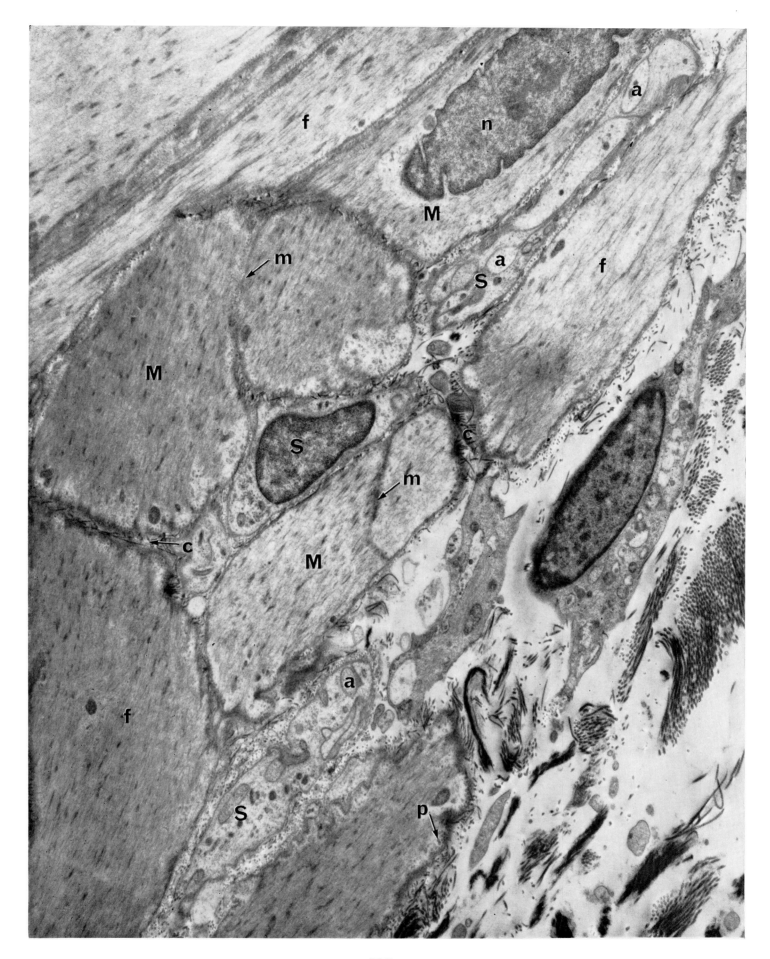

FIGURE 252

This features an area of the previous micrograph (Fig. 251) at higher magnification, and one may note again Schwann cells and processes (S), and collagen fibres (c) interspersed among the muscle cells. Associated with the myofilaments (f) are dense foci (d) similar to those present in vascular smooth muscle cells, and in myo-epithelial cells. Myofilaments of smooth muscle are not arranged in a regular pattern as in striated muscle, but form loose bundles orientated along the long axis of the cell.

FIGURE 253

Portions of four transversely-sectioned smooth muscle cells (M) are seen here. They surround a small Schwann cell process (S) containing two axons (Ax), and fusion of basal laminae (b) occurs in places. Pinocytotic vesicles (p), mitochondria (m), and individual dense glycogen particles (g) are concentrated in the region adjacent to the plasma membrane of the muscle cell, though some glycogen is also scattered among the myofilaments (f). The presence of vesicles (v) and mitochondria within the axoplasm of the axons, and the fact that one is merely indenting the Schwann cell process, indicates that these are very close to termination. They are, of course, autonomic terminals, and the primary transmission mechanism is neuronal, though the presence of direct membranous contacts between some of the muscle cells (see Fig. 251) indicates that intercellular transmission of the nervous impulse may also occur.

Fig. 252. Arrector pili muscle from scalp of man aged 32. Osmium fixation, PTA staining. × 18,000.

Fig. 253. Smooth muscle cells of arrector pili, and terminal axons from forearm skin of man aged 70. Osmium fixation, lead staining. × 56,000.

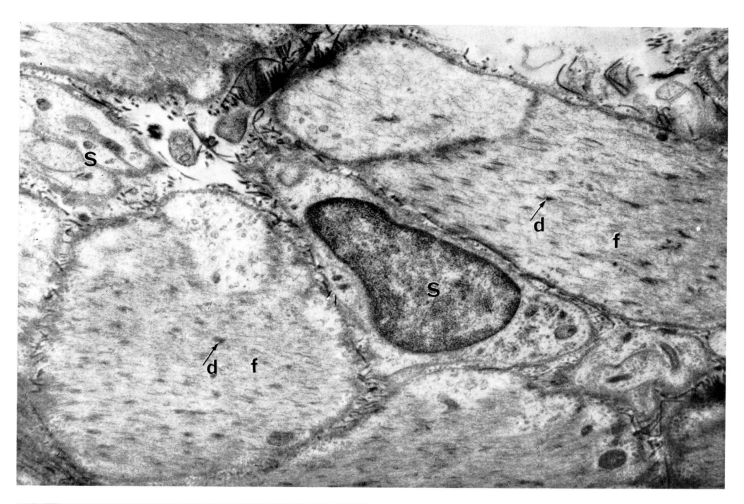

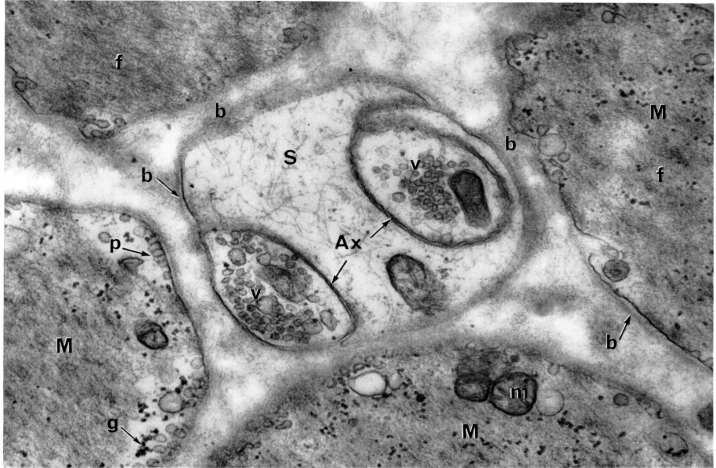

333

REFERENCES

Most of the references cited at the end of the previous section also apply to this.

HAIR

Birbeck, M. S. C. Keratin: an ultrastructural review. In: "Progress in the biological sciences in relation to dermatology—2", A. J. Rook and R. H. Champion, eds. Cambridge, University Press, 1964.

Matoltsy, A. G. What is keratin? In: "Advances in Biology of Skin, IX, Hair Growth", W. Montagna and R. L. Dobson, eds. Oxford, Pergamon, 1969.

Mercer, E. H. "Keratin and keratinization". Oxford, Pergamon, 1961.

Mercer, E. H. The use of the word "keratin". In: "Advances in Biology of Skin, IX, Hair Growth", W. Montagna and R. L. Dobson, eds. Oxford, Pergamon, 1969.

Orfanos, C. and Ruska, H. Die Feinstruktur des menschlichen Haares I. Die Haar-Cuticula: II Der Haar-Cortex. *Arch. klin. exp. Derm.*, **231**:97–110, 264–278, 1968.

Roth, S. I. and Helwig, E. B. The cytology of the cuticle of the cortex, the cortex and the medulla of the mouse hair. *J. Ultrastruct. Res.*, **11**:52, 1964.

ARRECTOR PILI

Bell, M. The ultrastructure of the arrector pili muscle of the rhesus monkey (*Macaca mulatta*). In: "Advances in Biology of Skin, IX, Hair Growth", W. Montagna and R. L. Dobson, eds. Oxford, Pergamon, 1969.

Orfanos, C. Electron microscopy of smooth muscle fibres of the skin and their innervation. *Dermatologica*, **132**:445, 1966.

14 Sebaceous Gland

Anlage: peripheral and central cells — early sebaceous differentiation — fully differentiated cells — development of sebaceous duct — post-natal sebaceous gland.

FIGURE 254

The anlage of the sebaceous gland first appears at the late hair-peg or early bulbous-peg stage of follicular development. It presents as a protuberant accumulation of cells (SG) along the posterior face of the follicle just below the angle (a) where this latter becomes continuous with the basal layer of the epidermis (E). The anlage of the apocrine gland (Fig. 269) usually appears at a slightly later stage of development, by which time the sebaceous swelling is situated at a deeper level than shown here, due to growth of the neck region of the follicle. The two therefore are unlikely to be confused, and each is distinguishable by position from a third more deeply situated swelling, the bulge (Fig. 194). In the case of follicles exhibiting only two swellings, the uppermost is the sebaceous gland anlage, partly because it develops earlier than the apocrine gland, and partly because some follicles entirely lack this latter structure.

At the stage of development illustrated here, the cells of the sebaceous gland anlage do not exhibit any distinguishing features in comparison with adjacent cells of the outer wall of the follicle. They can be distinguished from cells of the hair tract (HT), however, because of their different orientation.

FIGURE 255

As development proceeds, the sebaceous swelling becomes larger, and forms a rounded accumulation of cells projecting outwards and downwards from the posterior face of the bulbous peg (BP). The central cells (C) of the swelling rapidly acquire a foamy appearance due to the accumulation of lipid droplets (li) in the cytoplasm, and are enclosed by peripheral cells (P) containing prominent masses of glycogen (g). Further enlargement is achieved by budding from the primordial swelling to form a multi-acinar gland within which sebaceous differentiation takes place along lines illustrated in the following micrographs. Sebaceous glands become functional before birth, and their secretory products contribute towards the vernix caseosa.

Fig. 254. Sebaceous gland anlage and hair tract of bulbous peg from scalp of 109 mm C.R. (15½ weeks) human fetus. Osmium fixation, lead staining. × 7,000.

Fig. 255. Developing sebaceous bud of bulbous peg from scalp of 113 mm C.R. (16 weeks) human fetus. Osmium fixation, lead staining. × 4,000 approx.

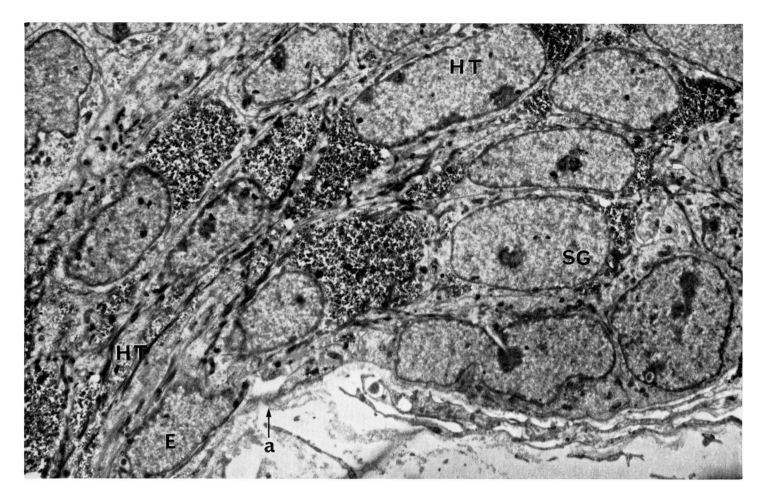

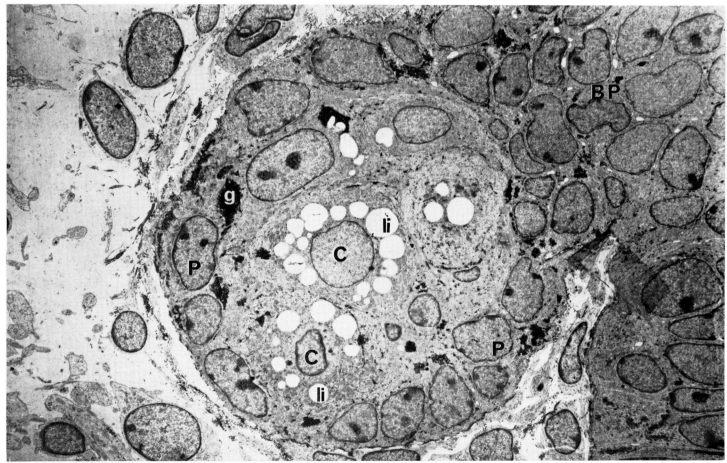

FIGURE 256

This illustrates general features of peripheral cells (P) of a sebaceous bud at a stage of development comparable to that seen in the preceding Fig. 255. The most prominent features of the cytoplasm are extensive aggregations of glycogen particles (g) and mitochondria (m). The membrane systems of the cell—Golgi, smooth and rough-surfaced endoplasmic reticulum —are barely evident at this stage, and filaments though present are not prominent. In general, these peripheral cells differ very little in appearance from cells of the outer wall of the follicle from which they stem. One cell contains a single lipid droplet (li), and larger droplets are present within the central cell occupying the top left-hand corner of the field. Peripheral cells of glands at later stages of development are illustrated in Figs. 258–260.

FIGURE 257

The cytoplasm of the central cells of the early sebaceous bud has a high concentration of ribosomes (r) and mitochondria (m), and short, compact, filamentous bundles (f) are scattered throughout. Lipid vacuoles (li), the contents of which have largely been leached during processing, are prominent. There is no evidence that these vacuoles have a limiting membrane, and one's impression, derived from examination of material at this and at later stages of development, is that the lipid droplets appear initially free in the cytoplasm. Certainly, at this stage, they cannot be said to be intimately related to any cytoplasmic membrane systems, none of which are, as yet, well developed. In this connection, it may be recalled that lipid droplets appearing free in the cytoplasm are an occasional feature of interfollicular basal cells (Fig. 50).

An interesting feature of the cytoplasm at this stage is the presence of elements of obscure structure and doubtful significance. These present as circular structures (w, and also inset) which appear to consist of ill-defined, wispy whorled material enclosing granules approximately the same size as ribosomes. Other, vesicular elements (v) seem to be derived from these, as far as one can interpret the appearances. It could be suggested that the elements in question represent early stages in the formation of lipid droplets, but there is no evidence to support this. The appearance and size of the vesicles (v) could suggest that they represent mitochondria in process of being transformed into lipid droplets, but again, this would be pure speculation.

Fig. 256. Peripheral cells of sebaceous bud of follicle from arm skin of 215 mm C.R. (24 weeks) human fetus. Osmium fixation, uranyl acetate and lead staining. × 13,500.

Fig. 257. Differentiation within sebaceous bud of follicle from arm skin of 169 mm C.R. (21 weeks) human fetus. Osmium fixation, lead staining. × 20,000. *Inset:* × 48,000.

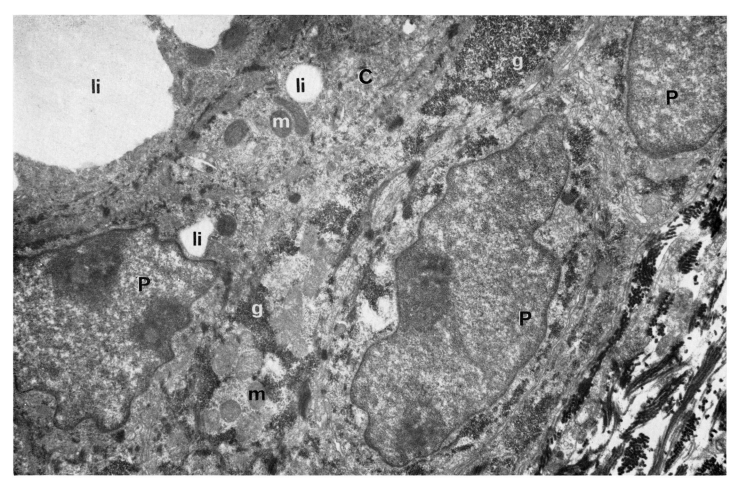

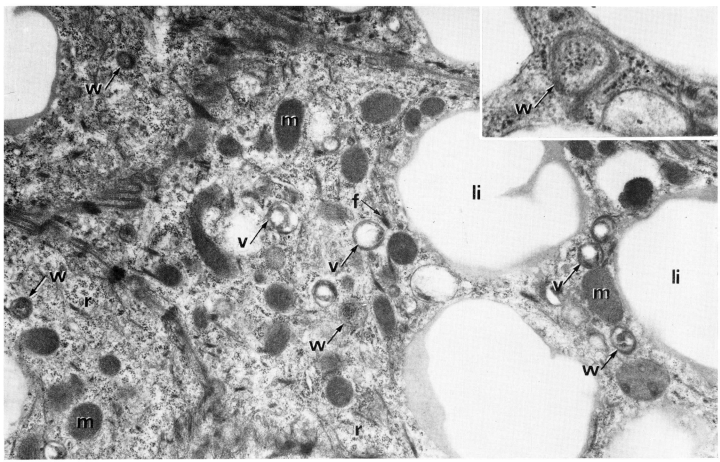

FIGURE 258

Acini developed from buds of the primordial swelling soon undergo sebaceous differentiation, and individually contain cells at various stages of this process. This micrograph illustrates the outer segment of a fairly mature acinus. (More centrally lying regions are illustrated in Figs. 261 and 262.) Peripheral cells rest upon a basal lamina, which separates them from the dermis (D), and two of them (P) present features essentially similar to peripheral cells of the primordium (Fig. 256). The third (P$_1$), however, has a different appearance. The cytoplasm in general appears less dense, though it contains many ribosomes (r), and mitochondria are very numerous. The glycogen deposit (g) appears to be breaking up, with individual granules becoming more widely dispersed in the cytoplasm, and there is a concentration of small vesicles (v) in the neighbourhood of the nucleus. A single lipid vacuole (li) is present. It seems reasonable to conclude that this cell represents one at a very early stage of sebaceous differentiation. More centrally situated cells (C) are evidently at a more advanced stage with numerous lipid vacuoles (li) and much denser cytoplasm, honeycombed with membrane-limited vesicles (see also Figs. 261 and 262). Mitochondria do not stand out prominently within these cells, as there is little contrast between them and the general dense cytoplasmic matrix which consists of ribosomes interspersed with small clusters of glycogen particles. From this and similar micrographs it may be concluded that sebaceous differentiation involves or, at any rate, is associated with an increase in the number of mitochondria, dispersal of glycogen deposits, and the appearance of vesicles throughout the cytoplasm. There is no evidence that the lipid droplets develop within, or are stored within, the vesicles. Similar vesicles are associated with sebaceous differentiation in glands of post-natal skin (Fig. 267) when they are thought to represent the smooth-surfaced endoplasmic reticulum, and to play, along with the Golgi apparatus, an important role in the synthesis of lipid. In this connection, it is of interest to point out that vesicles of smooth endoplasmic reticulum are almost entirely absent from lipid containing cells at an earlier stage of development (Fig. 257) and the Golgi apparatus of these cells is not very prominent.

Fig. 258. Sebaceous differentiation within multi-acinar gland from arm skin of 215 mm C.R. (24 weeks) human fetus. Osmium fixation, lead staining. ×8,750.

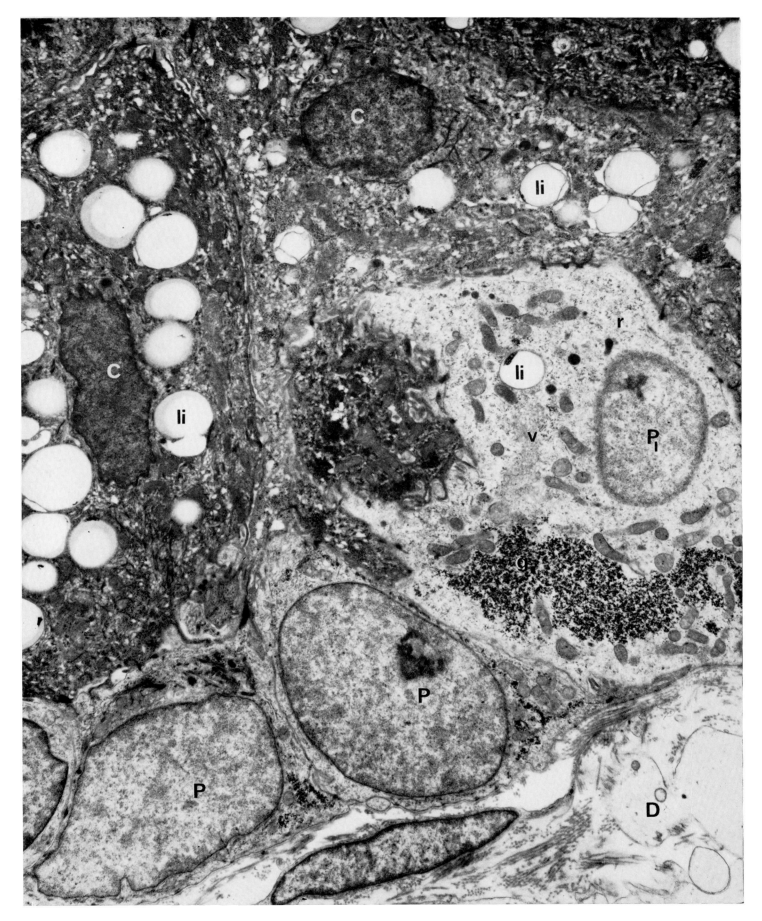

FIGURE 259

This micrograph illustrates further features of peripheral cells (P) of an acinus at a stage of development similar to that illustrated in Fig. 258. The cell on the left has a cilium (c) associated with the plasma membrane, and this is indenting a more deeply situated cell which is well advanced towards sebaceous differentiation with lipid droplets (li) and the peculiar structures (w) already referred to. The peripheral cell on the right presents an appearance which, it is suggested, represents a stage of differentiation intermediate between the other two. The glycogen deposit (g) has a loose arrangement of particles suggesting imminent dispersal, and three lipid droplets (li) are present within it. Vesicles, either of Golgi or smooth endoplasmic reticular nature, are not apparent and this and the previous micrographs serve to illustrate and emphasize the fact that in ontogeny, lipid droplets precede any exuberant development of either. A lysosome (ly) is present within this cell, and similar structures are seen in cells at all stages of differentiation.

FIGURE 260

One of the two peripheral cells (P) illustrated here is in process of dividing as may be seen from the condition of the nucleus (n). Mitotic activity of peripheral cells at an early stage of development is mainly concerned with the formation of new acinar buds, but later, when the gland becomes functional and has developed a duct, it is associated with the replenishing of cells lost in secretion. The more differentiated cell in the right lower half of the field is at a more advanced stage than the one illustrated in Fig. 259 above. Vesicles (v) are present in the cytoplasm, and it may be pointed out that the lipid droplets (li) are not specifically related to these, being concentrated rather in a region of the cytoplasm occupied by mitochondria (m), glycogen (g) and ribosomes (r). The peripheral osmiophilic husk which may be misinterpreted as a limiting membrane is well seen in association with some of the droplets.

Fig. 259. Peripheral cells of multi-acinar gland from arm skin of 215 mm C.R. (24 weeks) human fetus. Osmium fixation, lead staining. × 21,300.

Fig. 260. Peripheral and partially differentiated cells of multi-acinar gland from arm skin of 215 mm C.R. (24 weeks) human fetus. Osmium fixation, lead staining. × 18,000.

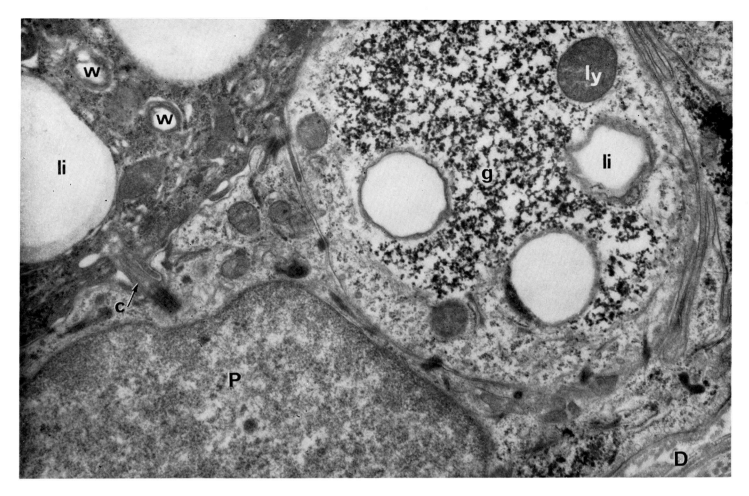

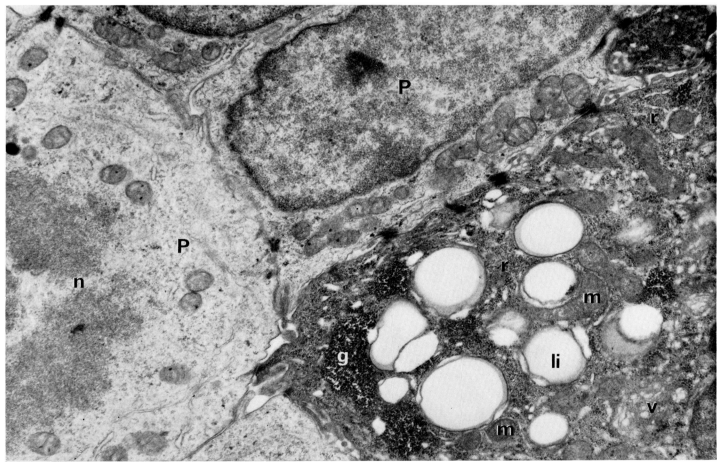

343

FIGURES 261 and 262

In mature glands, the structure of the cells alters progressively from the periphery to the centre of the acinus, presenting a picture of the sequence of changes involved in sebaceous transformation. Peripheral and partially differentiated cells were illustrated in previous micrographs, and the two opposite are taken from a central region of an acinus. Each picture features segments of partially differentiated cells (PD) and of more or less fully differentiated cells (FD), which have reached the final stage of transformation prior to rupture and discharge of their contents. The partially differentiated cells have reached a more advanced stage than the one shown in Fig. 260, and apart from lipid droplets (abundantly present in areas outside the field) the cytoplasm is characteristically dense and honeycombed with numerous small vesicles (v), among which are ribosomes, and the occasional individual glycogen particle. The mitochondria (m) have a particularly dense appearance, and granules and cristae, present in mitochondria of peripheral cells (Figs. 259 and 260), are not apparent.

The fully differentiated cells (FD) are loaded with lipid droplets (li) to the extent that many of these latter are separated only by narrow partitions of cytoplasm containing vesicles (v) and an occasional mitochondrion (m). In places, the periphery of lipid droplets is outlined by what appears as a regular row of vesicles (v). This appearance cannot be interpreted as evidence that the droplets are "membrane-limited", in the sense that they develop *ab initio* within, or are stored within, membrane-limited vesicles. Such is the concentration of vesicles within the cytoplasm that it is not surprising they should, in places, be marshalled in regular array by the compressing effect of an expanding lipid droplet.

Fig. 261. Partially and fully differentiated cells of multi-acinar gland from arm skin of 215 mm C.R. (24 weeks) human fetus. Osmium fixation, lead staining. × 36,000.

Fig. 262. Partially and fully differentiated cells of multi-acinar gland from arm skin of 215 mm C.R. (24 weeks) human fetus. Osmium fixation, lead staining. × 24,000.

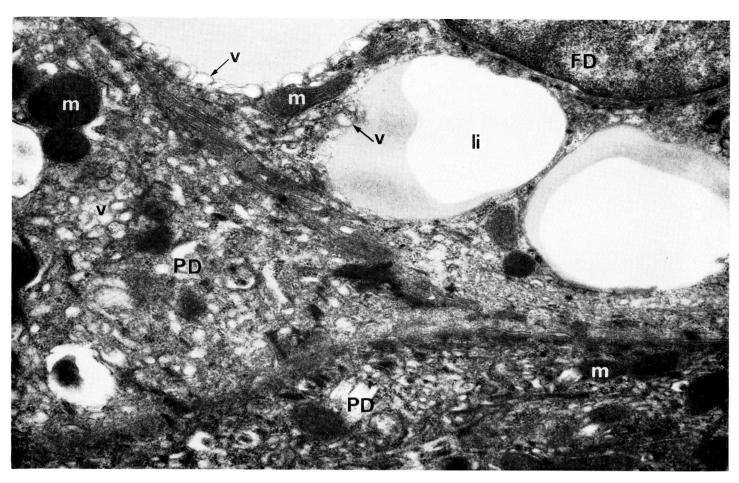

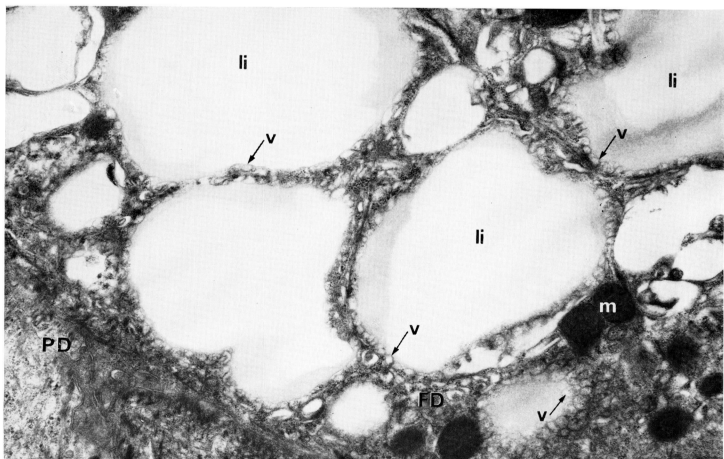

FIGURE 263

The sebaceous duct forms within the proximal part of the sebaceous outgrowth where it stems from the hair follicle. Originally, in this situation, typical sebaceous cells with lipid droplets (li) lie immediately adjacent to the already well-differentiated pilary canal (PC), the lumen of which (Lu) is occupied by the hair (fallen out of this section). At a later stage of development, the central sebaceous cells break down to form the lumen of the duct, peripheral cells remaining to form the wall which undergoes a degree of keratinization.

FIGURE 264

This micrograph illustrates a somewhat later stage in the development of the sebaceous duct. Towards the right of the field may be seen the Henle layer (He) of the inner root sheath of the hair, and the outer root sheath (ORS) with its keratinized (k) border. The immediately adjacent sebaceous cells are packed with lipid droplets (li), and the narrow septa between these latter are becoming characteristically dense in places (d) preparatory to breaking down. The margin of many of these septa exhibit dense globules (g), which, as far as can be determined, are derived from vesicles similar to those present beyond the periphery of lipid droplets of fully differentiated cells lower in the gland (Figs. 261 and 262). The cell labelled P is presumably a peripheral cell of the sebaceous outgrowth, though in this region of the follicle which is very close to the site of entry of the sebaceous duct, it could easily be taken for an outer root sheath cell. However, a narrow segment of outer root sheath cytoplasm (ORS) separates it from the Henle layer (He) of the inner root sheath. With breakdown of the septa, the lumen is formed, and the margin will be formed by the remaining edge of the peripheral cell. This shows a high concentration of filaments (f) and dense irregular material indicative of subsequent keratinization.

Fig. 263. Transverse section of pilary canal of follicle and adjacent part of sebaceous gland from arm skin of 215 mm C.R. (24 weeks) human fetus. Osmium fixation, lead staining. × 5,250.

Fig. 264. Transverse section of pilary canal and developing sebaceous duct from arm skin of 169 mm C.R. (21 weeks) human fetus. Osmium fixation, lead staining. × 7,800.

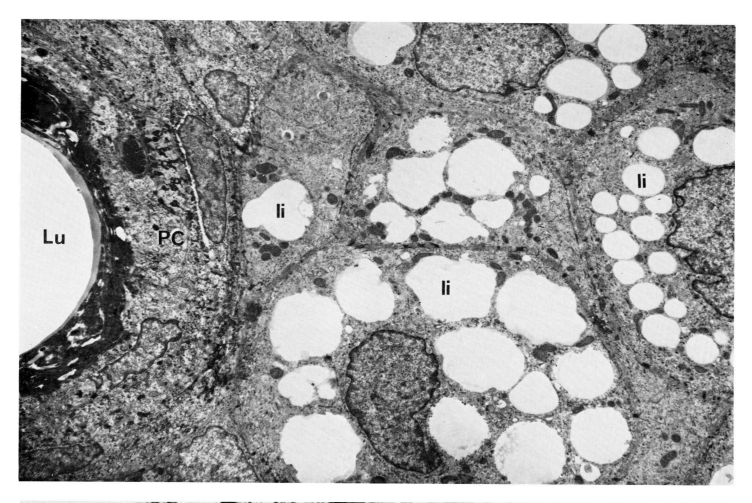

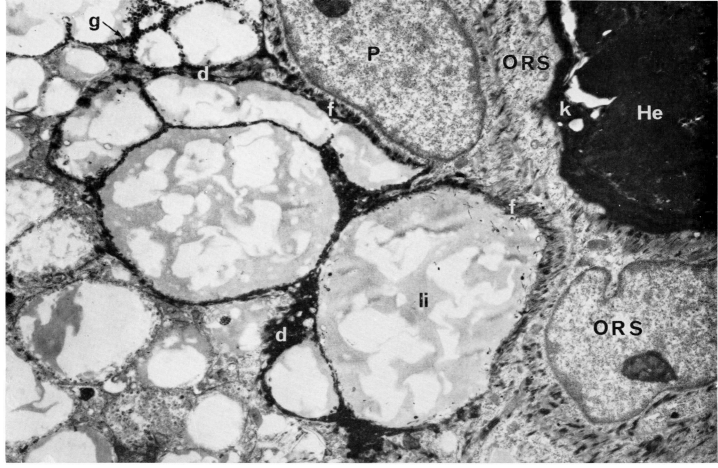

FIGURE 265

This features a longitudinal section of part of the wall of the developing sebaceous duct on the side of the lumen away from the hair. The wall is several layers thick, and the basal cells are separated from the mesenchymal tissue (M) by a basal lamina. Glycogen (g) is abundant within the cytoplasm of most cells, two of which contain lipid droplets (li) as well. Round dense granules (d), of either trichohyalin or keratohyalin, are present within the cells bordering the lumen (Lu), which is in process of formation by the breakdown of septa.

FIGURE 266

The entire width of the sebaceous duct is seen in this micrograph of a longitudinal section of the duct just below the level at which its lumen (Lu) communicates with the pilary canal. On the hair side (right) a narrow strip of layered keratinized tissue (k) separates the lumen from Henle's layer (He) of the inner root sheath of the hair. The bulk of this strip is almost certainly derived from the outer root sheath (see Fig. 264), though the ragged appearance of its luminal edge indicates the presence of some remnants of a sebaceous cell. Within the lumen some dense septa (d) are still present, and projecting from them and from the luminal margin of the opposite wall of the duct are finger-like processes (p). These present a certain problem of interpretation. They occupy the same position and are of approximately the same density as globules previously noted (Fig. 264). But, they appear more elongated, almost like micro-villi. It seems likely they are derived from the globules, and the difference in appearance may be related to plane of section. However, there is a minor point here which requires clearing up. With the final disappearance of all septa, canalization of the lumen is completed. It is bounded on the hair side by a keratinized layer derived mainly from the outer root sheath at this level, and on the opposite side by peripheral sebaceous cells (P) which also subsequently undergo some degree of keratinization.

Fig. 265. Longitudinal section along wall of developing sebaceous duct from arm skin of 215 mm C.R. (24 weeks) human fetus. Osmium fixation, lead staining. × 5,900.

Fig. 266. Longitudinal section along developing sebaceous duct from arm skin of 215 mm C.R. (24 weeks) human fetus. Osmium fixation, lead staining. × 13,750.

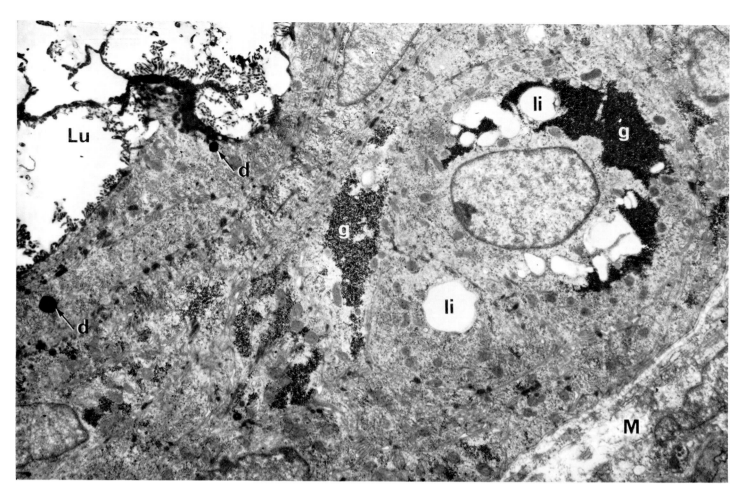

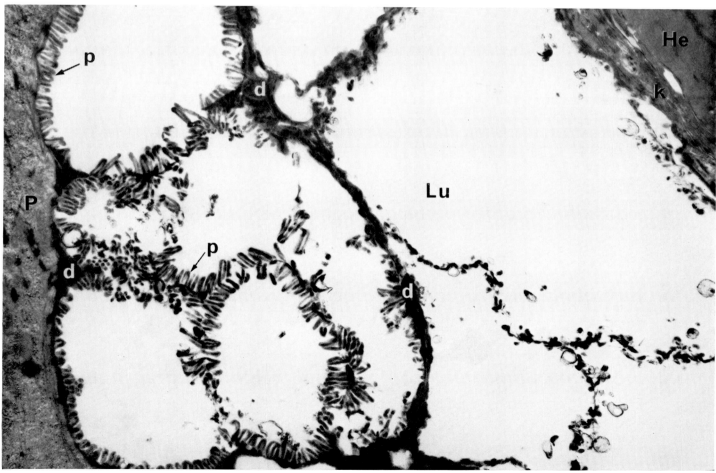

FIGURE 267

Shortly after birth the sebaceous glands become reduced in size, and remain relatively in-active until puberty, at which time they enlarge again with marked increase in functional activity. At this stage, their structure is essentially similar to that of fetal glands already illustrated, and peripheral, partially differentiated, and fully differentiated cells are seen in the acini. This micrograph illustrates cytoplasm of partially differentiated cells. One may note again mitochondria (m), vesicles (v), ribosomes (r) and lipid droplets (li). As in the fetus, there is no real evidence of a limiting membrane surrounding these latter. Most workers are of the opinion that the vesicles represent the smooth endoplasmic reticulum, and that this is intimately concerned with the synthesis of lipid. However, as already mentioned, one's im-pression from fetal studies is that the lipid droplets appear free in the cytoplasm, and they may be quite numerous before many vesicles are evident. It may be that the development of vesicles is associated with synthesis of some other product or, possibly, with the impending disintegration of the cell.

FIGURE 268

The cytoplasm of the fully differentiated cell is packed with lipid droplets (li) separated by extremely tenuous septa, and the nucleus (n) is dense and irregular in outline due to com-pression by adjacent droplets. It frequently contains inclusions of varying size and density, but in general remains recognizable until the cell finally ruptures and discharges its contents into the duct.

Fig. 267. Partially differentiated cells of sebaceous gland from axilla of man aged 25. Osmium fixation, lead staining. × 37,000.

Fig. 268. Fully differentiated cells of sebaceous gland from scalp of man aged 35. Osmium fixation, lead staining. × 7,750.

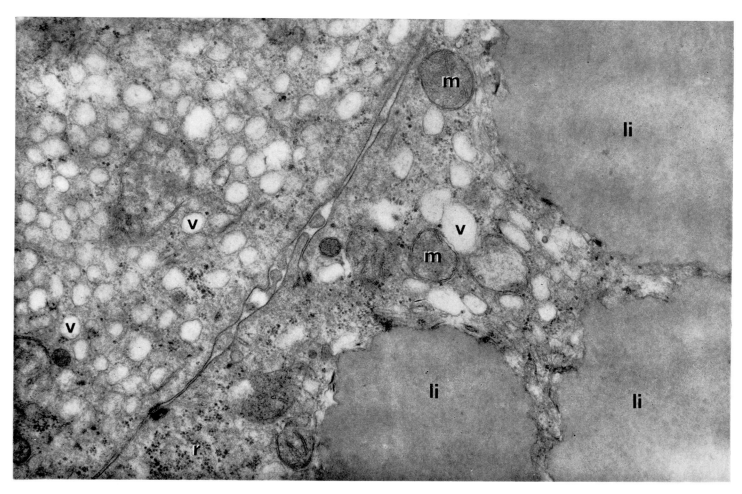

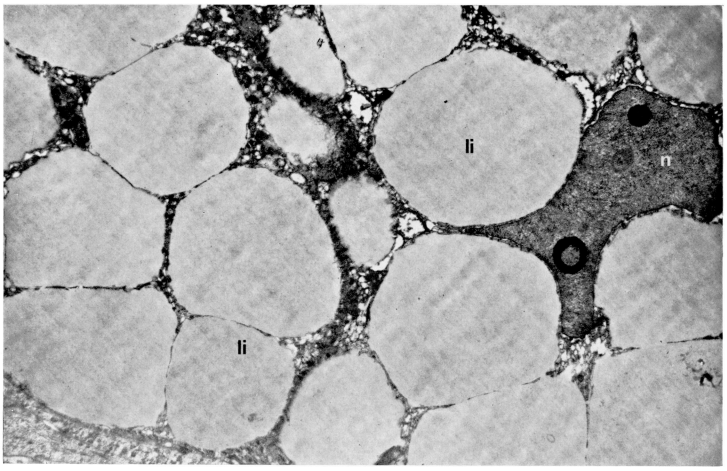

REFERENCES

Charles, A. Electron microscopic observations of the human sebaceous gland. *J. invest. Derm.*, **35**:31, 1960.

Ellis, R. A. Eccrine, sebaceous and apocrine glands. In, "Ultrastructure of normal and abnormal skin". A. S. Zelickson, ed. London, Kimpton, 1967.

Ellis, R. A. and Henrickson, R. C. The ultrastructure of the sebaceous glands of man. In, "Advances in biology of skin", Vol. IV. W. Montagna, R. A. Ellis and A. F. Silver, eds. New York, Pergamon, 1964.

Hibbs, R. G. Electron microscopy of human axillary sebaceous glands. *J. invest. Derm.*, **38**:329, 1962.

Kurosumi, K., Kitamura, T. and Kano, K. Electron microscopy of the human sebaceous gland. *Arch. hist. jap.*, **20**:235, 1960.

Morohashi, M. An electron microscope study of the sebaceous glands with special reference to the effect of the sexual hormones. *Jap. J. Derm.*, B, **78**:133, 1968.

15 Apocrine Gland. Fat Cell

Early apocrine differentiation — axillary apocrine gland: secretory coil: "clear" cells: secretory cells and granules: myo-epithelial cells — fat cell.

FIGURE 269

The anlage of the apocrine gland first appears as an accumulation of cells (Ap) projecting from the posterior face of the hair follicle at a stage when sebaceous (Fig. 254) and bulge (Fig. 194) primordia are already present. Initially, the cells of the three swellings are indistinguishable, but as development proceeds, the two glandular elements differentiate along rather different lines. To date, little or no attention has been paid at the ultrastructural level to developing human apocrine gland, and few details can be presented here. However, the succeeding Figs. 270–272 illustrating some features of its early differentiation may be compared with previous illustrations featuring primordial stages of development of sebaceous gland.

The dense structure (d) within one of the cells of the hair tract (HT) in this illustration is not indicative of impending keratinization, but rather of morphogenetic cell death.

FIGURE 270

The earliest sign of differentiation within the apocrine primordium appears while it is still a relatively small bud projecting from the posterior face of the bulbous peg (BP). At this stage, it consists of peripheral (P) and central (C) cells, and the latter exhibit a cytoplasm packed with membrane-limited vesicles (v). It is not possible at present to pronounce upon the significance of these central cells. It may be that their vesiculated character is associated with the development of the lumen which appears at an immediately later stage (Fig. 271). The appearance of this central cell may be compared with that of central cells of the primordial sebaceous bud (Fig. 255).

Fig. 269. Longitudinal section along neck region of bulbous peg follicle from scalp of 109 mm C.R. (15½ week) human fetus. Osmium fixation, lead staining. ×6,000 approx.

Fig. 270. Apocrine rudiment of bulbous peg follicle from scalp of 109 mm C.R. (15½ week) human fetus. Osmium fixation, lead staining. ×8,000.

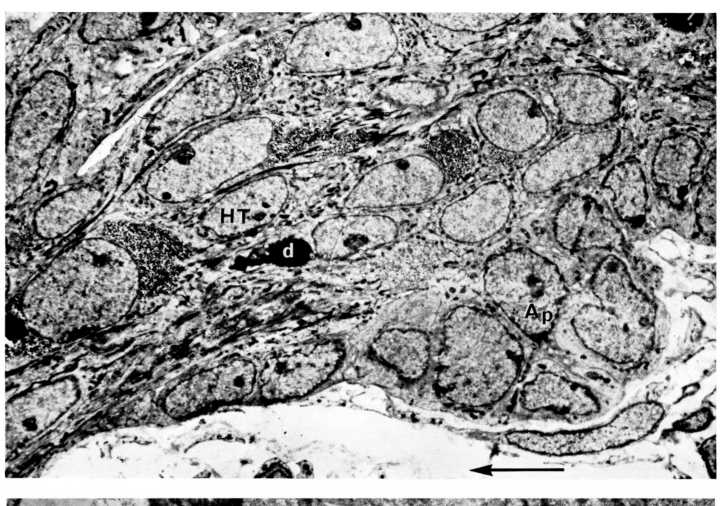

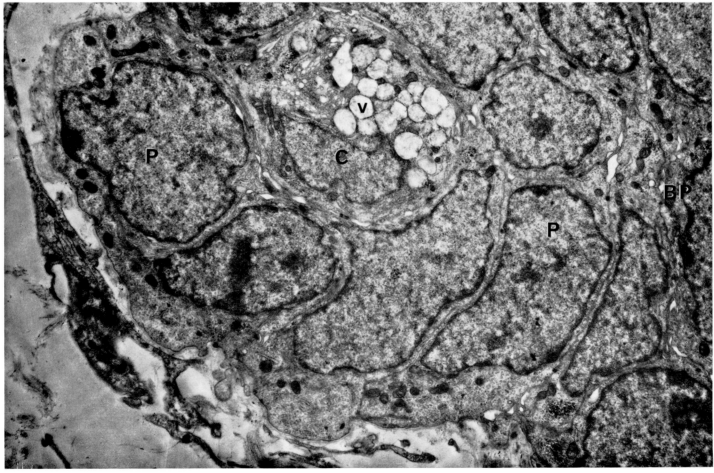

FIGURE 271

This longitudinal section along the adepidermal region of a bulbous peg follicle (BP) and associated apocrine rudiment (Ap) shows that lumen formation within the latter takes place at a relatively early stage of development, and before a distinct secretory part and duct can be distinguished. Exactly how the lumen is formed, i.e. whether intra-cellularly as in the case of the epidermal sweat duct (Fig. 171), or intercellularly as in the dermal portion of the sweat duct, is not yet clear. The presence of vesicles within central cells of the primordium at an immediately earlier stage (Fig. 270) could suggest the former method.

The apparently structureless areas (g) within cells of the bulbous peg represent glycogen deposits, which, as previously mentioned, do not stain with PTA.

FIGURE 272

This transverse section of an apocrine rudiment little bigger than that presented in Fig. 271, above, reveals cells connected by desmosomes and tight junctions surrounding a lumen (Lu) bordered by microvilli. Within the cytoplasm of the luminal cells are mitochondria (m), dense granules (d), and other more translucent granules (g) of variable size and structure. Whether these granules are similar to granules present in apocrine glands of post-natal skin (see Figs. 279–282) is impossible to say until further observations at this, and at later stages of development, are made. However, it is of interest to note that specific granules are present at a comparatively early stage of differentiation.

In post-natal skin, apocrine glands are found in the axilla, external auditory meatus, on the external genitalia, in the areola and nipple, and sparsely scattered on the face and abdomen. They do not attain full development until puberty, and it is generally believed that the fine structure of the cells varies with site, sex, and to a limited extent with cyclic activity. The micrographs which follow were obtained from sections of axillary apocrine gland of an adult male, and whereas they illustrate general and some specialized features, they cannot be said to cover all variations in structure which may be determined by the factors mentioned.

Fig. 271. Longitudinal section along bulbous peg follicle and apocrine rudiment from face of 142 mm C.R. (17 week) human fetus. Millonig fixation, PTA staining. ×3,120.

Fig. 272. Transverse section of luminal region of apocrine rudiment from scalp of 109 mm C.R. ($15\frac{1}{2}$ week) human fetus. Osmium fixation, lead staining. ×22,800.

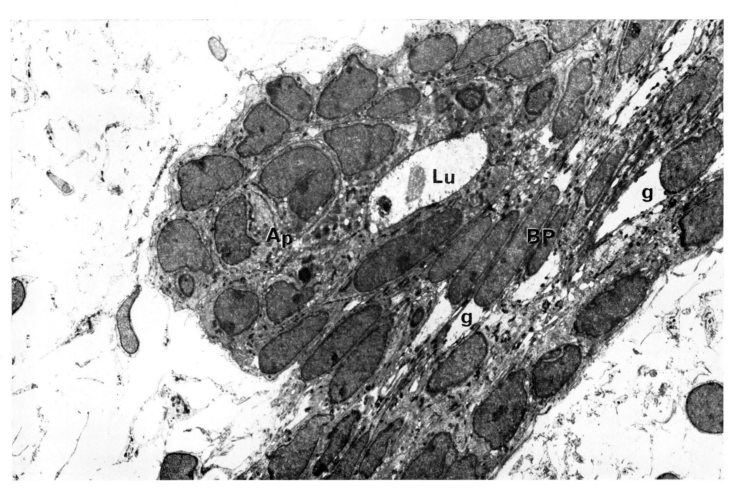

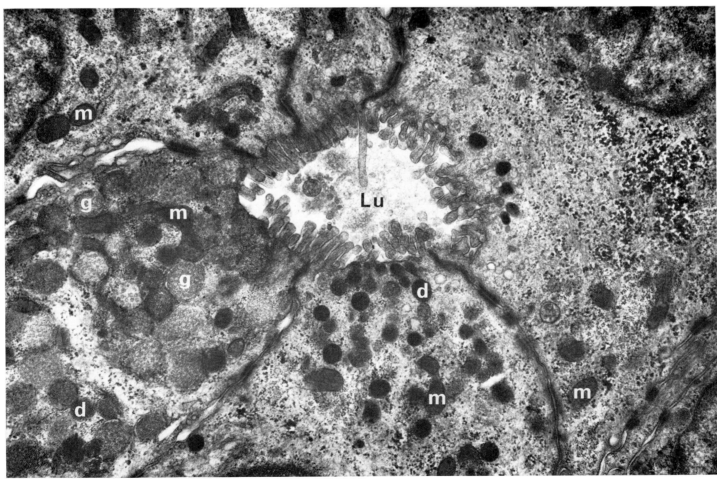

FIGURE 273

The axillary apocrine gland consists of a coiled secretory segment and a straight duct which opens into the pilary canal of the hair follicle. The duct consists of two layers of cells, and is essentially similar in structure to the duct of the eccrine sweat gland (Figs. 177, 178). The secretory segment of the gland is coiled, and anastomoses between adjacent loops may occur. Each coil is lined by secretory cells, resting upon a layer of myo-epithelial cells which is separated from the surrounding collagenous dermis by a well-defined basal lamina. The secretory cells are usually described as being cuboidal or columnar, but due to the fact that segments of individual coils exhibit different degrees of dilatation, and to differences in plane of section, the shape and height of cells as seen in individual micrographs may be extremely variable.

This more or less longitudinal section along a coil reveals the lumen (Lu) lined by secretory cells (S) with granules (g) of varying size and density located predominantly in the supra-nuclear region of the cytoplasm. Apical caps of cytoplasm (ap) project into the lumen beyond terminal junctional complexes (j) binding the apposed plasma membranes of the secretory cells. A myo-epithelial cell (M) is separated from surrounding collagen (c) by a broad basal lamina (b).

FIGURE 274

A number of tangentially-sectioned myo-epithelial cells (M) are seen in this micrograph which also shows clearly the considerable extent of basal lamina (b) which intervenes between them and the surrounding collagen (c). As will be seen later (Figs. 283 and 284) this broad basal lamina appears to have two components. Mitochondria (m) are a prominent feature of the infra-nuclear cytoplasm of the secretory cell (S).

Fig. 273. Secretory coil of axillary apocrine gland of man aged 23. Glutaraldehyde-osmium fixation, uranyl acetate and lead citrate staining. ×7,500.

Fig. 274. Basal region of secretory coil of axillary apocrine gland of man aged 23. Glutaraldehyde-osmium fixation, uranyl acetate and lead citrate staining. ×7,850.

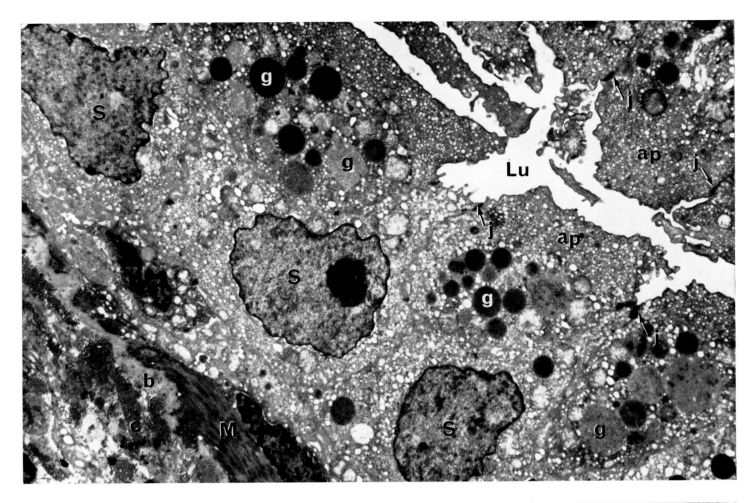

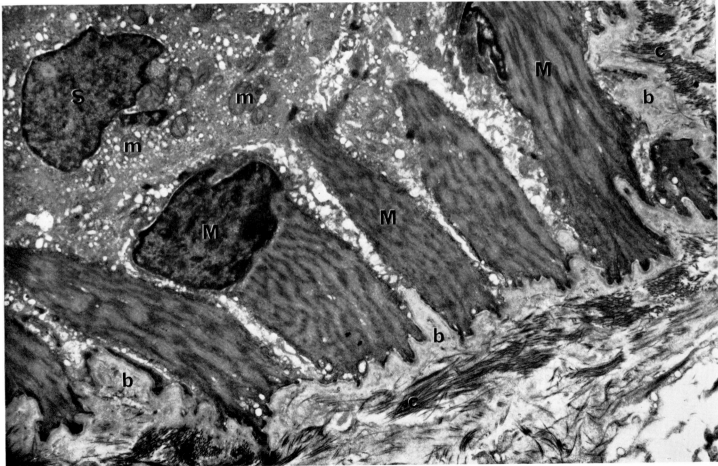

FIGURES 275 and 276

In some sections of axillary apocrine gland, individual cells of distinctive appearance (C) are seen among the myo-epithelial cells (M), or between these latter and the basal regions of the secretory cells (S). From the relatively translucent character of the cytoplasm (cy) these cells may be labelled "clear cells". They contain very few organelles, though centriolar structures (c), mitochondria (m), and ill-defined vesicles are present. The nucleus (n) tends to be indented, and desmosomes are absent from the plasma membrane.

The nature and significance of these "clear cells" is obscure. Some authors have reported degenerative changes in myo-epithelial cells, involving loss of myo-filaments with resulting increased "clarity" of the cytoplasm. It is possible that the cells illustrated here, therefore, are examples of degenerate myo-epithelial cells. It is equally possible, however, that what have previously been reported as degenerating myo-epithelial cells are in fact "clear cells" of entirely different character. The general appearance of the cells and the fact that they lack desmosomes inclines one to favour this latter view. If it be correct, then apocrine glands must contain cells differing in nature and lineage from either secretory cells or myo-epithelial cells. This need not be entirely surprising. The interfollicular epidermis, the outer root sheath of the hair, and the sebaceous gland, all contain elements of this character, i.e. Langerhans cells. Indeed, considering the common derivation of all the structures under consideration, the apocrine gland would be exceptional in not containing them. To date, typical Langerhans granules have not been observed within the cytoplasm of these apocrine "clear cells", and it will be of interest to see if they can be revealed by further studies.

Fig. 275. "Clear" cell in secretory coil of axillary apocrine gland of man aged 23. Glutaraldehyde-osmium fixation, uranyl acetate and lead citrate staining. × 16,200.

Fig. 276. "Clear" cell in secretory coil of axillary apocrine gland of man aged 23. Glutaraldehyde-osmium fixation, uranyl acetate and lead citrate staining. × 24,700.

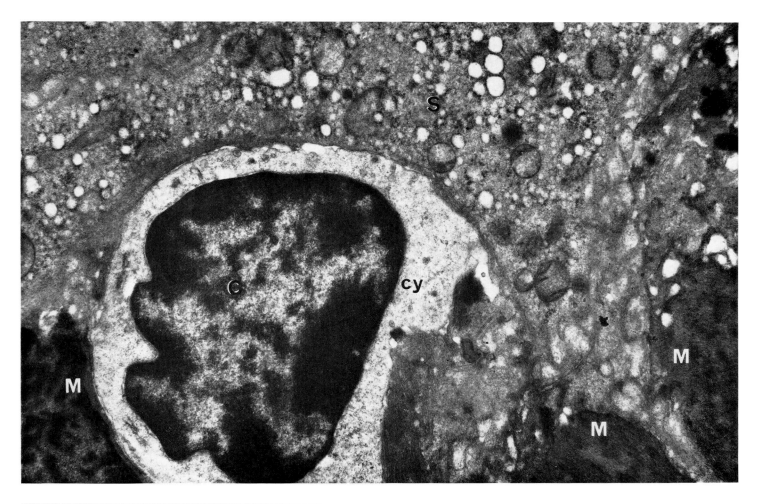

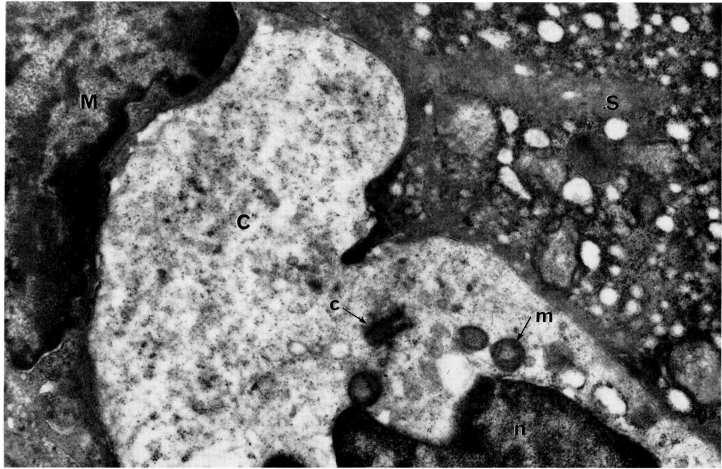

361

FIGURE 277

This micrograph, and the one below (Fig. 278), serves to illustrate the variable appearance presented by the luminal borders of adjacent secretory cells (S). The luminal plasma membrane of the cell on the left does not project appreciably into the lumen (Lu) beyond the terminal junctional complex (c), whereas an extensive apical cap (ap) is a feature of the cell on the right. Apical caps of this size and extent contain smooth vesicles, ribosomes and filaments, but relatively few of the large granules (g) which are a characteristic feature of the supra-nuclear cytoplasm.

FIGURE 278

Apical caps of four secretory cells (S) are seen here projecting into the lumen (Lu) beyond the terminal junctional complexes (c). One is somewhat broader than the others which taper to extremely narrow protrusions, in one instance, little wider than the double layer of plasma membrane in places. This appearance, together with appearances seen in Fig. 277 above, and in Fig. 273, suggests that the apical cap region of the cell may expand and retract, or collapse, possibly in relation to cyclic activity. There is no evidence from the present material that the apical cap is pinched off and extruded into the lumen during secretion, as suggested by some authors, nor is there any evidence that under physiological conditions, cellular products are passed into the lumen following extensive breakdown of the luminal plasma membrane. The latter appearance is almost certainly due to damage during processing, and the cellular contents visible within the lumen here come from cells outside the field which were obviously damaged. Otherwise, the luminal plasma membrane is invariably intact.

Microvilli are a prominent feature of the luminal plasma membranes of the cells of the fetal apocrine gland illustrated in Fig. 272, and they are also numerous in connection with cells of fully developed glands as illustrated by other authors. In the present material, micro-villi are, in general, very poorly developed, but this again may just be indicative of a particular phase of cyclic activity.

Fig. 277. Luminal border of secretory cells of axillary apocrine gland of man aged 23. Glutaraldehyde-osmium fixation, uranyl acetate and lead citrate staining. × 12,000.

Fig. 278. Luminal margins of secretory cells of axillary apocrine gland of man aged 23. Glutaraldehyde-osmium fixation, uranyl acetate and lead citrate staining. × 8,750.

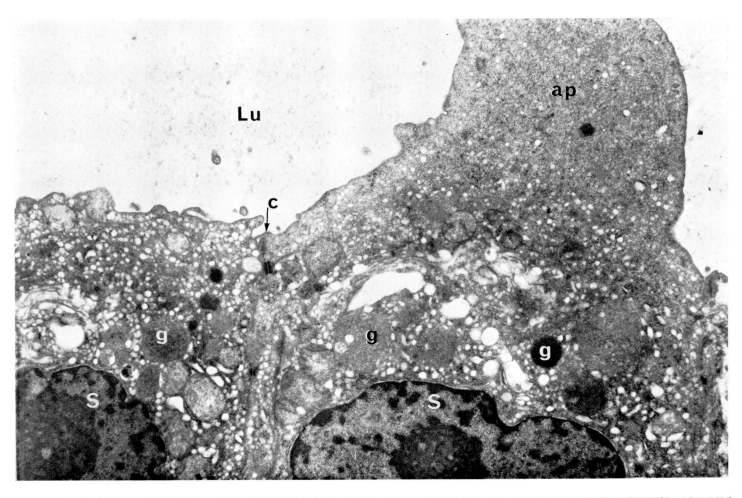

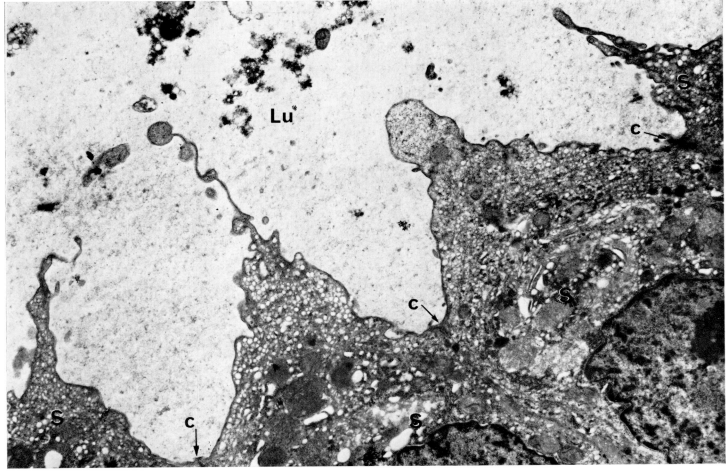

FIGURE 279

In a very general way, the cytoplasm of the secretory cell exhibits three regions with distinct characteristics, i.e. the apical cap region with vesicles, ribosomes, and few large granules (Figs. 277 and 278), the infra-nuclear region where mitochondria are very numerous, and the supra-nuclear region which contains granules of varying size and appearance. In this micrograph of an area immediately superficial to the nucleus (n) a Golgi area (go) is seen, and the general cytoplasm contains a high concentration of ribosomes and some fine filamentous bundles (f). Two mitochondria (m) with granular homogeneous matrix but no evident cristae are identified on the basis of a double limiting membrane, and two other granules (t) with similar matrix but only fragmented or indistinct limiting membranes are also present. It would appear that these latter granules are modified mitochondria which ultimately undergo disintegration. Two dense granules (d) with single limiting membranes are also present, as well as another type (c), with limiting membrane and containing a core of dense material set in a more translucent matrix.

FIGURE 280

This micrograph of the supra-nuclear region of another cell shows dense granules (d), cored granules (c), and a group of the large mitochondria which are such a characteristic feature of the apocrine secretory cell. The cristae are relatively sparse, and tend to be curved. The inset figures two mitochondria apparently undergoing modification; cristae are no longer evident, and electron dense material (perhaps derived from the cristae) is being deposited in the matrix.

Fig. 279. Supra-nuclear cytoplasm of secretory cell of axillary apocrine gland of man aged 23. Glutaraldehyde-osmium fixation, uranyl acetate and lead citrate staining. × 37,500.

Fig. 280. Granules in cytoplasm of secretory cell of axillary apocrine gland of man aged 23. Glutaraldehyde-osmium fixation, uranyl acetate and lead citrate staining. × 37,000. *Inset:* Modified mitochondria. × 36,000.

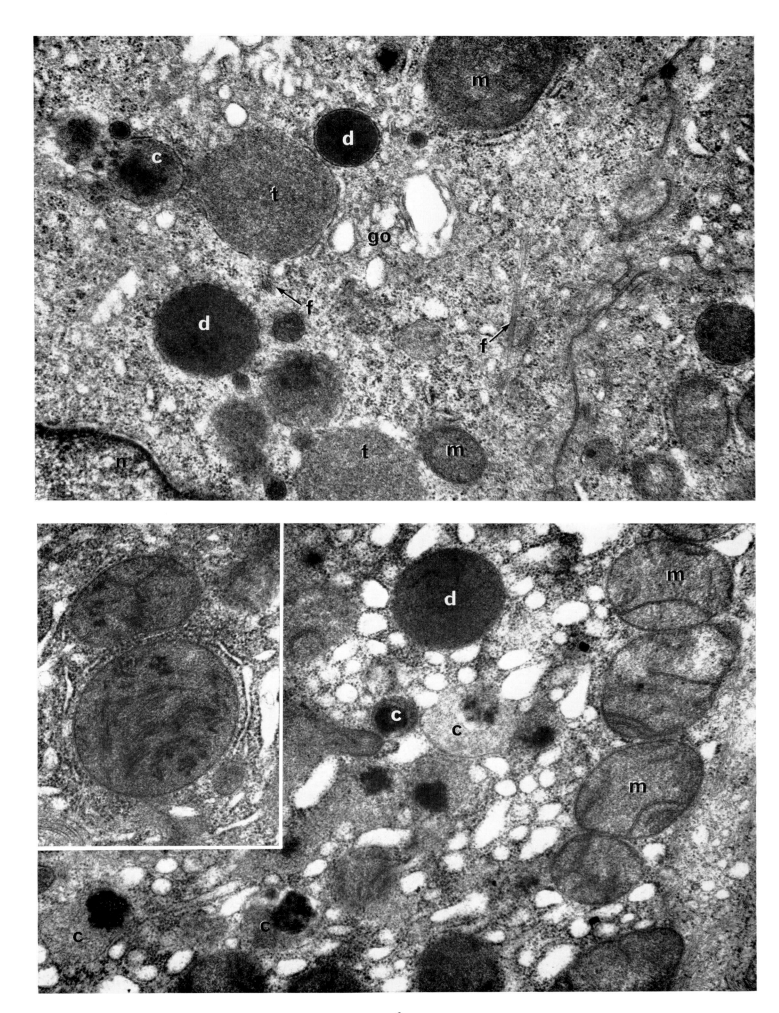

FIGURE 281

These granules located in the juxta-Golgi (go) region of the supra-nuclear cytoplasm exhibit varying degrees of electron-density. The matrix is not entirely uniform, being more coarsely granular at the periphery than centrally. Two typically large mitochondria (m) are also seen. The inset figures two dense granules, one of which contains a small round spot of increased density, and the other a spot of similar size, but less dense than the surrounding matrix (arrows). In some secretory cells as figured by other authors, much larger granules of this type are abundant, and their internal structure in terms of circumscribed dense or translucent loculi varies enormously. Such large and heterogeneous granules were very rarely seen in the present material, possibly because at the time of biopsy the glands were at a relatively inactive phase when only early formative stages of dense granules were present.

FIGURE 282

Segments of apical cap of two secretory cells are figured here. Within the cell on the right can be seen a dense granule (d), and a modified mitochondrion (mi). These are located very close to the luminal plasma membrane, and this could suggest that they are about to be discharged into the lumen (Lu). However, as mentioned already, there is no real evidence that this occurs during the normal process of secretion. Note a microvillus (m) projecting from the plasma membrane, and the presence of ribosomes (r) and smooth vesicles (v) within the apical cap cytoplasm.

Fig. 281. Granules in cytoplasm of secretory cell of axillary apocrine gland of man aged 23. Glutaraldehyde-osmium fixation, uranyl acetate and lead citrate staining. × 40,000. *Inset:* Dense granules. × 27,000.

Fig. 282. Apical caps of secretory cells of axillary apocrine gland of man aged 23. Glutaraldehyde-osmium fixation, uranyl acetate and lead citrate staining. × 57,000.

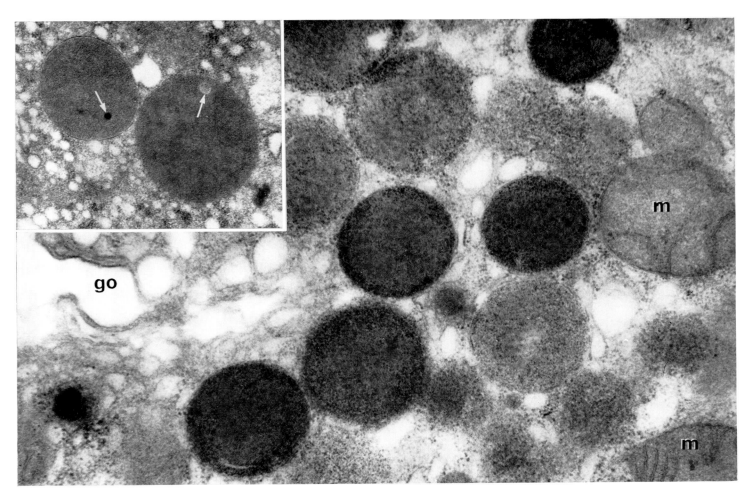

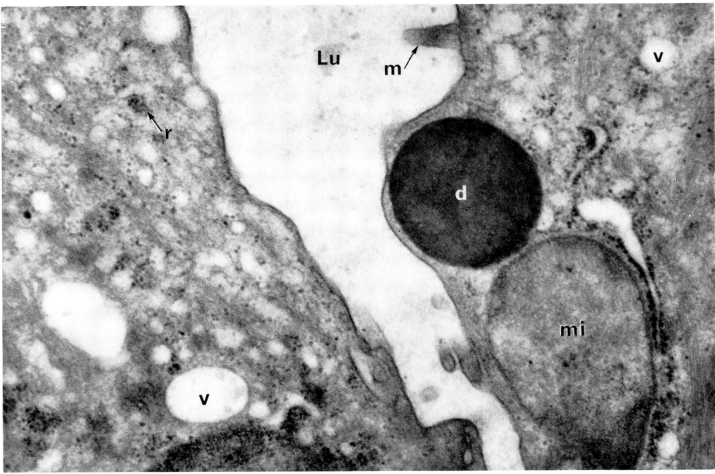

FIGURE 283

The myo-epithelial cells (M) upon which the apocrine secretory cells rest (Figs. 273 and 274) are essentially similar to those of the eccrine sweat gland (Figs. 187 and 188). Like the latter, they do not form a complete layer and processes of secretory cells (S) exhibiting terminal villous folds (v) extend to the basal lamina between them. When sectioned transversely as here, typical myofilaments and dense areas are seen. Paralleling the basal plasma membrane is a basal lamina (b) of typical depth and appearance, and beyond this is a more extensive zone of similar but more translucent amorphous material (a).

FIGURE 284

In this longitudinal section of a myo-epithelial cell, myofilaments (m) and dense areas (d) are also seen. The dense areas are regions where myofilaments are associated with some additional matrix substance. The basal lamina (b) is seen here as a well-defined narrow zone, beyond which is the more extensive zone of amorphous material (a) already referred to. Isolated collagen fibres and fine filaments (f) may be seen within this latter zone. A similar zone is not present in association with the basal lamina of interfollicular epidermis, and its significance is obscure. From the appearances presented it certainly seems to constitute an additional element deep to a typical basal lamina, and not to result from tangential sectioning of this latter.

Fig. 283. Transverse section of myo-epithelial cells of axillary apocrine gland of man aged 23. Glutaraldehyde-osmium fixation, uranyl acetate and lead citrate staining. × 36,700. *Inset:* Enlarged segment of cell on right. × 64,000.

Fig. 284. Longitudinal section of myo-epithelial cell and basal lamina of axillary apocrine gland of man aged 23. Glutaraldehyde-osmium fixation, uranyl acetate and lead citrate staining. × 40,300.

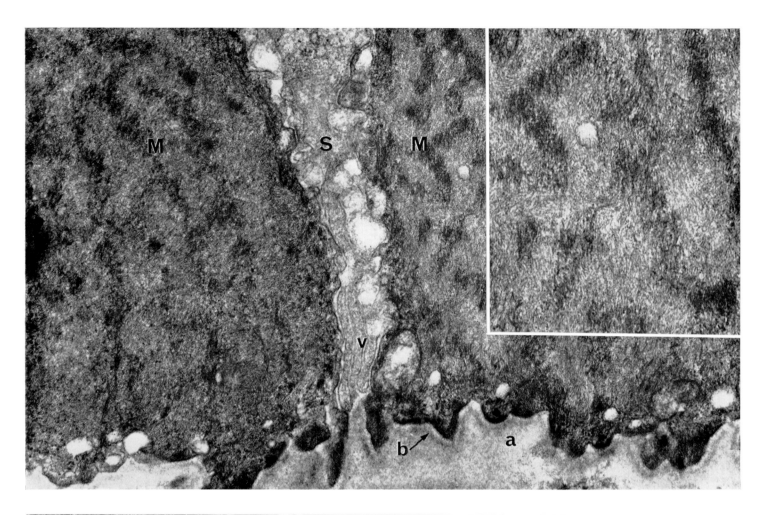

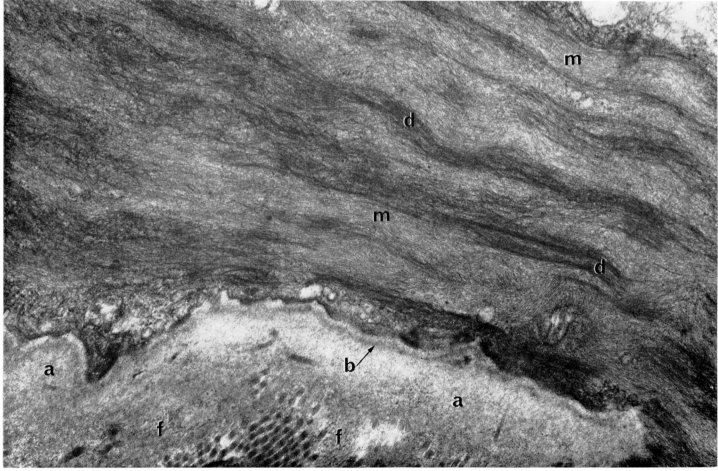

FIGURE 285

Fat cells, occurring singly, or in groups, are frequently encountered in the deeper regions of the dermis, where it merges with the subcutaneous fatty tissue. The cells are very large, and at powers of magnification commonly employed in examination (and particularly with small-holed grids) usually only a portion of the cell is available for observation in any field. Fat cells of human skin are unilocular, i.e. they consist of a single droplet of lipid enclosed by a narrow rim of cytoplasm containing a flattened nucleus and the common organelles.

Segments of two fat cells are seen in this micrograph. The nucleus (n) has been sectioned in one instance, and in connection with both, the attenuated layer of peripheral cytoplasm (cy) enclosing the lipid (li) is seen. The interface between cytoplasm and lipid is irregular in places due to the presence of organelles such as mitochondria (m, inset), and the droplet is not limited by a membrane.

FIGURE 286

This micrograph figures portion of the nucleus (n) and adjacent cytoplasm of a fat cell. Mito-chondria (m) tend to be concentrated in the juxta-nuclear region, and a poorly-developed Golgi apparatus may also be present in this situation. The rough-surfaced endoplasmic reticulum is never prominent, though free ribosomes are moderately abundant. One may note again the irregular character of the periphery of the lipid droplet (li), and the absence of a limiting membrane. In developing fat cells an orthogonal array of fine filaments is frequently seen at the interface between cytoplasm and lipid, but these are only rarely encountered in fully developed cells. A basal lamina (b) is associated with the plasma membrane of the fat cell.

Fig. 285. Fat cells from axillary dermis of man aged 23. Glutaraldehyde-osmium fixation, lead staining. ×7,300. *Inset:* Cytoplasmic rim of fat cell. ×50,000.

Fig. 286. Nuclear region of fat cell from axillary dermis of man aged 23. Glutaraldehyde-osmium fixation, lead staining. ×39,000.

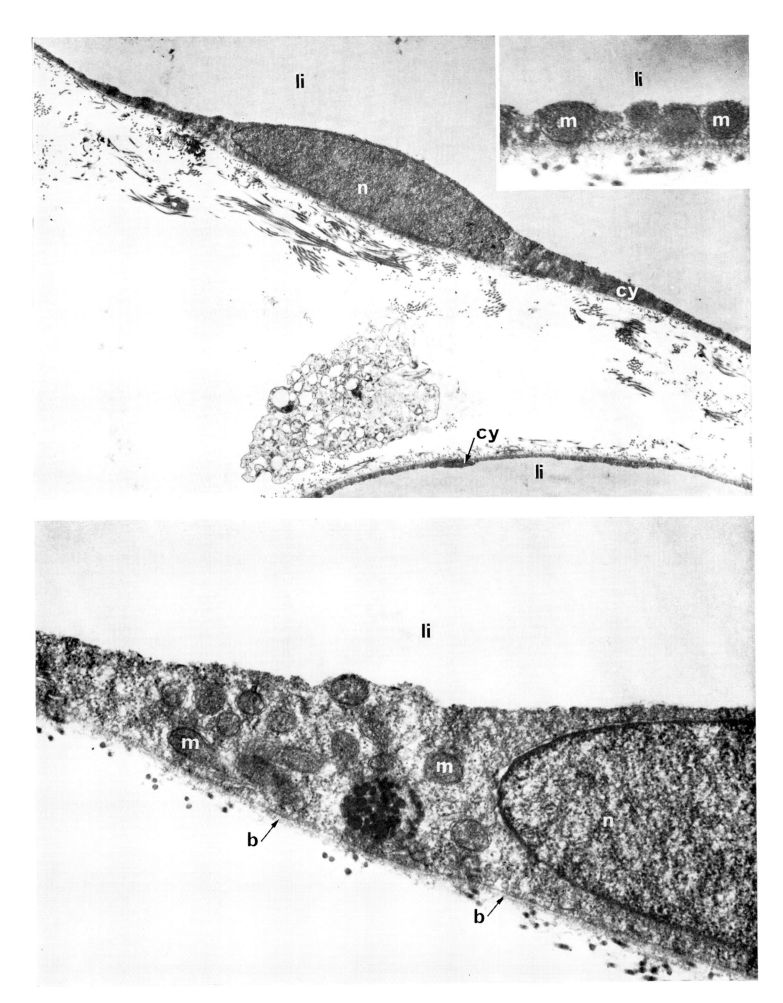

FIGURE 287

This gives an impression of the general environment of the fat cells of the deeper region of the dermis. Segments of lipid (li) and enclosing cytoplasm (cy) of a fat cell are seen in relation to collagenous bundles (C), vessels (V) and individual cells of different types, one of which is a mast-cell (M). Fat cells are also closely related to the secretory coils of eccrine and apocrine glands.

FIGURE 288

Segments of three apposed fat cells are illustrated here enclosing a space which is almost certainly enlarged due to shrinkage during processing and to retraction which tends to occur as the electron beam hits the section. Nevertheless, owing to the circular sectional profile of the fat cell, intervals of this character must exist wherever more than two cells abut against one another. They are never, of course, "empty", but occupied by collagenous tissue which is intimately associated with the cytoplasmic rim of the cell (c, inset).

There is nothing like the lipid droplet of a fat cell for showing up irregularities of the cutting edge of an apparently satisfactory glass knife.

Fig. 287. Fat cell and surrounds from axillary dermis of man aged 23. Glutaraldehyde-osmium fixation, lead staining. × 7,500.

Fig. 288. Fat cells from axillary dermis of man aged 23. Glutaraldehyde-osmium fixation, lead staining. × 8,200. *Inset:* × 10,300.

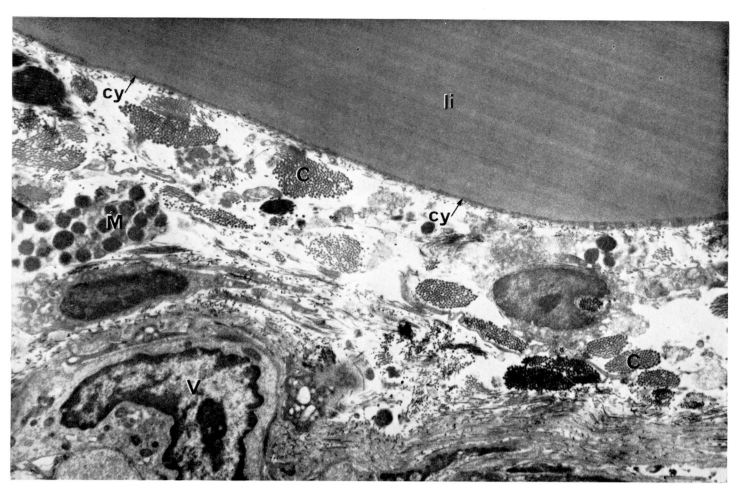

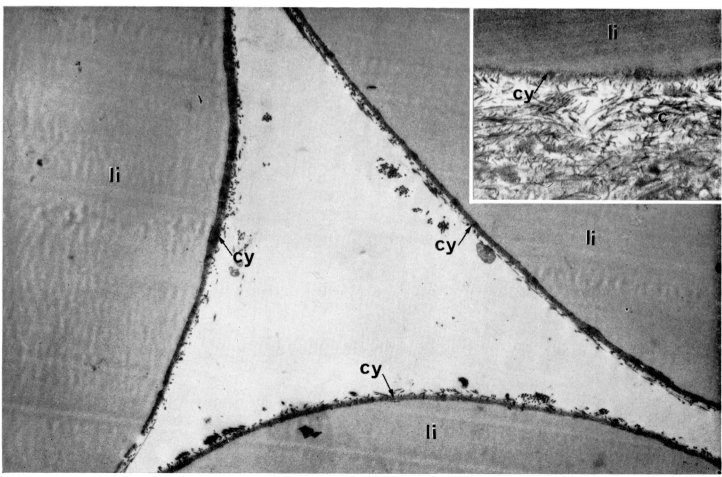

REFERENCES

APOCRINE GLAND

Biempica, L. and Montes, L. F. Secretory epithelium of the large axillary sweat glands. *Am. J. Anat.*, **117**:47, 1965.

Charles, A. An electron microscopic study of the human axillary apocrine gland. *J. Anat.*, **93**:226, 1959.

Ellis, R. A. Eccrine, sebaceous, and apocrine glands. In, "Ultrastructure of normal and abnormal skin". A. S. Zelickson, ed. London, Henry Kimpton, 1967.

Hashimoto, K., Gross, B. G. and Lever, W. F. Electron microscopic study of apocrine secretion. *J. invest. Derm.*, **46**:378, 1966.

Hibbs, R. G. Electron microscopy of human apocrine sweat glands. *J. invest. Derm.*, **38**:77, 1962.

FAT CELL

Fujita, H., Asagami, C., Oda, Y., Mori, T. and Sentoni, Y. Electron microscopic studies of the differentiation of fat cells in human fetal skin. *J. invest. Derm.*, **53**:122, 1969.

16 Fetal Nail

Nails begin to develop about the end of the third month, and a month later, all portions of the nail organ are well differentiated. The micrographs in this Section illustrate features of the nail organ at 16 weeks, by which time it has reached a condition essentially similar to that seen post-natally.

FIGURE 289

The nail primordium is formed by a solid plate of epidermal cells which extends obliquely into the dermis on the dorsal aspect of the terminal phalanx. This epidermal plate forms the nail organ, and the deeper cells proliferate to give rise to cells which differentiate into the keratinized or hardened elements of the nail at a more superficial level. With continuing proliferation and differentiation of cells, a nail plate is formed, which is pushed towards the surface and along the dorsal aspect of the distal phalanx.

This micrograph illustrates ventral cells of the deeper region of the nail organ, i.e. deep to the level at which keratinization commences. At this level, it consists of a peripheral layer of basal cells (B), and a core of central cells containing glycogen deposits (g) and compact filamentous bundles (f). As might be expected, these central cells are very similar to the intermediate layer cells of interfollicular epidermis (Fig. 59) with which they correspond.

FIGURE 290

This features the central region of the nail organ at a slightly more superficial level. One may note again the presence of glycogen (g) and filamentous bundles (f) within the more peripheral ventral cells. At the very centre is a cell of somewhat different appearance. The cytoplasm is more translucent, and it contains irregular dense deposits (d). At this magnification, these deposits resemble the keratohyalin granules of granulosa cells of interfollicular epidermis (Fig. 57). However, they differ significantly in fine structure (see Fig. 292).

Fig. 289. Longitudinal section along nail organ of finger of 130 mm C.R. (16 week) human fetus deep to level at which keratinization commences. Osmium fixation, uranyl acetate and lead staining. × 11,600.

Fig. 290. Longitudinal section along nail organ of finger of 130 mm C.R. (16 week) human fetus just deep to the level at which keratinization commences. Osmium fixation, uranyl acetate and lead staining. × 11,200.

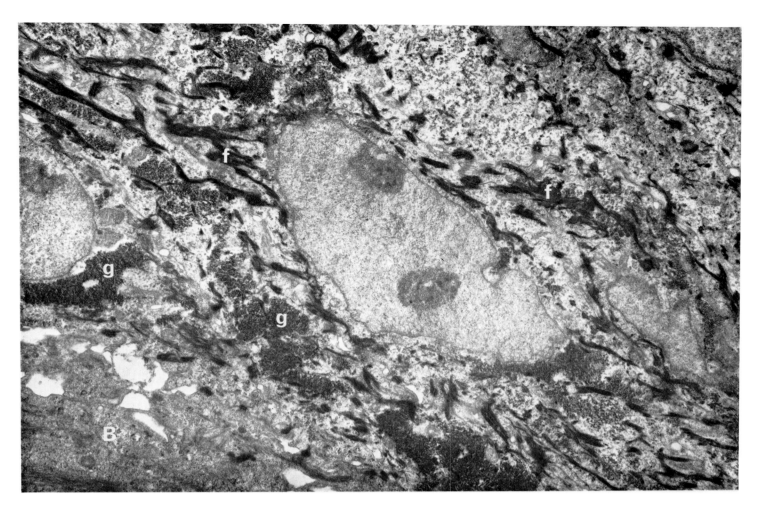

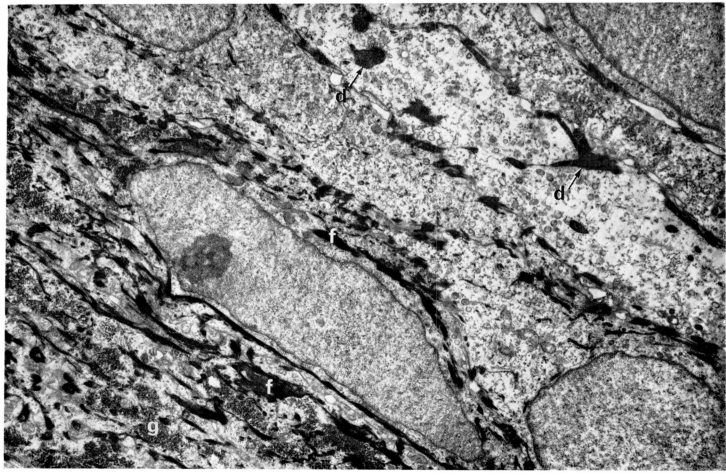

FIGURE 291

In this section along the nail organ, three central cells (N) are seen to be undergoing keratinization to form the deepest elements of the nail root. At this, and more superficial levels, the cells lying dorsal to the developing nail belong to the proximal nail fold (PNF) and those lying ventrally form the ventral matrix (VeM) of the nail. Even at this level, they present a somewhat different appearance. The cytoplasm of ventral cells adjoining keratinized elements of the nail root is generally more translucent than the cytoplasm of correspondingly positioned dorsal cells, and contains the irregular dense deposits (d) already mentioned. These differences are maintained at more superficial levels where, in addition, typical keratohyalin granules are present within the cells of the proximal nail fold (Fig. 294). Lamellar granules (l) are present within the non-keratinized cells.

The three nail root cells (N) exhibit the thickened plasma membrane (p) characteristic of keratinized cells, but none can be said to be completely keratinized because their contents are by no means homogenous. They would correspond in a sense to the "transition cells", occasionally encountered in interfollicular epidermis (Fig. 101), and the most ventrally situated one would appear to be less differentiated than the other two.

FIGURE 292

The dense deposits present within central cells immediately deep to the level of initial keratinization, and within ventral matrix cells superficial to this, are made up of two components. A major and more translucent component (t) is almost certainly derived from coalesced tonofilamentous bundles, and at higher magnification (see inset) exhibits an amorphous structure without any definite pattern. A much denser component (d) is usually located at the periphery of the deposit, and almost invariably associated with a local concentration of ribosomes (r). These deposits present a certain problem of interpretation. They are present within cells which apparently correspond to the granulosa cells of interfollicular epidermis, yet their structure is different to that of the trichohyalin granules of these latter. Identical deposits have been described by Farbman within cells producing the "hard" keratin of the filiform papillae of rat tongue, and this identity, as pointed out later (p. 380), is relevant to the question of the origin of the nail plate, and to whether or not the proximal nail fold makes any contribution to it.

Fig. 291. Longitudinal section along nail organ of finger of 130 mm C.R. (16 week) human fetus at level of initial keratinization. Osmium fixation, lead staining. × 16,200.

Fig. 292. Dense deposit in ventral matrix cell of nail organ of finger of 130 mm C.R. (16 week) human fetus. Osmium fixation, lead staining. × 42,500. *Inset:* × 78,700.

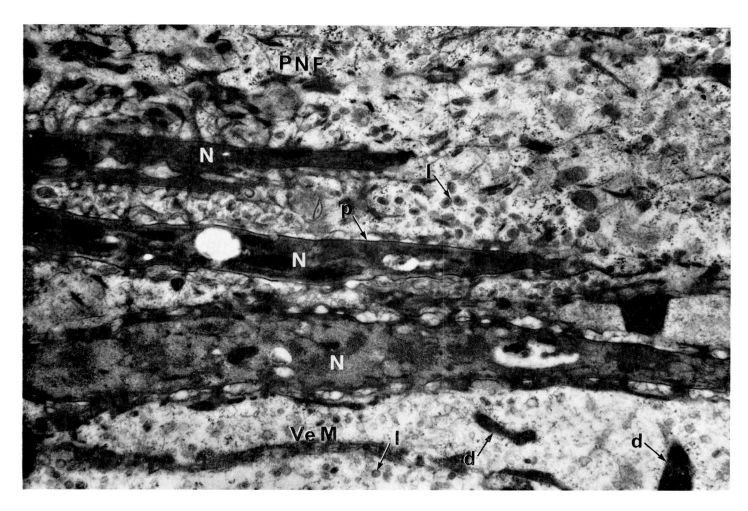

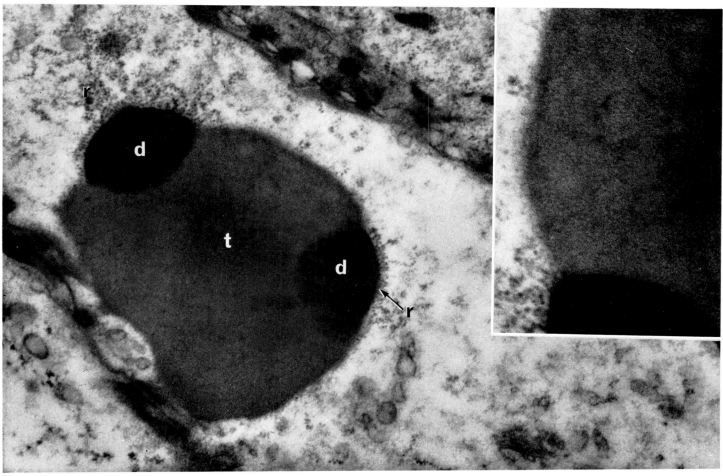

FIGURE 293

Here, just above the level at which keratinization commences, the nail root (N) is represented by three flattened cells interposed between proximal nail fold (PNF) and ventral matrix (VeM) cells. As in the previous Fig. 291, the nail cells are incompletely keratinized and dense deposits (d) and remnants of cytoplasmic organelles are evident within them. It may be recalled that when keratinization of interfollicular epidermis was being considered, it was pointed out that the abruptness of transition between the stratum granulosum and stratum corneum prevented any detailed morphological analysis of this process. With nail, however, the transition appears to be more gradual, and it is possible that further studies on fetal material may yield additional information.

FIGURE 294

In this micrograph, which is taken from a somewhat higher level of the nail root than the one above, the nail (N) consists of seven or eight flattened elements which have advanced further towards complete keratinization. The ventral matrix cells (VeM) exhibit features previously described, and one may note again the characteristic cytoplasmic deposits (d). The dorsally situated cells of the proximal nail fold are different in that they contain typical keratohyalin granules (k). The position here is that flanking the keratinized elements are keratogenous cells of different appearance. Dorsally are granulosa cells typically associated with the production of "soft" keratin as in interfollicular surface epidermis. Ventrally, however, are cells with no keratohyalin granules, but deposits compounded of coalesced filaments and foci of a more dense substance (see Fig. 292). This latter type of keratogenous cell, as Farbman has demonstrated in rat filiform papillae, is characteristic of epithelia producing "hard" keratin. This difference raises the question as to the nature of the keratinized cells between the two in the present micrograph. Do they consist of "hard" or "soft" keratin, or are both types represented regionally? Morphological observations to date provide no information on this question. However, a recent autoradiographic study of squirrel monkey nail by Zaias and Alvarez would indicate that, at the level illustrated here, and superficially to the level where the nail becomes visible, the more dorsally situated keratinized elements contain "soft" keratin produced by proximal nail fold cells, and that they ultimately form the eponychium or stratum corneum component of the cuticle, which, though originally adherent to the buried part of the definitive nail plate, is ultimately shed, and is not represented in the fully developed visible nail plate. This latter would appear to be derived exclusively from cells of the ventral matrix and to consist of "hard" keratin.

Fig. 293. Longitudinal section along nail organ of finger of 130 mm C.R. (16 week) human fetus at level of nail root. Osmium fixation, lead staining. × 16,200.

Fig. 294. Longitudinal section along nail organ of finger of 130 mm C.R. (16 week) human fetus at more superficial level than that illustrated in Fig. 293. Osmium fixation, uranyl acetate and lead staining. × 12,600.

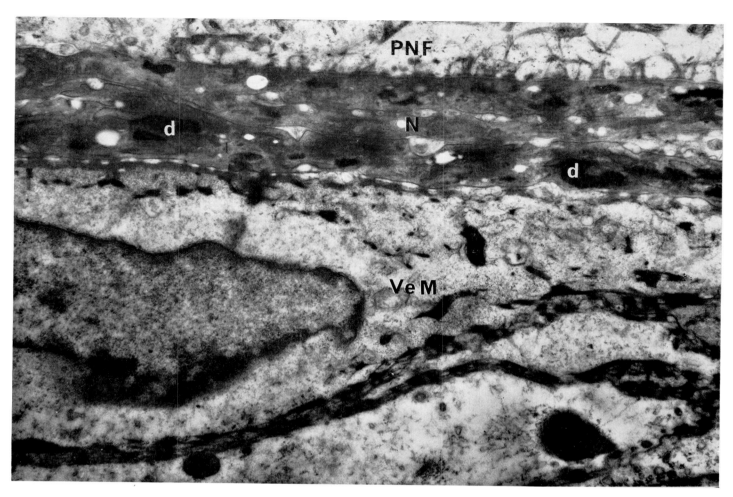

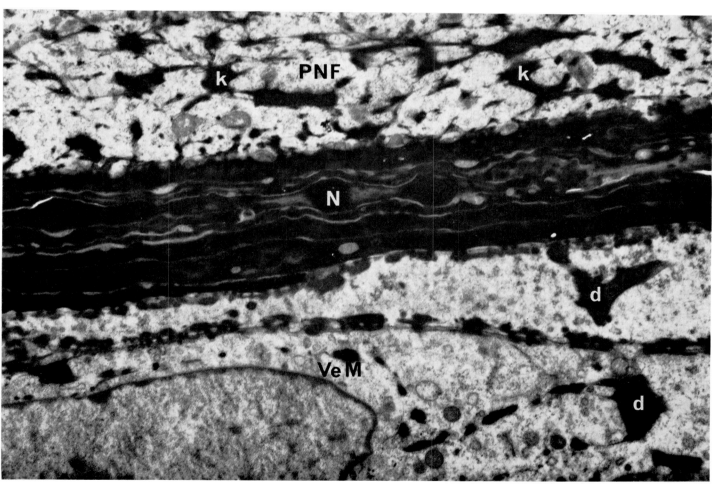

FIGURE 295

This field from a region one-third the way up from the apex of the nail primordium includes the full thickness of the proximal nail fold (PNF), the buried nail plate (N), and subjacent cells of the ventral matrix (VeM). The proximal nail fold comprises a basal layer of cells adjacent to the dermis (D), several intermediate layers of cells containing glycogen and filamentous bundles, and, adjacent to the keratinized elements, a layer of typical granulosa cells. The overall picture is very similar to that of interfollicular surface epidermis at a certain stage of development (cf. Fig. 59). Melanocytes are frequently encountered in the basal layer, and the basal cells included here contain some melanosomes derived from melanocytes outside the field.

FIGURE 296

As the surface is approached, increasing numbers of keratinized cells are found intervening between proximal nail fold (PNF) and ventral matrix (VeM) cells; here, between twelve and sixteen may be counted. In line with what has been said previously (p. 380), those lying more ventrally may be regarded as going to form the definitive nail plate (N), and those situated more dorsally, the eponychium (E). Beyond a difference in position there seems little justification at this magnification for making a distinction between the two, though high resolution studies may establish fine differences.

Fig. 295. Longitudinal section along nail organ of finger of 130 mm C.R. (16 week) human fetus at level approximately one-third way up. Osmium fixation, uranyl acetate and lead staining.   × 4,000 approx.

Fig. 296. Longitudinal section along nail organ of finger of 130 mm C.R. (16 week) human fetus just deep to level at which the nail plate reaches the surface. Glutaraldehyde-osmium fixation, uranyl acetate and lead staining.   × 7,500.

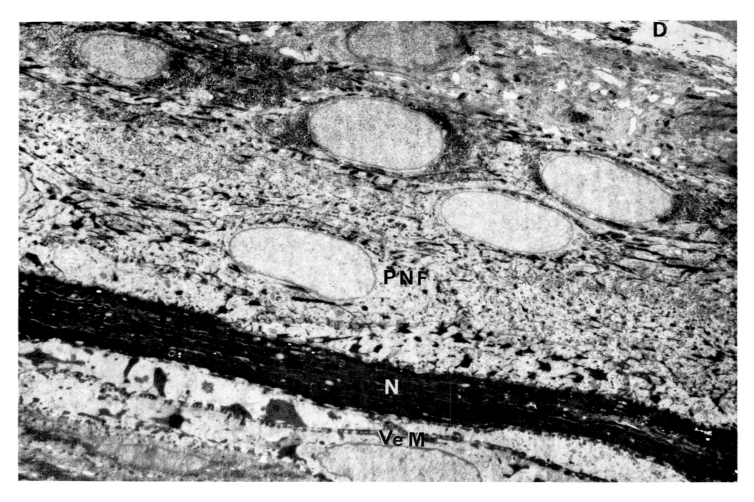

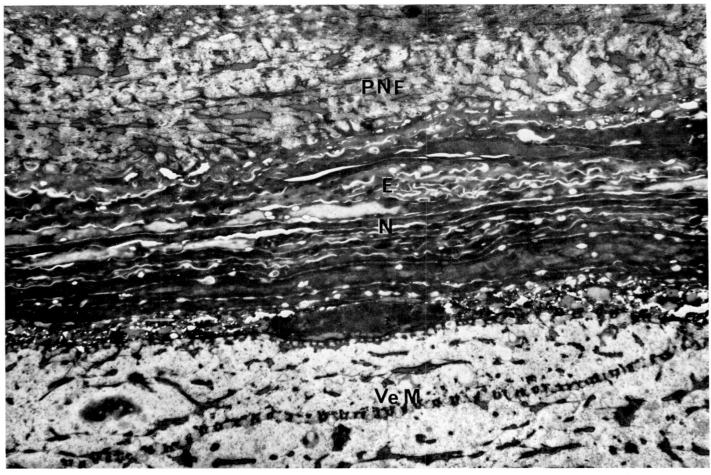

383

FIGURE 297

Just deep to the level at which the nail plate reaches the surface, the epithelium of the proximal nail fold (PNF) becomes continuous with the epidermis (Ep) on the dorsal aspect of the phalanx. Dorsal to the nail plate (N) and adherent eponychium (E), therefore, will be found successively, the granulosa layer of the proximal nail fold, several layers of intermediate or spinous cells, and most superficially, the granulosa layer and stratum corneum of the dorsal surface epidermis.

FIGURE 298

In this micrograph the eponychium (E), or keratinized component of the proximal nail fold, is seen to join the stratum corneum (SC) of the dorsal surface epidermis beyond the limit reached by keratohyalin (k) containing granulosa cells (G) of the apex of the nail fold, and to extend distally superficial to the nail plate (NP) which has split. In the fully developed post-natal condition, this combined corneal and eponychial component covers only the extreme basal part of the exposed portion of the nail plate, where it forms the cuticle. In the fetus, however, it extends further distally to a variable extent, depending upon age. In this sense, the proximal nail fold might be regarded as contributing for a period to the fetal nail plate. The fully developed nail, on the other hand, is exclusively the product of the ventral matrix.

Fig. 297. Longitudinal section along nail fold, nail plate, and ventral matrix of finger of 130 mm C.R. (16 week) human fetus. Osmium fixation, uranyl acetate and lead staining.   × 3,500 approx.

Fig. 298. Longitudinal section along tip of nail fold, eponychium, and nail plate of finger of 130 mm C.R. (16 week) human fetus. Osmium fixation, lead staining.   × 5,500 approx.

FIGURES 299 and 300

The epidermis immediately distal to the advancing tip of the nail plate is thickened, with many layers of intermediate or spinous cells (S) intervening between the basal layer, and a granular layer (G) the cells of which are packed with keratohyalin granules (k). The surface of the hyponychium is ridged and undulant (Fig. 300) and the stratum corneum (SC) is constantly being shed. In the fully developed condition, the hyponychium lies under the free edge of the nail.

Fig. 299. Upper layers of epidermis of hyponychium of finger of 130 mm C.R. (16 week) human fetus. Osmium fixation, lead staining. × 7,800. *Inset:* Keratohyalin in granular layer cells. × 12,800.

Fig. 300. Granular layer and stratum corneum of hyponychium of finger of 130 mm C.R. (16 week) human fetus. Osmium fixation, lead staining. × 6,800.

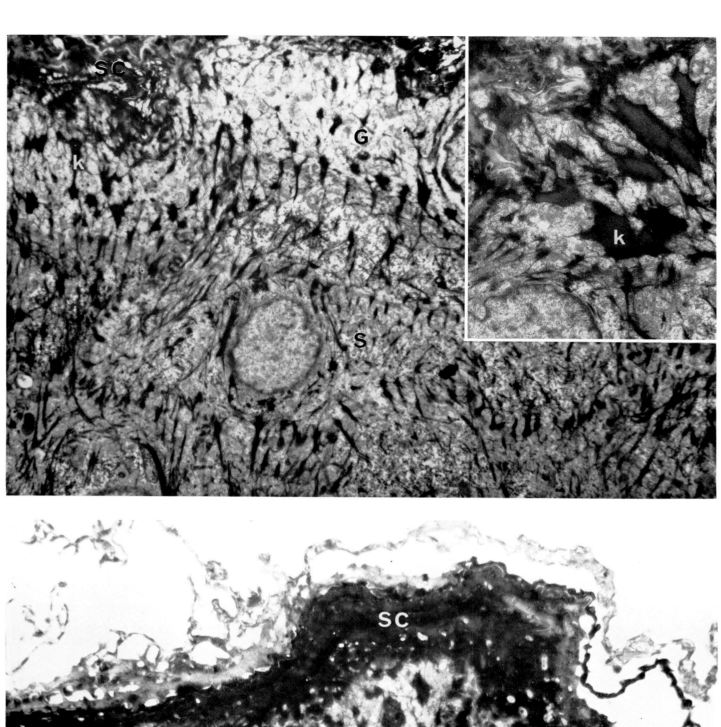

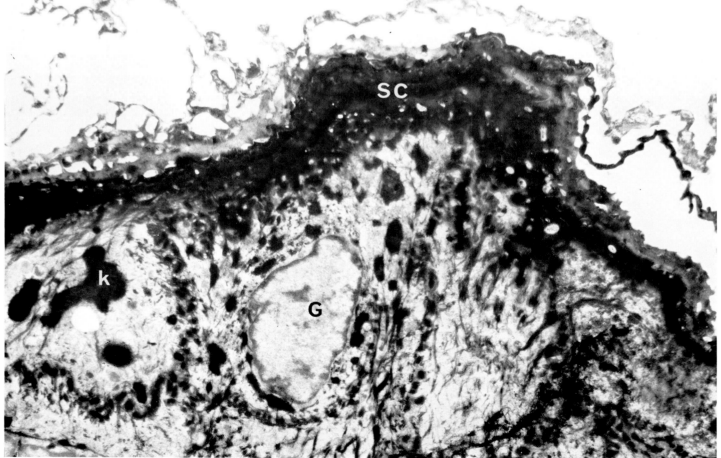

FIGURE 301

The epidermis in the hyponychial region and over the tip of the developing distal phalanx is particularly thick, and the basal epidermal cells (E) exhibit a characteristic palisade arrangement. The dermis (D) in this situation is packed with cells of relatively undifferentiated type containing large cytoplasmic vesicles (v) and the arrangement is such that, particularly at lower powers of magnification, it may be difficult to follow the line of the epidermal-dermal junction with precision; narrow bundles of collagen fibres (c) may resemble tonofibrils. However, the line of the junction is indicated by the basal lamina (b). The over-all appearance of the skin in this region resembles that described in regenerating skin of experimental animals, where the epidermis forms an "apical cap" overlying a dermal "blastema".

FIGURE 302

It may be recalled that in the course of a discussion on the origin of the Merkel cell (p. 76), it was suggested that it may stem originally from the mesoderm, and Fig. 63 was presented as probably illustrating a cell in process of migrating from mesoderm into the outer root sheath of the hair follicle. At the time, no micrograph was available showing a Merkel cell lying entirely free in the mesoderm. However, during the course of the subsequent study of fetal nail for this Section, Merkel cells located entirely in the dermis (mesoderm) of the nail fold and hyponychium were seen, and one such is presented here. It (M) contains the typical dense cytoplasmic granules, and is clearly separate from the overlying epidermis (E) and its basal lamina (b).

Fig. 301. Basal layer of epidermis and subjacent dermis from tip of finger of 130 mm C.R. (16 week) human fetus. Osmium fixation, uranyl acetate and lead staining. × 11,200.

Fig. 302. Dermal Merkel cell from finger-tip region of 130 mm C.R. (16 week) human fetus. Osmium fixation, uranyl acetate and lead staining. × 20,000.

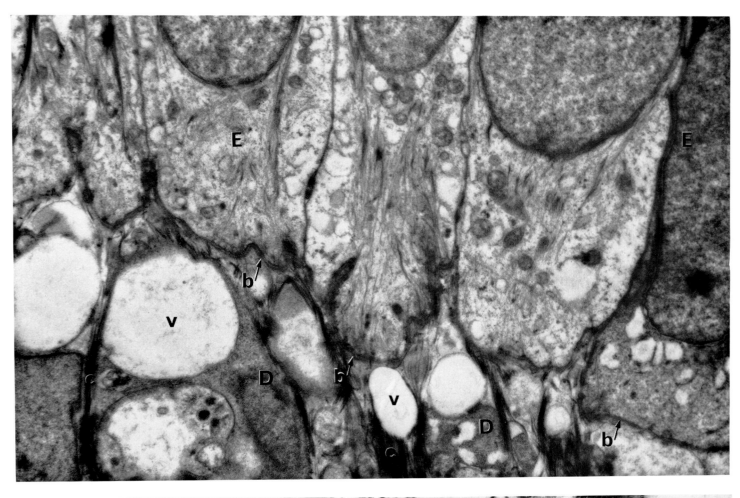

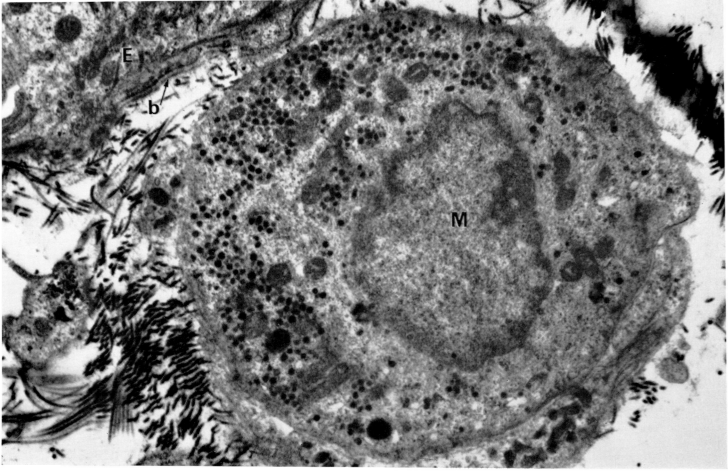

FIGURE 303

Fully-hardened post-natal nail consists of flattened cells with closely apposed tortuous, and interlocking plasma membranes (p). Infolded segments of plasma membrane (f) may appear in sections apparently within the cytoplasm (f_1). When stained with uranyl acetate, as in this instance, the general cell contents present a somewhat flocculent appearance, and extensive deposits of denser material (d) may also be seen. Whether or not these correspond in whole or in part to the deposits seen in ventral matrix and keratinizing cells of fetal nail (Figs. 292 and 293) is impossible to say.

FIGURE 304

The flocculent appearance of the contents of fully-hardened nail cells stained with uranyl acetate is well seen in this micrograph. It would appear to be due to a variation in stainability, the significance of which is not apparent. Each of the cells illustrated contains a localized dense deposit. At higher magnification (see inset) the contents present an appearance of fine granularity which resembles that seen in the cuticle of the hair (Fig. 238). No pattern such as may be seen in stratum corneum cells of interfollicular epidermis (Fig. 107) or in the cells of the hair cortex (Fig. 246) is discernible.

Fig. 303. Fully-hardened finger nail of woman aged 27. Glutaraldehyde-osmium fixation, uranyl acetate staining. × 50,700.

Fig. 304. Fully-hardened finger nail of woman aged 27. Glutaraldehyde-osmium fixation, uranyl acetate staining. × 112,200. *Inset:* × 150,000.

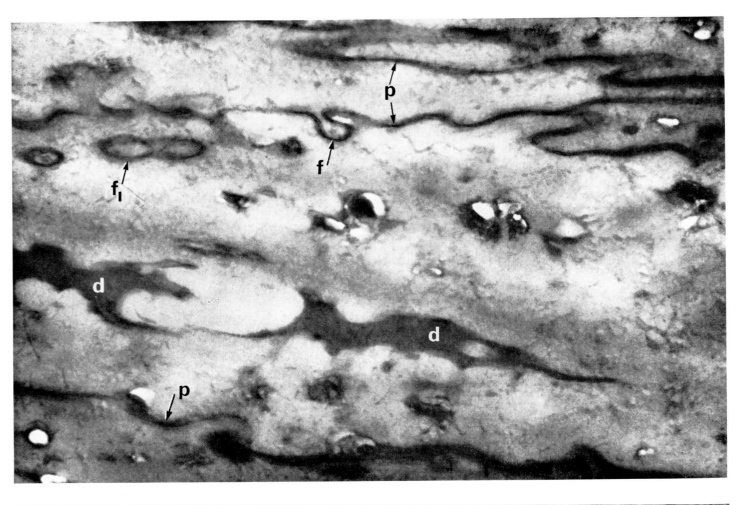

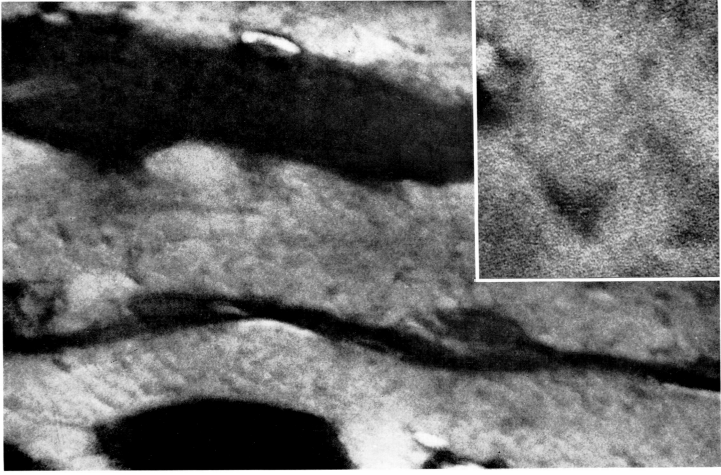

REFERENCES

Farbman, A. I. The dual pattern of keratinization in filiform papillae on rat tongue. *J. Anat.*, **106**:233, 1970.

Hashimoto, K., Gross, B. G., Nelson, R. and Lever, W. F. The ultrastructure of the skin of human embryos. III. The formation of the nail in 16–18 week old embryos. *J. invest. Derm.*, **47**:205, 1966.

Zaias, N. and Alvarez, J. The formation of the primate nail plate. An autoradiographic study in squirrel monkey. *J. invest. Derm.*, **51**:120, 1968.

Index

394